The New Hite Report

The New Hite Report

**The Revolutionary Report on Female
Sexuality Updated**

Shere Hite

hamlyn

This revised and updated edition published in Great Britain in 2000 by Hamlyn, a division of Octopus Publishing Group Limited, 2–4 Heron Quays, Docklands, London E14 4JP

The Hite Report: A Nationwide Study of Female Sexuality first published by Macmillan Publishing Co., Inc in 1976.

A CIP catalogue record of this book is available from the British Library

ISBN 0 600 60116 1

Typeset by Dorchester Typesetting Group Ltd
Printed in Italy by Rotolito

By the same author

THE HITE REPORT ON MALE SEXUALITY
WOMEN AND LOVE: A CULTURAL REVOLUTION IN PROGRESS
THE DIVINE COMEDY OF ARIADNE AND JUPITER
WOMEN AS REVOLUTIONARY AGENTS OF CHANGE
THE HITE REPORT ON THE FAMILY: GROWING UP UNDER PATRIARCHY
WOMEN WITH WOMEN: A THIRD WAY
SEX AND BUSINESS: ETHICS AT WORK
THE HITE REPORT ON HITE

Acknowledgements

The author gratefully acknowledges permission to reprint material from the following sources:

Basic Books, Inc. for material from *Understanding the Female Orgasm* by Seymour Fisher. Copyright © 1973 by Basic Books, Inc., Publishers, New York. Brunner/Mazel, Inc., New York, for material from *The New Sex Therapy*. Copyright © 1974 by Helen Singer Kaplan, M.D., Ph.D. Ernest Been Ltd., London, for material from *The Sex Factor in Marriage*. Copyright © 1947 by Helena Wright. André Deutsch Ltd., London, for material from *The Sex Researchers*. Copyright © 1970 by Edward M. Brecher. The Institute for Sex Research and W.B. Saunders for material from *Sexual Behaviour in the Human Female* by Alfred Kinsey, et al. Copyright © 1953 by W.B. Saunders Co. Little, Brown and Co. for material from *The Sex Researchers*. Copyright © 1969 by Edward B. Brecher, by permission of Little, Brown and Co. The National Council on Family Relations for material from "Sister Love: An Exploration of the Need for Homosexual Experience" by Janis Kelly from *The Family Coordinator*, October 1972. Copyright © 1972 by the National Council on Family Relations. Reprinted by permission. Penguin Books, Ltd., England, for material from *The Female Orgasm: Psychology Physiology Fantasy* by Seymour Fisher. Copyright © 1973 by Basic Books, Inc. First published in Great Britain by Allen Lane, a division of Penguin Books, Ltd. Random House, Inc. for material from *The Nature and Evolution of Female Sexuality*. Copyright © 1966, 1972 by Mary Jane Sherfey, Dr Pepper Schwartz for material from the paper "Female Sexuality and Monogamy." Available from the Department of Sociology, University of

Washington, Seattle, Washington. Drs Pepper Schwartz and Philip Blumstein for material from their paper "Bisexuality: Some Sociological Observations." Available from the Department of Sociology, University of Washington, Seattle, Washington.

Contents

Introduction 2000:
The New Hite Report

The female orgasm as metaphor

The most mysterious of organs—the female vulva, labia, vagina, uterus and especially the clitoris—the intricate, elegant clitoral system, that large network that extends deep inside the female genitals and fills with blood to allow intensely vivid sensations and pleasures—names and information about these organs and how female sexuality functions has been suppressed for long periods of history.

The suppression of knowledge about female orgasm is part of a very long tradition of the suppression of women. The culture's denial of women's sexual needs mirrored the larger social system, in which women were given second-class status. Orgasm is therefore a metaphor for women's power in society.

Today, the United Nations Declaration of the Rights of Women focuses worldwide attention on women's rights to information about their bodies, and autonomy over their sexual and reproductive choices.

A new understanding of female sexuality

For centuries, it was said that women had "difficulty" having orgasm, that female orgasms were much weaker and not as "real" as men's; that men achieved orgasms more easily, their orgasms were stronger, their sexual organs larger and more important, and so on. Further, it was claimed that women were only "blocked" from having orgasm during intercourse (as men do) by either their own psychological fears and neuroses, or men's haste in having orgasm themselves, i.e., women would have orgasm during coitus if men would be "more sensitive" and "not orgasm too soon" themselves. Though these *idées fixes* are erroneous and full of prejudice, for centuries they were considered unquestionable.

The twentieth century saw a breakthrough as women determined to gain equal rights and power in society. From fighting for the right to vote early in the century to equal pay issues (still being fought), women made impressive advances, going on to raise more personal issues such as sexuality and family-reproductive matters—the right to autonomy over their own bodies and reproduction. In fact, even today sexuality (central to the system oppressing women) is one of the principal keys to women's freedom and equal status, as the United Nations Declaration, signed by 140 countries in Beijing in 1995, makes clear. Women have come a long way in half a century from a time when the existence of women's orgasms was doubted, when women were legally (and economically) owned as property in marriage, to their status today.

Women at the start of the new millennium are reinventing themselves, work and love—reclaiming space to breathe, experiment and discover what sexuality and love mean—to decide on their own terms how they want to express themselves, after centuries of being force-fed a passive reproductive role in sex, and after the endless public distortion of female sexuality. The images we see of "the new free sexual woman" in magazine layouts are not exactly who women today "are".

A great distance remains between how women say they feel sexually, how they orgasm, and public visual images of how women experience sexuality and orgasm. Sex videos and internet pornography continue to show women imitating men sexually (acting like male fantasies of women): attempting to have orgasm from the same stimulation men do (i.e., intercourse), exhibiting lust for stereotypically male-pleasing activities, wearing clichéd sex–tart "provocative clothing", and of course, by being ever young.

The assumption continues to be—in films and sex videos today (and in our minds?)—that intercourse is the only "real" way to have "sex", and that a "normal woman" should orgasm during "penetration", like a man. However, this research shows that most women, however much they may like coitus, need specific stimulation of their exterior vulva or clitoris in order to orgasm fully.

In the beginning . . .

Who was I when I first began this research? I was at university, studying history in graduate school. At that time I also discovered feminist activism: my friends and I attended demonstrations together, wrote pamphlets about "women's rights" and "equal pay"—and talked about our personal lives. Gradually it became clear that our bodies were as important as equal pay: that as women we deserved the right to own our own bodies. After two degrees, I left university and devoted myself fully to preparing this report.

This research began from the starting point of asking women themselves to describe exactly how they feel during various sexual activities, and when they most often orgasm.

Society has long known that it is easier for women to orgasm during self-stimulation (masturbation) than coitus—and that masturbation is clitoral and exterior, not vaginal. Yet society condemned women, as if their needs and feelings were wrong, incorrect. For example, in the twentieth century, though both Freud and Kinsey knew that women could orgasm much more easily with clitoral stimulation (exterior stimulation) than "vaginal penetration", both failed to draw the logical conclusion: that it is "normal" for women to orgasm via stimulation of the exterior clitoral area, not "abnormal", and that the definition of sex should change. Instead of seeing that society was oppressing women, they expected women to change; Freud believed women should grow up to "adjust" and become "mature", while Kinsey thought that when a woman had been married for a while, and had more experience sexually, she would achieve this result. Masters and Johnson believed women should seek their clinical treatment for their "sexual dysfunction".

On the basis of the testimony of the over 3,000 women here, the facts are clear: most women can orgasm easily during clitoral or pubic area stimulation (either by themselves or with another person, by hand or by mouth), while only one-third of women orgasm easily during the actual act, i.e., penetration or intercourse (with no additional stimulation by hand). (By the way, why is the beginning of intercourse almost always described as "vaginal penetration"—couldn't one as easily say "penile covering"?)

The conclusion: it is normal for women to orgasm from clitoral stimulation, not "immature" or dysfunctional. The way women orgasm is something to celebrate, not to decry! It is not women who have a "problem" sexually, but society which has had a problem accepting and understanding women's sexuality.

The understanding of female orgasm has improved since the first publication of this study in 1976. Women today do not usually believe that there is "something terribly wrong with them" if they do not orgasm during "the act", though they often wish they could; yet men often indicate by their actions that they assume a woman will orgasm from intercourse "unless she tells me something different"—putting a woman in the awkward position of asking for something with no name that must be "special" since it is not automatically offered (as women during sex expect to offer coitus to orgasm for a man). Thus there is an ongoing gap between men's idea of women and women's reality—and this undercurrent in sex makes emotions even more fragile than they would normally be.

Are we modern?
Although we may think of ourselves as "modern" ("we already know all that"), yet . . . have you ever seen a Hollywood film or a sex video that shows clitoral stimulation by hand to orgasm? Even in the year 2000, the myth is alive that only coitus is "real sex".

A theory that became popular in the 1980s (helping to keep this myth alive) was that women have an interior "g-spot" inside the vagina, that causes orgasm if stimulated. Yet my research for this book indicates that it is the "c-spot", or clitoris, rather than the "g-spot", that is most important for women. If the g-spot was effective, then why haven't more women been having orgasms for centuries during coitus when this g-spot was supposedly contacted? Why don't more women masturbate by insertion, trying to touch themselves inside the vagina, instead of caressing their pubic and clitoral areas? Clearly women are voting with their actions.

This is the only book, presenting the evidence, to state the case for women's right to clitoral or exterior pubic stimulation to orgasm during sex with a partner. Not only does this book present a new theory of female sexuality—and sexuality itself*—it is the only book to document in detail, in women's own voices, the ways that women masturbate, classifying, based on a large and diverse sample, the differences. The vast majority of women can masturbate easily to one or more orgasms by simply placing their hand or fingers externally on their bodies, caressing the clitoris and mons area of their vulva, sometimes lower. Why can't this type of stimulation be built into the sexual scenario between two people? Though certainly some—especially during the last two decades—have learned to do this, no such mutual activity to orgasm has ever been the subject of the glamorizing treatment of Hollywood films or videos, which is reserved for intercourse.

It is not a crime—or sexual inadequacy—for a woman not to orgasm during "the act": clitoral stimulation to orgasm is not some lesser form of sexuality! Clitoral stimulation is very erotic and exciting when two people share it, and should be celebrated and enjoyed.

Women today want their partners to understand the beauty and functioning of the clitoris.

*This book was first to propose that the institution we know as "sex" is culturally created and not simply a biological given.

A missing name

One stumbling block remains: how is anyone to speak of this stimulation, describe it—or ask for it?

Why doesn't "clitoral stimulation to orgasm" have a name? It is stranger than fiction that the way in which most women orgasm actually has no name.

We could think of a name—christen ourselves, in a manner of speaking. There *is* a name (of sorts) for oral stimulation of the clitoris and vulva—"cunnilingus". It is rather long and Latin-sounding, a little difficult to pronounce (a mouthful), but at least it's a name. However, "clitoral stimulation by hand to orgasm"—the most common means to orgasm, as women testify—has no name at all.

This lack of a word for clitoral stimulation to orgasm during most (or all?) of Western history shows clearly how the culture has tried to suppress knowledge of women's bodies, and to stamp out women's enjoyment and pleasure.

A new view of anatomy

Anatomy like you've never seen it before

Overleaf a drawing that I commissioned, from a woman, Suzann Gage, shows a cross-section of a woman's interior sexual anatomy, seen from the side. It was (and may still be) the first in-depth drawing of its kind, showing the entire clitoral system.

Usually, the clitoris is thought of as a small bud. But what we think of as the clitoris is really only its exterior portion. The clitoris is a much larger, interior network.

In this drawing, note the larger, outside lips of the vulva which end just at the opening of the vagina—the vagina is not in the middle of the lips, as is often thought—as well as

Similarities between clitoris and penis anatomy

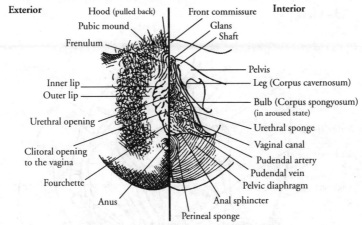

The clitoral system during arousal

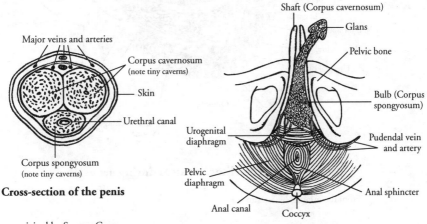

Cross-section of the penis

From an original by Suzann Gage

The penile system

There is a widespread misunderstanding of women's sexual anatomy. What we usually think of as the "clitoris" is simply the exterior part of a larger interior structure. The extent of this interior clitoral network is quite large—comparable to the size of the penis and testicles in men. Inside the penis there are two cavernous bulbs the length of the shaft that fill with blood and thus cause erection. These same two cavernous bulbs exist in the female; however, in the female they are separate, each extending on one side of the vulva, beginning at the pubic area (the exterior clitoris) and going back on either side of the vagina. During arousal they fill with blood and cause the entire area to swell: this is why a woman's vulva becomes swollen and puffy, pleasurably sensitive to the touch. When orgasm occurs, the blood is sent out of these structures in waves by muscle contractions. In other words, the clitoral system is similar in size to the penis, but the clitoral system is interior, while the penis is exterior. Both systems are the same in the early embryo.

These drawings appear in my 1982 edition of *The Hite Report on Male Sexuality* (Knopf, 1981). The explanation printed underneath appears in *Women as Revolutionary Agents of Change* (Bloomsbury, 1993).

Side View

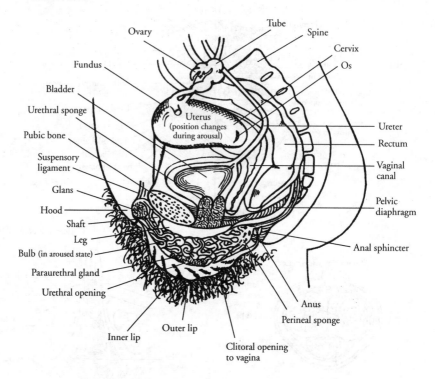

Ovary · **Tube** · **Spine** · **Cervix** · **Os**

Fundus

Bladder

Urethral sponge

Pubic bone

Suspensory ligament

Glans

Hood

Shaft

Leg

Bulb (in aroused state)

Paraurethral gland

Urethral opening

Uterus
(position changes
during arousal)

Ureter

Rectum

Vaginal canal

Pelvic diaphragm

Anal sphincter

Anus

Perineal sponge

Inner lip

Outer lip

Clitoral opening
to vagina

The clitoral system during arousal

From the original by Suzann Gage

If men could understand the similarities of their structures to those of women, they could understand clitoral stimulation much more easily. For example, most men need stimulation at the top of their penis for orgasm, even though they feel the orgasm basically at the base of the penis and inside their bodies: stimulation at the sensitive tip and around the rim leads to sensations deeper inside the body. In the same way, stimulation of the exterior clitoral area causes sensations deeper in the body and vaginal area, culminating in orgasm.

A version of this drawing was incorporated by the Chinese public school system into its 1999–2000 public information manual on sex education.

the inner, smaller lips. Inside, a larger venous network comprises the clitoral system, which fills with blood when a woman becomes sexually aroused.

It is commonly thought that a woman's sexual anatomy, the clitoris, is smaller than a man's sexual anatomy. The reason for this idea is that the penis is exterior, while most of the female anatomy is interior. The penis, the part of a man's body identified as 'THE male sexual organ', becomes dramatically larger during arousal.

A woman's arousal is also sizeable; it is simply less visible because it is inside her body. The changes may not be seen at all if, for example, a woman is standing up, or her legs are together. What one can see, if looking directly at the vulva, is the beautiful, fleshy engorgement of the lips and the shimmering tissues just inside.

The interior structure or network increases dramatically in size and volume inside women, in the same way that the penis fills with blood and becomes larger during arousal in men.

There are two tubes inside the penis that fill with blood to cause the erection. These same two tubes exist in women, but they are separated: one is located on either side of the vulva, nestled up inside the body, one just above each of the lips of the vulva. As a woman becomes aroused, so these two areas—the lips and the surrounding tissues above—fill with blood, becoming fatter and more plushy-looking (and feeling!) The labia majora of the vulva are like two plush, full curtains that draw back on either side of the entrance to the vagina . . .

Why are the structures underlying male and female sexual anatomy so similar? Because in the embryo, male and female are one and the same: the gender of a baby's genitals is only differentiated in the third month of pregnancy inside the womb, when certain hormones come into play, causing boys' genitals to develop outside the body, while girls' remain and develop inside.

In adults, the two structures have even more in common—most importantly, their sensitive spots are in the same place; most men stimulate themselves for orgasm at the top of the penis, but actually feel the orgasm inside their bodies, at the base of the penis and deeper inside.

The tip of the penis is like the front of the vulva, i.e., the small bud we usually think of as the clitoris. Think of a penis as a vertical vulva, or think of the vulva as a penis horizontally placed inside a woman's body; the tip is the clitoral or pubic area, the base is the entrance to the vagina.

Women usually like to be stimulated around the exterior clitoral area (pubic area), that is, towards the front of the vulva (this is the 'top' of the clitoral system, like the top of the penis). This is where most women stimulate themselves while masturbating to orgasm.

'How do I look?'

How do you feel looking at these drawings, and reading these words?

For centuries, women's sexuality has been considered 'dirty', 'unclean' or 'smelly'—viz., the Latin term for the vulva. Names in common usage are often pejorative: 'cunt', for example, is a swear word.

Yet women's genital appearance—the vulva—is individual and quite lovely, with a variety of natural differences in colour, shape and texture. Many people believe that Georgia O'Keeffe's famous flower paintings, which hang in museums around the world, are really paintings symbolic of the vulva and female anatomy.

Women can feel proud of their bodies. Women's genitals, especially when aroused, filled with blood, become full like luxuriant cushions, or ripe, rounded fruit.

Arousal, or this swollen state, in men, is called 'erection'. In women, it again has no name.

The fragrance of the vulva changes when a woman is aroused; it becomes muskier, heavier, stronger. Is this a too strong or bad smell? Although some describe it as having a fishy quality, I cannot agree with this. I believe this is not an accurate description, but a hold-over from old medieval stereotypes and prejudices about women's sexuality.

Actually I doubt that these stereotypes were ever made up by anyone who had a first-hand knowledge of women's scents; they must have been made up by people who had very little actual knowledge of things female! Poets—both male and female—have written of the exotic scents that women's bodies waft over the senses of a lover, creating a heady atmosphere, a time and a space that is theirs alone.

Un-defining sex

Our definition of sex is antiquated, out of date. The sexual scenario presented to us, both men and women ("what we should feel" and "what we should want to do") is too rigid, repetitive and reproductively focused. (Ironically, most women use birth control until beyond the age of reproduction; men today use condoms.)

In brief, the definition of sex for the last 2,000 years (the way we have institutionalized erotic and emotional desires for each other) has been a rigid reproductive scenario, with "the main event" always centred around intercourse—coitus. Everything coming before ("foreplay") was considered "trimming" or the "warm-up". Even today, very little physical contact lasting more than one minute is condoned unless it is between lovers or sex is intended; friends cannot or rarely do walk down the street holding hands together, for example.

The categories "homosexual" and "heterosexual" are much too rigid, and reflect the focus on reproduction. Surprisingly these terms were only created in the nineteenth century (by German sexologists). Such categories are meaningless, as Kinsey suggested in the 1950s, proposing that "homosexual" be used as an adjective to characterize activities, not to label people.

Sex should be un-defined. It should include clitoral stimulation to orgasm for women, of course, but further than that, we should un-define (or deconstruct) sex, to make it an individual vocabulary of ways to touch another person. Our feelings are much more subtle and interesting than the body vocabularies currently available to express them. We can invent new ones—in fact, we are already doing so.

Preface to first edition

Women have never been asked how they felt about sex. Researchers, looking for statistical "norms," have asked all the wrong questions for all the wrong reasons—and all too often wound up *telling* women how they should feel rather than *asking* them how they do feel. Female sexuality has been seen essentially as a response to male sexuality and intercourse. There has rarely been any acknowledgement that female sexuality might have a complex nature of its own which would be more than just the logical counterpart of (what we think of as) male sexuality.

What these questionnaires have attempted to do is to ask *women* themselves how they feel, what they like, and what they think of sex. This is not to imply that the only thing that stands between a woman and "satisfactory" sex is her realization of her own physical needs. "Sex" as we define it is part of the whole cultural picture; a woman's place in sex mirrors her place in the rest of society.

This book presents what the women who answered said—in their own words and in their own way. The intention is to get acquainted, to share how we have experienced our sexuality, how we feel about it—and to see our personal lives more clearly, thus redefining our sexuality and strengthening our identities as women. This book is also meant to stimulate a public discussion and re-evaluation of sexuality. We must begin to devise more kind, generous, and personal ways of relating which will be positive and constructive for the future.

In addition, this book presents a new theory of female sexuality, which unfolds gradually, chapter by chapter, and can best be understood by reading the book in chapter order. The first half of the book is devoted basically to a discussion of orgasm, and the second half to a critique of our culture's definition of sex.

The experience of receiving these replies has been enriching, warming, and enlightening—for me, and, I hope, for all who read them. What these women have shared (anonymously), with so much love and honesty, comes from the wealth of female experience that is usually hidden, but which foreshadows women's great courage and potential for the future.

It has been my privilege to conduct this project for the last four years, and it is with great joy that I present the results.

Shere Hite
February 1976

The questions asked

NATION AL ORGANIZATION FOR WOMEN,*
NYC CHAPTER
47 EAST 19 ST., NYC 10003

I. Orgasm

1. Do you have orgasms? If not, what do you think would contribute to your having them?
2. Is having orgasms important to you? Would you enjoy sex just as much without having them? Does having good sex have anything to do with having orgasms?
3. Do you have orgasms during the following (please indicate whether always, usually, sometimes, rarely, or never):
    masturbation:_____
    intercourse (vaginal penetration):_____
    manual clitoral stimulation by a partner:_____
    oral stimulation by a partner:_____
    intercourse plus manual clitoral stimulation:_____
    never have orgasms:_____
    Also indicate above how many orgasms you usually have during each activity, and how long you usually take. Space for comments, if desired:
4. Please describe what an orgasm feels like to you. How does your body feel?
5. Is there more than one kind of orgasm? If you orgasm during vaginal penetration/intercourse, does the orgasm feel different than orgasm without penetration? How?

*This project is connected with the National Organization for Women's New York chapter only in that, as a member, I was granted permission to use the name and address as a heading for the questions, to give the reader some idea of their orientation. There was no funding involved, although part of any profit which this project may make will be donated to the chapter.

6. Are you more aroused before or after orgasms? Would you use the word "satisfied" to describe your feeling after orgasm? "Loving"? "Elated"? A "feeling of well-being"? What word would you use?

7. Is one orgasm physically satisfying to you? Do successive orgasms become stronger or weaker? Does the place to be stimulated change or "move around" slightly from one orgasm to the next?

8. Please give a graphic description of how your body could best be stimulated to orgasm.

9. If you are just about to have an orgasm and then don't because of withdrawal of stimulation or some similar reason, do you feel frustrated? When does this tend to happen?

10. What bodily "symptoms" do you show at the moment of orgasm? For example, does your body become tense and rigid, or are you moving? What position are your legs in? What is your facial expression?

11. Is an orgasm something that "happens to" your body, or is it something you create yourself in your own body?

II. Sexual activities

12. What do you think is the importance of masturbation? Did you ever see anyone else masturbating? How did they look? Can you imagine women you admire masturbating?

13. Do you enjoy masturbating? Physically? Psychologically? How often? _____. Does it lead to orgasm always, usually, sometimes, rarely, or never? _____. How long does it/do you usually take?_____. How many orgasms do you usually have? _____.

14. How do you masturbate? Please give a detailed description. For example, what do you use for stimulation—your fingers or hand or the bed, etc.? *Exactly* where do you touch yourself? Are your legs together or apart? What sequence of events do you do?

15. Do(es) your partner(s) stimulate your clitoral area manually? How? Is it usually for purposes of orgasm or arousal? If for orgasm, does it lead to orgasm always, usually, sometimes, rarely, or never? Is this form of sex important to you?

16. Do(es) your partner(s) stimulate you orally (cunnilingus)? Is this stimulation oral/clitoral or oral/ vaginal, or both? Is it for orgasm or arousal? If for orgasm, does it lead to orgasm always, usually, sometimes, rarely or never? _____. Do you like it?

17. Is breast stimulation important to you? What kind?

18. Do you like vaginal penetration/intercourse? Physically? Psychologically? Does it lead to orgasm always, usually, sometimes, rarely, or never?

19. If you orgasm during vaginal penetration/intercourse, are other accompanying stimuli usually present? What would you say is your method of obtaining clitoral stimulation during intercourse: a) long foreplay, b) simultaneous manual stimulation of the clitoris, c) indirect stimulation from thrusting, d) "grinding" or pressing together during penetration, or e) some other method?

20. If you orgasm during intercourse, which kinds of movements do you like to make during penetration to increase your stimulation—soft or hard, slow or fast, complete or partial penetration, thrusting in and out or holding still, etc. Which positions do you prefer for orgasm? Are your legs together or apart at orgasm? Do you use vaginal or other muscles to help you orgasm?

21. Do you ever have physical discomfort during intercourse? Do you usually have "adequate" lubrication? Do you sometimes feel less excited the longer intercourse continues?

22. Is the emotional or psychological relationship more important during penetration than during other forms of sex? What is your emotional reaction to penetration?

23. Is it easier for you to have an orgasm by clitoral stimulation when intercourse is not in progress? If you had

to choose between intercourse and clitoral stimulation by your partner, which would you pick? Why?

24. Do you like rectal penetration? What kind?

25. What forms of non-genital sex are important to you (for example, hugging and kissing? talking intimately? looking at each other? smelling?) Do you enjoy these activities as much as regular genital sex? Is the best sex genital?

III. Relationships

26. Answer whichever are or were relevant to you:

If you are *married,* how many years have you been married? Do you like being married? What is the effect on sex? Have you had "extra-marital" experiences (how many and how long)? If so, what was the effect on you as an individual, and on your marriage? Were they of the "open marriage" type, or unknown to your partner. What is your opinion of the "open marriage" concept?

If you are *single,* do you enjoy being "single"? Or is it difficult? Do you think of "single" as a temporary way of life or a basic one? Do you have sexual activities very often? What kind?

If you have a *regular sex partner* (not married), how does this compare with other life styles you have tried? Would you rather be married? Do you consider this temporary or permanent? Are you comfortable?

If you are a *lesbian* (relate sexually to women), please answer any of the preceding questions which may have applied to you, and also: How many years have you been relating physically to women? How do you feel sexual relationships with other women "compare" with relationships with men (or would compare, if you have never had heterosexual sex)? Physically? Psychologically? Please also explain how to relate to another woman physically, as this information is not always widely available.

If you are still *living at home* with parents or family, how do rules against sex for younger women affect you? Do they protect you or hurt you or what? Would you like less or more restrictions on sex? Are parents or relatives willing to discuss sex realistically with you? Friends? Teachers? Is getting information a problem? And finally, if you have had sex with a partner, do your parents know? How did they react?

If you have *not yet had sex with a partner,* what do you think sex will be like? What physical sensations have you enjoyed most so far?

If you are currently *asexual or celibate* (that is, you have no sexual relations except perhaps masturbation), how do you like this way of life? Would you recommend it to other women? How long do you plan to remain asexual?

27. Which "life style" do you feel *would* be best for you? Extended periods of monogamy? Two or three or four regular lovers? Casual sexual relationships? Relatively long periods of no sex at all? "Swinging"? Or some other style which has not yet been invented?

28. Rate the following in numerical order of their importance to sex (1, 2, 3, etc.), adding comments, if desired:
    - passion
    - romance
    - friendship
    - non-romantic love (deep caring)
    - long-term commitment, marriage
    - being "in love"
    - economics
    - hostility and feelings of violence

29. Describe the first time you fell in love. How did you feel? How did the relationship develop and grow, or die? If you have fallen in love more than once, do you think there is a pattern of emotional developments which takes place in romantic sexual relationships?

30. What have your deepest relationships been like, with both men and women? How were they satisfying or unsatisfying? Emotionally? Physically?
31. What are your deepest longings for a relationship with another person(s)?

IV. Life stages

32. How old were you when you first masturbated? _____. To orgasm? _____. Did you discover it on your own, or did you learn how from someone, or somewhere, else?
33. How old were you when you had your first orgasm with another person? _____. During what activity? _____.
34. What were your feelings about "losing your virginity"? Was there any pain or bleeding involved? How old were you?
35. Can you remember your sexual feelings during childhood? Grade school? High school? What were they?
36. Do you think that child and/or teenage sexuality should be repressed? Why or why not? Why is it presently repressed?
37. Have you had sexual feelings for members of your family? Brothers or sisters? Parents? Have your children (if applicable) ever shown sexual responses to your touch, or have you ever had sexual feelings for them? How did you react?
38. Did pregnancy and childbearing/birth have sexual aspects for you?
39. Have you had sexual contact with people who were quite a bit younger or older than you? Was it different in any way, either physically or psychologically, from other sex you have had?
40. How does age affect sex? Does desire for sex increase or decrease, or neither, with age? Enjoyment of sex? Does this have anything to do with the age of your partners?

41. Does menopause ("change of life") affect sexuality, either physically or psychologically? How? Did it affect your partner(s)'s reactions to you?

42. If you have had a hysterectomy, did this affect your sexual activities or feelings? Physically? Psychologically? How?

43. What is your age and background—occupation, education, upbringing, race, or anything you may consider important?

V. In addition

44. Have physical sexual relations with men followed any particular patterns? What were they? (How have most men had sex with you?)

45. Is (are) your partner(s) sensitive to the stimulation you want? If not, do you ask for it, or stimulate yourself? Is this embarrassing?

46. Do you ever find it necessary to masturbate to achieve orgasm after "making love"?

47. Do you often feel your partner(s) is (are) not emotionally involved during sex? Or, what emotional responses do you most often feel from your partner(s)?

48. Do you ever fake orgasms? During which sexual activities? Under which conditions? How often?

49. Have you ever been afraid to say "no" to someone for fear of "making a scene" or "turning them off"? If so, how did you feel during sex? Would you define this as rape?

50. How do you feel about fellatio (mouth stimulation of the penis)? To orgasm? How do you feel about "performing" cunnilingus (oral sex) on another woman?

51. Do you think your vagina and genital area are ugly or beautiful? Smell good or bad? What other parts of your body do you like or dislike? Are you comfortable naked with another person?

52. Do you fantasize? (During masturbation, or during sex with a partner?) Is it to help bring on an orgasm, or just for general pleasure? Do you think of stories with plots, or just visualize specific images? What are they?
53. What do you think of sado-masochism (domination-submission)? Have you ever experienced it?
54. What books on sex have you read? What did you think of them?
55. What do you think of the "sexual revolution"?
56. Do you think that sex is in any way political?
57. Is there anything on your mind you would like to speak about which was left untouched by this questionnaire? If so, please add it here.
58. Why did you answer this questionnaire (*thank you!*), where did you get it, and how did you like it?

Responses

"Why did you answer this questionnaire?"

"I answered this questionnaire because I think the time is long overdue for women to speak out about their own feelings about sex. As for whether I liked it I can only say it was a great relief to say these things out loud at last. I for one am heartily sick of reading what men have to say about my sexuality."

"This was a great questionnaire. I really enjoyed thinking about how I felt about things. Women need to communicate with each other so much more, because we can really give so much to each other. I've learned a lot about my sexuality the hard way—but it doesn't have to be so hard. Sharing is easier."

"I am grateful because finally I got to tell how I *really* feel about sex and my sex life. There's no one I can talk to that would understand, and now I really feel good, like a burden's been lifted. I'd felt like this for so long I was ready to burst."

"I answered because I like the whole idea of it—that for once a group of women are going to be able to say what we like and don't like and what we want and don't want. I am tired of having some man tell me what I should want and feel and what my sexuality is or should be. I would never try to tell a man what his should be because I have no way of knowing."

"Because I believe the findings will be significant. Since this is anonymous and written, instead of verbal, one can be completely honest without any discomfort. I would find it very hard to have to *say* all these things to another person, and I'm sure many women would feel the same as I. I believe it's terribly important for all

women to know what most other women experience—
not just what the more sexually free women experience,
like those who don't mind relating publicly their
experiences, or who could manage to perform in a
laboratory situation. I don't believe those more
uninhibited women represent the general female
population. And if we are to help the rest of us, we have
to know what the *average* woman experiences, women
we can all identify with."

"I answered this questionnaire because I hoped that
in some way it would shed some light for other women,
so that they might not go through what I went through
to realize they are not 'frigid,' 'inadequate,' or 'have
something wrong with them.' Even though more is
being written about sex, many psychiatrists,
psychologists, M.D.s, etc., are still too uptight and
unknowledgeable to be of any service at all. Even in
some large metropolitan areas, the heads of psychology
departments at universities, for example, don't yet feel
that it is important or necessary for women to orgasm!
My own O.B. in a large metropolitan area six years ago
told me orgasms 'would come' one day when I was 'least
looking for them'. I'm glad I didn't just sit back and wait!"

"I really enjoyed this questionnaire. I found out a lot
about myself and quite a few things are really clearer to
me after writing them down. I sure didn't think it would
take so much time but it was worth it. I wish I could
keep a copy for myself but if my husband found it, it
would hurt him too much and I can't do that to him,
because he has been good to me. I do wish he were more
of a feminist, but that's the way it goes. I hope my
answers have helped."

"I answered it because I'd like to help add to our
collective knowledge of ourselves, and it seems a good
approach to begin to define female sexuality without
theorizing. I trust the answers you might get more than
the answers male gynaecologists and male analysts have
gotten on women's sexuality. We need to know, but we

don't get to know with all the studies being done by men. I liked the questions—they made me feel very deeply about things."

"I suppose I just wanted to tell someone how I really feel and get it out in the open. I would like to know more about sex, but most of the books I have read are not very revealing. They don't answer the important questions. All my friends don't know the answers either. At our age (I am eighteen years old—almost nineteen) we really are in the dark about sex."

"It was *great!* Had to do with *my* sex life, not how to please a man!"

"My husband has read through the questionnaire—but not through my answers—and I am going to try to discuss the questions with him, though some of them may be painful. I wanted to answer them all first, however, without getting any comment from him. Perhaps we can find out more about what each of us wants and needs, though that wasn't what the questionnaire was set up for."

"I answered it for cheap therapy, and introspection. I'm glad I did it—I was able to tie together patterns that I hadn't thought about before, despite the fact that I do think about these things and introspect a lot. Looking over it, I want to go back and rewrite and explain and qualify it all—but probably I wouldn't do a better job than this on a second time around, only a different one—there are lots of contradictions and inconsistencies and complexities in my thinking. I do think the questionnaire is aimed towards women who have done a lot of sex with a lot of different people; I feel defensive about having been with one man so long. But on the whole, thank you greatly—I don't spend my average day writing ten pages on my sexuality and it's been a good thing to do."

"The questions sure got me thinking about myself! I was slightly embarrassed writing out the answers, thinking at certain points the questions were too personal—if it hadn't been anonymous I never could have answered. I learned more than you have about myself."

"I answered because it seemed like a good way of having a dialogue with myself—only incidental to sharing me with you. Now I'm glad I did it. I've kept a journal for fourteen years without ever being able to write this candidly about my sex life. I was able to let out hidden things I'd otherwise never tell a soul!"

"What I like best about it is the thought that I'm talking to other women."

"I am only grateful I don't have to sign this, as all hell would break loose if this ever got into the wrong hands. I can't say I liked answering these questions, I would die of embarrassment to do so in person. This way I don't mind. My only reason for doing so is to be of some help and that is all.'"

"I cried when I first read through this. There is so much I've lied about for so long; I'd already come to understand that, but wanted to fill out the questionnaire to make myself write it all down. Undoubtedly, you will have helped many women in just this way, and publication of the results will reach many more who as I did, will read the truth they couldn't tell themselves."

"I had an experience into myself, my past and my sexuality in answering. I can only say it brings to mind the lack of areas for 'ageing' sexually active women to find satisfaction whether in or out of love relationships."

"I wanted to make sure you had at least one questionnaire with my viewpoint. It was difficult for me to answer this, but I did so in the hope that I could reach someone out there."

"I thought that some input from a person who was extremely slow and conventional in sexual development might be helpful to you. Not being a swinger—I had to force myself to be frank in my answers. It was worth it."

"Anything that helps women define their own sexuality on their own terms, and thus have more control over their own lives, is something I want to be part of."

"After I wrote reams, you ask me why I answered this—hah! I feel that all people regardless of age and experience have to be more open and honest and learn from each other. *Some* young people feel they have the market on sexual experience. They have a lot to learn!"

"Because I felt there were not enough statistics about women septuagenarians nor enough understanding of the widows' situation. At my age and without responsibilities I do not want matrimony, but I have a continuing sex drive. Also I had heart surgery two years ago, which has completely rejuvenated me. I want to live to the fullest extent of my capabilities."

"I have a twenty-three-year-old daughter, to whom I still owe much in the way of truth-telling. So, what I have to say here is for her as well as for all young women."

"Saw an ad in the paper, thought you should have the opinion of a middle-aged woman concerning her sexual attitudes. Interesting questions, thought-provoking; some were hard for me to answer because I had never thought about them. I would not have answered honestly without anonymity, and I would not have answered as carefully had it been a multiple-choice questionnaire. For the most part I enjoyed seeing my reactions to many of the questions; but I found most of the questions dealing with masturbation disturbing . . . and I guess that only shows I have not dealt with my feelings regarding it. And if I haven't dealt with my 'hang-ups,' will I pass them on to my children?"

"I have read the results of a few sex questionnaires before, and all the women seemed happy, well-adjusted, and in control—that is, they all had orgasms. I felt lonely, left out, and odd. I answered this because I wanted you to hear from someone like me who is still struggling with it—but putting up a good fight, too!"

"This questionnaire was hard to answer. I felt

blanked out, confused. I didn't want to face what's hard to look at for me. I didn't feel as lucid or as happy with my answers as I usually do when I write. I usually feel clear when I write. I can express myself well, get more in touch with myself, through writing usually—not here; this was hard. But I wanted to hear about/from women who were where I'm at or who had hassled through the same shit and this seemed like the only way to do it."

"Being non-orgasmic, sex is often on my mind and takes a lot of my energy. So it helped me feel a little better to have a chance to voice my frustrations."

"I answered because I feel the women's point of view should be publicized. I have read many of the sex books available, and they are all written of the male, for the male, and by the male. I would like to ask Dr Freud how many orgasms Mrs Freud had?! And Dr Reuben is another one."

"I think real information on women's sexuality should be made available to other women. It's time we began understanding each other instead of only trying to understand men."

"Actually writing out the answers to it was a chore for me; I did it doggedly to help other women."

"I feel that I owe the women's movement a lot for my own personal sexual satisfaction, which I might never have discovered otherwise. That's why I filled out this questionnaire. I hope it shakes male assumptions to the roots."

"It made me uncomfortable and especially the questions I don't have answers to. But I think it's an important body of knowledge—so I forced myself to be honest. I feel very strongly that sexual education for women will be one of the greatest single factors in our liberation. That's why I answered."

"Why did I answer? Heaven knows, there has already been masses written re female sexuality, every paper is filled with it, so much that I feel drowned in it, there's nothing more to learn, I guess. So what possessed me to fill it out? I wanted to clean out my own head and put down my own ideas about what sexuality means to me. I sat with it alone at my table after midnight after everyone else had gone to bed, and just thought about it."

"I wrote to you because I have read a lot about sex in every newspaper and magazine until I can't read any more of that rubbish. I think we should get back on the track we women were on before our sex habits became trendy media items. We have a lot to say, especially to each other, and I want to be part of that effort. I hope what I have said is helpful to another woman – even if it is just my experience."

Analysis of replies*

One woman who answered wrote, "Though this the most fascinating sex survey I ever participated in, I am baffled how you could compile an essay type of study in an accurate form." Had I not written my Master's thesis on the methodology of the social sciences, undoubtedly it would have been more difficult than it was. Actually, it was difficult and time-consuming, but the results made it more than worth it. There were probably over 13,000 woman hours involved in analysing the answers, plus at least another 10,000 put in by the women who answered the questionnaires.

Specifically, the information was analysed in this way: first, a large chart was made for each question asked. Each person's answer to the question being analysed was then copied onto that chart (which was usually many pages long), next to its individual identification number. The many days required to copy the 1,844 answers to each question were actually very valuable in that they provided extensive time for reflecting on the answers. Once the charts had been prepared, it was a relatively simple, though again

* For more information, see the Appendices of this book, and a long methodological essay in the third Hite Report, *Women and Love* (Knopf, 1987).

time-consuming, process to categorize the answers. Usually patterns had begun to stand out during the copying process, so that the categories more or less formed themselves. Then figures were prepared by totalling the number of women in each category, following which representative quotes were selected. This procedure was followed for each of the fifty-odd questions.

In addition, one main chart was kept onto which much of the information from other charts was coded for each individual woman, including preferred type of stimulation, type of masturbation, number of orgasms desired, age, and many other facts. This chart, which acted as a kind of hand-made computer, was the basis for the majority of statements in the orgasm, intercourse, and clitoral stimulation chapters.

Project financing

There was no foundation grant or other funding involved in this project. Originally, extensive funds were not needed, as printing was inexpensive. Luckily, there is a free press (Come! Unity Press) in New York that makes space available for non-commercial printing—for whatever donation you can afford, as long as the material printed is free to everyone.* Eventually I printed all the 100,000 questionnaires at this press, with the help of other women—in many different colours, and on many different kinds of paper, including scrap from old bingo score cards. Thus, until the analysis of the information was begun, the main expense of the project, besides paper and moderate contributions to the press, was postage, since over 75,000 questionnaires were mailed.

The larger the project became, the more apparent it became that the results could best be made available in

*Of course the questionnaires were always free, and *Sexual Honesty* was available free to anyone who wrote me for it. Unfortunately, the present book could not be offered free but many N.O.W. chapters are receiving free copies so that anyone who is interested, member or not, can have access to the book.

book form. *Sexual Honesty by Women for Women* was an early attempt to share these replies in the form of an inexpensive paperback. However, since paperbacks do not generally receive as much attention as hardcovers (in terms of publicity or book reviews), it seems that in the long run, the information in hardcover books reaches more people. As for contributing to the financing of the project, the book advance for *Sexual Honesty* was of course small and only contributed to the continuing printing and mailing of the questionnaires. It was really the generous advance, through the sponsorship of Regina Ryan, which made possible the time necessary for the analysis of the answers. The debt I owe to Regina Ryan is enormous. Without her perceptive understanding of the project and belief in its importance from the very beginning, and her unerring good judgement at so many points in the work, the wheels of progress would undoubtedly have ground to a halt many times.

Eventually, it also became necessary to borrow money from friends, some of whom went into debt themselves to loan me money. For this very important support for the project I am especially grateful to Cecile Rice, Michael Wilson and Virginio Del Toro. However, since loans must eventually be repaid, and since book advances are in themselves a sort of loan, in a very real sense it will be the people who buy this book who will, in the long run, have financed this project.

Women who contributed

There were many people who contributed to this project, to whom I am deeply grateful. I am indebted to Veronica di Napoli for so freely and ably giving of her intelligence, time, and resources for two years, not only preparing and analysing the charts, but also in many other critical aspects of the project. She also made some funds available to the project at a time when they were greatly needed, for which I send her my warmest personal regards. Dylan Landis also gave enormous amounts of time and energy to the project, and waited for over a year to be paid. Without the help of these two women, this book would undoubtedly have taken another two years to complete. Other women who worked painstakingly and with great dedication for hours and weeks on end, for very low pay, were Claire Cowdery, Helen Ferraioli, Maria Finchenko, Diane Maller, Ruth Matthews, Susan Olup, Andrea Selkirk, Julia Spears, and Carol Timko. To all of them I send my thanks and personal greetings.

Many other people helped in other ways, including Sydelle Beiner, Jan Crawford, Stefanie Erickson, Heather Florence, Polly Kellog, Helen Kirschner, Barbara Love, Carol Lowenberg, Naomi Mankes, Mercure, Frances Moulder, Trudy Rosen, Joyce Snyder, Laura Spadicini, Lee Walker, Vicki Wilson, C. K. Yearley, and Sara Zarem. I would also like to thank Dorothy Crouch for her great support for the project from the very beginning. In addition, I am deeply grateful to Barbara Seaman for her own book, *Free and Female,* and for her enthusiastic support and encouragement throughout the entire period of this project, which was a source of great help to me, and a real example of sisterhood.

I would also like to thank the women who produced this book. Not only were the questionnaires printed by women, and the replies analysed by women, but some very talented women were responsible for the production of the book. Again, without Regina Ryan one wonders what the fate of this book might have been. I cannot thank her enough. At every step of the way, her criticism was invaluable, and her long-term vision and enthusiasm regarding the project provided me with an infinite source on energy and encouragement. Lindy Hess was also extremely important in producing this book, and deserves a large amount of credit and praise for her skilful work in many areas and her intelligent and carefully considered criticisms of the book's content, which influenced the shape of the book. She was enormously helpful, and enormously kind, and I am very grateful to her. Suzi Arensberg took on the gigantic job of copy-editing the manuscript, and did so in a remarkably sensitive, skilful, and thoughtful manner. Christine Aulicino is responsible for the book's beautiful design. Finally, had it not been for the women who answered the questionnaires, there would have been no book, and to them I send my warmest greetings and my deepest personal appreciation—and congratulations.

1 Masturbation

Masturbation is, in a very real sense, one of the most important subjects discussed in this book and a cause for celebration, because it is such an easy source of orgasms for most women. Women in this study said they could masturbate and orgasm with ease in just a few minutes. Of the 82 per cent of women who said they masturbated, 95 per cent could orgasm easily and regularly, whenever they wanted. Many women used the term "masturbation" synonymously with orgasm: women assume masturbation includes orgasm.

The ease with which women orgasm during masturbation certainly contradicts old stereotypes about female sexuality—that women are slow to become aroused, and are able to orgasm only irregularly. The truth seems to be that female sexuality is thriving—but unfortunately underground.

How women masturbate is one of the most important keys to understanding female sexuality (from the point of view of orgasm): since it is usually done alone and since in most cases no one is taught how to do it, masturbation provides a source of almost pure biological feedback—it is one of the few forms of instinctive behaviour to which we have access. Although some women did not masturbate until after they had had sex with another person, most women discovered it on their own, very early: "I've never needed anyone to tell me where I have to be touched to have an orgasm; I've just been masturbating ever since I can remember."*

Surprisingly, most researchers have not shown much interest in masturbation. Generally, they approach the study of sexuality through intercourse, with masturbation as a sidelight—since, it is argued, the "sex drive" is fundamentally for purposes of reproduction. However, to take intercourse as the starting point is an assumption†—one that

*As Betty Dodson has written in "Liberating Masturbation," "Masturbation is our primary sex life. It is *the sexual base.* Everything we do beyond that is simply how we choose to socialize our sex life." In addition, primates also masturbate more or less instinctively from childhood on.[1]
†The basis for this assumption is analysed in the chapter on intercourse.

has led to widespread misunderstanding of female sexuality. To assume that intercourse is the basic expression of female sexuality, during which women should orgasm, and then to analyse women's "responses" to intercourse—is to look at the issue backwards. What should be done is to look at what women are actually experiencing, what they enjoy, and when they orgasm—and then draw conclusions. In other words, researchers must stop telling women what they *should* feel sexually, and start asking them what they *do* feel sexually. This is what these questionnaires have attempted to do.

The fact that women can orgasm easily and pleasurably whenever they want (many women several times in a row) shows beyond a doubt that women *know* how to enjoy their bodies; no one needs to tell them how. It is not female sexuality that has a problem ("dysfunction") but society that has a problem in its definition of sex and the subordinate role that definition gives women. Sharing our hidden sexuality by telling how we masturbate is a first step towards bringing our sexuality out into the world and towards redefining sex and physical relations as we know them.

Feelings about masturbation

Masturbation seems to have so much to recommend it—easy and intense orgasms, an unending source of pleasure—but, unfortunately, we are all suffering in some degree from a culture that says people should not masturbate. This deeply ingrained prejudice is reflected in a quote from a woman who was in other ways very aware of the culture's influences on her: "A problem is definitions and usage of words. Probably one of the most offensive statements I've seen in this regard in a long, long time is your question, 'Do most men masturbate you?' To some extent, my difficulty with that is that I give a negative connotation to masturbation when compared with intercourse; that is, I would rather have intercourse than masturbation. I take masturbation to mean what I do to myself, alone. Intercourse is what I do with another person, regardless of what takes place. To call vaginal stimulation of the penis intercourse, and to call manual stimulation of the clitoris masturbation, insults me and makes me angry."

Actually the term "masturbate" had been used (really misused) as a euphemism for someone giving someone else manual clitoral stimulation with the express purpose of gauging the reaction to this usage. The meaning was perfectly understood by the overwhelming majority of women, but the implication was *hated:* sex with a partner legitimizes the activity, whatever it is, and to call it masturbation demeans it.

We have arrived at a point in our thinking as a society where it has become acceptable for women to enjoy sex, as long as we are fulfilling our roles as women—that is, giving pleasure to men, participating in mutual activities. Perhaps we are reaching the time now when we feel we have the right to enjoy masturbation too—to touch, explore, and enjoy our own bodies in any way we desire, not only when we are alone but also when we are with another person. "The importance of masturbation," as one woman put it, "is really to love and care for yourself totally, as a natural way of relating to your own body. It is a normal activity that would logically be a part of any woman's life."

"Do you enjoy masturbating?"

Many women said they enjoyed masturbation physically (after all, it did lead to orgasm), but usually not psychologically.
Psychologically, to describe their feelings, they used words that included "uncomfortable, adrift, uneasy, pathetic, ashamed, empty, cheap, dirty, self-centred, silly, disgusted," and "self-conscious." As one woman said, "To me, masturbation seems lonely, childish, self-absorbed; everything I'd rather *not* have as part of my sex experience. I do it sometimes, but I wouldn't brag about it in public." Other women gave similar opinions:

"Physically, I enjoy it, especially if I'm not in a hurry. Psychologically, I sometimes enjoy it, but often I feel too self-conscious or embarrassed, or even guilty, to really get into it. I don't masturbate too often, because I'm sort of prejudiced in favour of sex with a partner, and I'm living with a man (my husband) from whom I'm almost never separated and who usually wants to have sex with me as often as I want to with him. But sometimes I just feel like masturbating and sometimes if we fuck and I don't come, I masturbate afterwards, and sometimes we like for him to hold me while I masturbate, but not really all that often. I probably only masturbate about once a month at most."

"Yes, I enjoy masturbating. Psychologically, I'm not sure. It's not so much that I feel I am doing something 'dirty,' but it does tend to reinforce my fears of being 'frigid' or just fucked up. (I'm afraid I've been terribly influenced by all that 'literature' that says if you masturbate but can't orgasm during intercourse, you are very screwed up.) I always orgasm when I masturbate. It's more intense alone. I usually orgasm once or twice."

"I enjoy masturbation physically, but psychologically, as much as I 'know' that it is good and there is 'nothing wrong with it,' I also know that it is not socially acceptable by the majority, and I suffer a guilty fear of being 'discovered' and rejected for it."

"I only started to masturbate recently, after a long abstinence since childhood. It was hard to begin—I felt self-conscious and a little silly. Physically I enjoy it, but psychologically I still have difficulties—a fantasy is necessary. I masturbate about once a week under the bathtub faucet. I do it only for the orgasm—it takes about half an hour to orgasm, but I try to prolong it."

"I very often feel an indefinable uneasiness afterwards (after masturbating). This is only the second time in my life that I have admitted to masturbating. The first time was when my sexual partner asked me."

"I'm rather bored with masturbation, truthfully. If anything I enjoy it more physically than psychologically. If I am dependent upon it, I sometimes masturbate twice a day and it usually leads to orgasm. I think it would be more intense with someone although most men consider 'playing with yourself' something not quite to be shared—unless they are at the same time playing with themselves—I have found men's hands often go towards their genitals when they relax, yet I have been criticized for touching myself by my partner who could not accept the idea that after *he* had come, I was still unsatisfied and he was already on his way to the bathroom."

"Physically yes, psychologically no—there is a feeling of foolishness attached to the act—I prefer mostly waiting for the 'real thing.' I know my associations of loneliness, rejection, childhood punishment, and social ridicule are non-rational. But physical sensation is also non-rational, and it doesn't help to lecture myself."

"I enjoy masturbating. The physical stimulation and the orgasm is nice, but I often feel ashamed afterwards like there is something wrong with me because I should have a man to do this any time I want, and I don't."

"Yes, I like masturbation. Some of my sexual fantasies wouldn't even make grade C movies. And God, the number of reruns in a season. Couldn't really say how often I masturbate. At a guess, somewhere between every seven to fourteen days. It used to always lead to orgasm, but sometimes now my heart just ain't in it (I have been known to fall asleep halfway through.) I started masturbating around age twelve, but it wasn't until age twenty-two that I actually made love to myself, if that makes any sense. Up to then there had been more dislike and disgust than tenderness. It has only happened half a dozen times or so since (I'm twenty-five now), but I'm sure it is significant. I have never masturbated in anyone's presence."

"I enjoy masturbation physically, but not psychologically. I masturbate maybe three times a month. It always leads to orgasm and is equally intense by myself or with someone, but I feel more at ease by myself. A partner's ego is hurt because you can achieve so many orgasms to his one climax! I usually have only one orgasm with a partner, but several if I'm alone."

"To me it means to have sex with yourself and I think of that in terms of also being by yourself and not with someone else present. Physically I enjoy masturbation; psychologically, I have a lot of guilt and 'dirty' feelings although in my head I recognized fully that I shouldn't feel bad about it. I think it's as valid as any other sex, and to be alienated from your own body would not be good. It's an active experience for me since it's hard to have passive moments when you're alone."

"It's great to be able to have an orgasm whenever and however I please, no questions asked, no seduction (pretty undies, etc.) by me, no wondering what he's thinking after. But there is something missing. Is it just my imagination, am I still suffering from old taboos? Somehow I feel psychologically rewarded by the amount of desire, need, want, whatever you want to call it, that someone else shows me—and by responding, I am creating something (even if it's a moment, an illusory moment) with another human, something no one can deny is very real. This is satisfying."

"I love masturbating with my girlfriend! It's easier to come as much as I want when I'm alone and this is a thrilling feeling, to explore my body with no 'distractions', but when someone wants me (a woman in my case, I'm gay) that takes the prize."

"I haven't lived long enough with the fact that, yes Virginia, girls do masturbate. I did it often when I was young and then I 'prayed' for the strength to give it up. My sinful ways! But all too often 'strength' would fail me and I'd be back praying to God that lightning wouldn't strike me. I knew I was a Sinner."

"I'm liking masturbation more and more, it's quick and easy and satisfying. Psychologically, it's a little lonely, sometimes, but then, so is making love with a person who doesn't love you. I masturbate most evenings before I fall asleep. I always have at least one orgasm and usually am satisfied with half a dozen. It is the same intensity, whether alone or with a partner."

Some women used to feel guilty about masturbating, but had gotten over it.

"Before other women began to talk about it I was sure there was something wrong with me for needing it. (I usually masturbate two times a week, and have three or so orgasms each time, in about one hour's time.) I resent not learning how to masturbate until I was an adult. I was too much of a prude to experiment and invent it until I had already been married for several years. I could have had a lot better time in adolescence if I had."

"I like to masturbate. I used to feel a little guilty (or

frigid) psychologically but not any more. There was much guilt involved with my early masturbation as mother always sneaked around on tiptoe trying to catch me at it."

"For a long time I had a psychological hang-up, I felt it was wrong, but it felt so good I didn't want to quit it. But when I started reading that it was natural, I began to feel more relaxed and realized I wasn't weird or perverted."

"At first I thought it was wrong to masturbate, because that's the way I was brought up and because nobody talks about it now either, so I assume they all think it's bad. But I personally enjoy it and think it's a healthy part of my life."

"I was always afraid of being caught. Then at nineteen, after I finished once, I thought: this cannot be a sin. It always makes me feel better afterwards and I'm not harming myself or anyone else. So God cannot think it wrong. So I went to an old and very strict priest for confession and asked him about it. To my surprise and relief he said it was not a sin. That *every* woman and man did it. There had been new research in psychology and it was found to fulfil a psychological and physical need and therefore it was normal and natural. This was from a priest who was not liberal or new church. He was so compassionate. After that it didn't bother me any more."

Other women could not let themselves enjoy masturbating, even physically.

"I seem to prefer suffering with my own horniness to masturbating. I guess I don't blame others for doing it, but I was taught that it was indecent and to hold myself 'above' such behaviour. So I developed a tolerance for others' masturbation, but not mine. I'm a snob."

"I have too many mental blocks about masturbation. Kids in elementary school had the attitude that people who 'played with themselves' were somehow emotionally incomplete. At this time I masturbated but quit because of what they were saying."

"I don't enjoy masturbation at all. It's my only sexual release right now but I dislike it intensely, because it's lonely, cold, and not satisfactory at all. I have one orgasm, alone, and try to forget it."

"When I masturbate I psychologically feel guilty or disgusted with myself. I did it once and that's all for me."

"I've only tried it once and I actually broke down in tears because I felt so guilty."

"Masturbation could be very damaging to me, so I try to avoid it unless it's absolutely necessary."

But some women completely enjoyed it.

"I never masturbated when I was young, and when I found out about it, I was filled with a sense of power and liberation. Masturbating helped me learn a great deal about the changes my body goes through in achieving orgasm."

"I enjoy physical masturbation at least five days a week. Ninety-nine per cent of the time I do it alone simply because most males think it is 'dirty' to see a female masturbate. If the prejudice weren't there I would do it in front of them."

"Yes, I enjoy masturbating, although masturbation is not *only* a substitute for fucking because I enjoy it immensely as something *different*. I always have orgasms, at least three or four. It's more intense when I'm alone, as I'm more relaxed and less inhibited."

"Masturbation is my only sexual activity at the moment, as I have been a widow for the last two years and haven't yet felt like making new friends. It really isn't bad. I did masturbate all my life, off and on, whenever the need arose, but now it has become a more regular daily part of life. Actually, I rather like it."

"At this point I must make my masturbation confession. Masturbation has not been important to me until last night when I masturbated for the first time, after reading several confessions in *Sexual Honesty*. This is not shit, masturbation was always a sort of vague abstract concept to me because I never knew how nor felt the need to. Of course I had read a lot about it but I lost interest. After last night I will venture to say that it will definitely become a regular part of my sex life. It was great!"

"Masturbation is one of the sacred rituals that women can enjoy amongst themselves. I say it is 'sacred' because it is *self*-initiated, *self*-controlled, and *self*-gratifying—coming from a position of strength. It is not only about a physical or emotional (they are inseparable) closeness to one's own body, but a conquest of all the fears that families and men have instilled in women about their bodies and sexual dependencies. Try it—you'll like it."

"Today it's okay to masturbate. Madonna did it! On her video my friends and I couldn't believe it, we used to watch it over and over, they would come over to my house and we would sit in my room and look at it. Once my mom complained that I watched Madonna and 'that video' too much, so I hid it—but it made me wonder, does my mom do it? She would probably want to kill me if she knew I imagined her doing it, like I do, but neither of us talks about it. My friends sort of know."

Almost all women had been brought up not to masturbate.

"The earliest I remember masturbating was at age seven, although I didn't know what 'it' was until I was fifteen. Up until then, it was just something that felt good—but that I was feeling very guilty about, because it was in a 'naughty' part of my body."

"I don't think my mother ever taught me anything about masturbation that I can remember. When I was a teenager, and started to masturbate, I had read in a book that it was normal and not wrong, and my mother had not said anything to me, nor had anyone else that I can recall, yet I felt that I had to hide it. I still can't talk about it as comfortably as I can everything else about sex."

"My first experience with myself was in the pre-school age. I would masturbate (I didn't know that was what it was) by clutching stuffed toys between my legs and sort of wiggling up and down. I remember it very clearly for two reasons: it felt so good, and my mother was so completely horrified when she noticed me doing it. She got very angry, and threatened to take my toys away."

"Once my mother caught me masturbating (just last year) and she was shocked, although she pretends to be enlightened and liberal about sex. She also told me about every part of my body except my clitoris."

"I used to feel terribly guilty about masturbating, and up to the age of fifteen or so, I periodically confessed to my parents that I had been doing it and promised never to do it again, but always found myself unable to keep that promise. I know that the modern point of view is that the guilt and fear I suffered was unnecessary, deplorable, and unhealthy. But I place great value on the whole experience, guilt and all: I view the fact that I did continually masturbate, in spite of my guilt and my fears, as a very positive act of courage and self-assertion, as a dawning recognition of, and respect for, a power that I did not understand, a power greater than my parents and other authority figures, a power greater than reason."

"I believe that my parents' selectively negative reactions helped me to focus my interest on this forbidden part of my body. At first, I just enjoyed exploring. Gradually, as I became older, the feeling that I was doing something shameful and bizarre became part of the pleasure. I began to have masochistic fantasies about being alternately encouraged (by dirty-minded, leering men) to be 'naughty,' and then being punished for it (by the same men or by other adults—not my parents though). These fantasies, of which I felt terribly ashamed, became an essential part of masturbating. So I began to realize that perhaps other children masturbated too, but still couldn't quite believe it. The first time I came I was about twelve, I think. I was frightened—I thought I had really screwed up my body, and this strange spasm was the onset of some kind of fit. I sort of held my breath and waited to see what would happen next. Nothing further happened and I seemed to be all right. Still, I decided I better cool it. But after a few days I had calmed down, and cautiously tried again, and came again, and this time I was less frightened. Soon I accepted the orgasm as a natural event, and began to enjoy it."

"What is the importance of masturbation?"*

Most women felt that the main importance of masturbation was as a substitute for sex (or orgasm) with a partner.

"It keeps you from going nuts when you need sex."

"It is relatively important when *real* sex is not available."

"It is my only present form of sexual activity, and it serves the purpose of giving relief from sexual tensions."

"It enables you to be less demanding of your partner when he is not able."

"It's important to women without men who can gain relief that way."

"I think masturbation is essential to one's health. One cannot always have a partner, and—as I learned in my marriage—a partner is not always good sexually, though he may be wonderful in other ways—so I think everyone should know how to masturbate, know her own body."

*See Appendix 3 for a statistical breakdown of the answers. Generally, statistical breakdowns of all the main topics in this book will be found in the appendices at the back of the book.

"The difference between this and sex with a partner is that the intense heat of another body is missing, plus the stimulation of other parts of the body. But you can do it alone, quickly, and you're always sure of an orgasm."

"If your partner rolls over and goes to sleep, you can do it yourself."

"If I can come to an orgasm by myself, I don't feel I have to have sex for that reason alone. Since I usually don't have orgasm with my partner, this is very important for me."

"It's important for survival: my husband can't spend as much time as I'd like in bed."

"They used to say it made you crazy—but I'd *go crazy* without it."

"It's a safe, readily available means of sexual gratification. Better than bad sex with an incompatible partner."

Others saw it as a learning experience.

"Masturbation has helped me know how to have an orgasm, and to recognize the stages of arousal I go through."

"It teaches you to have orgasms and how to accept them; what they feel like, how you react and feel after you climax."

"Masturbation was a release valve when intercourse did not lead to orgasm for long periods of time. It allowed me to examine and learn about my own sexuality: what actually happens to me during arousal, orgasm, what I find pleasurable. It has made it easier for me to tell what feels good, has made me like myself more, and given me insights into the depths of me."

"Masturbation gave me the knowledge I *could* achieve orgasm. Now I know what it feels like and know I'm *normal.*"

"I'm convinced auto-erotic stimulation is essential to most women—it may be the only adequate introduction to their bodies they receive."

"Through masturbation I can learn how my body can feel and how it wants and likes to feel."

"It's important in finding the stimulation points of your body, discovering your own body."

Some women also felt masturbation helped them to express themselves better sexually.

"Masturbation teaches you to know your own body, and to gratify it, which leads to increasing your sense of independence and may also increase your ability to relate to someone else; being able to tell someone else what gives one pleasure can do a lot for a relationship."

"How can you love or satisfy someone else if you can't satisfy your own self?"

"Masturbation develops one's sexuality, because you learn how to touch yourself and therefore others. Perhaps the danger is that you can make it *too* good, because you can make it as you like it, which lovers may not be able to do as well."

And some women saw it as a means of independence and self-reliance.

"It's important because it is always there as an alternative. It has given me a sense of dignity since I realized that I could have sexual pleasure without a man."

"It feels good without feeling guilty about having sex with just anyone, or feeling like he has just used you, and also you don't have to worry about getting pregnant or V.D."

"It relieves tension and preserves human dignity *vis à vis* other people."

"Masturbation enables you to have self-determination on when and how much sex to have."

"Masturbation is sex on a solo level—that's like saying I can take care of myself. Get in touch with my body and self. I am *here*. I am sexy. I am okay. I *like* myself."

"Masturbation relieves frustration and releases energy."

"A way of taking responsibility for my own body. I should be able to make myself as happy as others make me."

"Given the historic horror of our culture for masturbation, I suppose being able to masturbate and not be upset by it in others is some small degree of freedom."

"To me its importance is in being able to have an orgasm all by myself, which means: I'm proud of myself. Right after orgasm I usually feel overwhelmingly proud of myself and fond of myself for having given me such a wonderful thing!"

Others described it as pure pleasure, important in its own right.

"Masturbation is important for pleasure, as a different aspect of any person's sexuality, just like heterosexuality and homosexuality. I don't think enough people have thought it all through. I also strongly feel that my church is wrong in saying that masturbation detracts from sex with other persons. It doesn't; it's just different."

"The attitude that masturbation is just for when you can't relate to someone else sexually for whatever reason is nonsense. Masturbation is another form of sex and should be seen as such."

I used to feel guilty if I masturbated while I was living with someone, but now I think that's ridiculous."

"Masturbation is self-love, giving yourself pleasure, a natural part of regular, everyday life."

"Masturbation is important to relieve tension, to indulge in fantasies, plus, I feel I owe it to myself, as a belated form of self-love. Until I was twenty-nine I never masturbated despite the fact that I was tempted to. After shyly joining the women's movement, however, feelings of worth and self-respect grew and I gradually dropped the mantle of 'professional Martyr' which my husband, Church, and mother were only too willing to help me possess. A door mat feels she doesn't deserve the pleasure of masturbating. So masturbation had a symbolic meaning for me. It was one of my first overt expressions of self-love, the dissolution of guilt and the beginning of self-confidence."

"I think the importance is for pleasure. I used to masturbate in the bathtub with my girlfriend, under the faucet, taking turns. It makes me feel good seeing someone I care for having pleasure that intense."

"For me, masturbation was symbolic of getting rid of attitudes about sex being bad. Being Catholic, I was brought up to think that I should not obtain power or pleasure from my body. I felt that my body was dirty and I equated sex with being dirty. For me the act of masturbating showed me that I had learned to accept my own body as a means of deriving pleasure."

"I think masturbation can be very beautiful, like a dance with oneself. T. and I are just now learning to watch each other masturbate, but I find it embarrassing. I guess I have some inset rules about 'sex is supposed to come from the other person.'"

"It helps me calm down, feel warm (I get very cold at night), go to sleep, work out my fantasies, and meet the sexual needs of the day."

"It is important to relate to one's own body in a total way. Loving and respecting oneself should include physical love."

"The importance of masturbation is to come to an orgasm."

"Masturbation wakes me up in the morning. An energy-starter."

"I think it is important that women be freed from the myth that the only road to pleasure is the penis in the vagina."

"Masturbation is important because sometimes I don't feel like sharing my body. It's just for me."

"Masturbation is important, it gives you a sense of incredible sensuality."

"Masturbation is a beautiful fulfilling gratification, almost a revitalizing force."

"It lets you satisfy yourself best, when you want to get into having an *intense,* very heavy, strong orgasm."

"When I met my lover, she asked me if I masturbate. I was too shy to say yes, so I said no, and she said, how can we have a sexual relationship then??? (At that moment, we were already in bed together, deep throat kissing.) Now I realize that she just wanted me to show her how I do it, so she could fulfil me like that. She has a lot of self-confidence about her sexuality, and showed me straightaway how she does it to herself. Now I value doing it to myself a lot more (even though she and I broke up two months go), and I don't feel unhappy about doing it anymore. It's my body!"

Types of masturbation

Six basic types of masturbation were found.

%	Type	Description
73.0%	I	Stimulating your clitoral/vulval area with your hand while lying on your back.
(47%)	IA	Clitoral area stimulation.
(17%)	IA	Clitoral area stimulation with variations: IA direct: direct stimulation of the clitoris itself. IA_1–IA_5: clitoral stimulation sometimes accompanied by vaginal entry.
(8.8%)	IB	Clitoral/vulval area stimulation.
5.5%	II	Stimulating your clitoral/vulval area with your hand while lying on your stomach. Same subheadings as I.
4.0%	III	Pressing and thrusting your clitoral/vulval area against a soft object. Sometimes also includes vaginal entry: III_1–III_5.
3.0%	IV	Pressing your thighs together rhythmically. Sometimes also includes vaginal entry: IV_1–IV_5.

%	Type	Description
2.0%	V	Water massage of your clitoral/vulval area. Sometimes also includes vaginal entry: V_1-V_5.
1.5%	VI	Vaginal entry.
11.0%		Women who masturbate in more than one of the above ways:
4.4%		IA
0.3%		IB
1.5%		II
1.2%		III
0.9%		IV
2.1%		V
0.4%		VI

In view of the difficulties women sometimes have in explaining to another person the stimulation necessary for them to have an orgasm—especially in view of the general misunderstanding of female sexuality—these classifications may be useful as "labels" of basic body types. They can be used to provide a convenient means of discussing things that heretofore required lengthy and sometimes awkward explanations.

Type I

Type IA

Type IA (manual/clitoral)* was used by the overwhelming majority of women who answered. Forty-seven per cent of the women who described how they masturbate (plus 2 per

*It is important to clarify the usage of the word "clitoris" in the following quotes. "Clitoris" is a term that came into popular usage only recently, thanks particularly to Masters and Johnson and feminist writers; a drawing of it can be seen on page 18. In most of these quotes "clitoris" seems clearly to be used to refer to the general clitoral area, and not the clitoris itself, which is only approximately one fourth of an inch in diameter.

cent who could also masturbate in other ways) used this type of masturbation, and another 17 per cent used it with variations. Basically, it means lying on your back and stimulating your clitoral area with your hand (or a vibrator). This type of masturbation is so classic that popular usage of the term "masturbation" seems to be synonymous with it.

"To masturbate, fantasizing, or getting into an aroused state mentally is important. Also, for me, being alone is important. I use the tips of my fingers for actual stimulation, but it's better to start with patting motions or light rubbing motions over the general area. As excitement increases I begin stroking above the clitoris and finally reach a climax with a rapid, jerky circular motion over the clitoral hood. Usually my legs are apart, and occasionally I also stimulate my nipples with the other hand."

"If I'm in a hurry (pressed for time), I use the vibrator on the base of the clitoris, with my legs open. But usually I use my fingers rubbing around the base of my clitoris, and when I'm near orgasm, I move my fingers to a circular motion on top of my clitoris. My legs are always apart, and I alternate hands because one gets tired. My other hand will caress my breasts or just rest. And I move my body a lot when I have the orgasm."

"Wow! What a question! Usually I lie on my back, my legs apart. I almost always have my panties on, as rubbing the clitoris itself directly is just annoying. I use one hand, two fingers together, rubbing up and down in short, quick strokes right over my clitoris. As I get closer to climax, my legs tend to spread apart and my pelvis tilts up more. I don't move around too much, but sometimes during climax I roll from side to side."

"I use my hands and my imagination, and have probably tried every imaginable position and motion—the basic stimulation remains the same. I use my finger to stimulate the clitoris, sometimes inserting another finger into my vagina at the same time. I touch only my genital area when I masturbate, because I am not stimulated by touching my body in general, as I am if my partner touches me all over."

"I stimulate the clitoris on either side with my legs apart, and do not move any other part of my body. It is as though I allow myself very efficient masturbation without guilt because anything else (touching myself all over, etc.) would be sick."

"When I masturbate I simply think locally stimulating thoughts, then a brief touch of fingers and it's over. Ha! Sneaky, isn't it!"

"I masturbate with my fingers on my clitoris, and other fingers gently pinching, pulling, scratching, across the surface of my nipples. It is necessary to maintain moisture on the clitoris. Sometimes I rub up and down, sometimes in circles. And my legs are sometimes together, and sometimes apart. It is especially exciting to hold my hand still and get the friction by movement of the body against the stationary finger. I also like to see and feel my breasts in motion. Usually I stand in front of a full-length mirror."

"I masturbate with my middle finger rubbing around my clitoris very fast until I come again and again and again. I rarely fantasize during masturbation, I simply want the sensation."

"First there is an up and down rubbing of the clitoris, then a slight pressure, then faster rubbing with pressure all over my mons area. I use my fingers first then my entire hand (palm for clitoral pressure). My legs are flapping or crossed, and high muscle tension is a must."

"I use my middle finger in up and down or circular motions on the clitoris and the area around it. I get stimulated better with my legs apart. I use the other hand on one of my breasts: I rub the nipple and pinch it, pull on it, etc. Sometimes I move a lot, sometimes I don't. I like to feel the erection of my clitoris with my finger."

"I masturbate in bed with my hand. I lie down, pet my skin all over then go straight for the clitoris and move in very rapid motions—sometimes touching the clitoris directly, sometimes just near it."

"I must still have hang-ups because it sort of embarrassed me to answer this. I rub the thumb of my left hand (I am right-handed) with a circular and up and down motion on my clitoris, legs together, starting out slowly and then more forcefully, sometimes massaging my breast with the other hand. I almost always fantasize and use 'dirty words.' And by the way, I have just turned myself on by writing this."

"Oddly enough, although I'm right-handed in most things, I always masturbate with my left hand. I lie on my right side and use my left hand from underneath me, the second and third fingers stroking my clitoris up and down the shaft. Usually I use a little Vaseline to lubricate it. With my right hand, I gently press down on my lower abdomen. Sometimes I cross my left leg over my right leg and press down as I feel the orgasm coming. I move about a bit—sort of wriggling. I would like to try a vibrator, but I haven't had the opportunity yet."

"Sometimes I dress in erotic costumes and view myself in the mirror. Usually I smoke a cigarette, and sometimes put on makeup. If there is time, I lubricate my breasts and genitals with oil or cream. I prefer looking in the mirror rather than directly at myself. Usually I begin playing with my breasts, rubbing my thighs together, then concentrating on orgasm, using the fingers on my right hand in a circular motion on my clitoris. I start with my legs apart, but enjoy having them fight together at orgasm, squeezing the muscles. At that point, I can't move very much."

"I use only one hand and mainly rub up and down. Does everyone answer these questions so frankly? I feel a little wanton, but I feel you must be true or else why try to understand yourself? My legs are apart and I touch only my clitoris."

"I just start right in rubbing my clitoris. I used to touch my breasts and stomach, but it seemed redundant. Now I just rub my clitoris, and generally admire the qualities of me!"

"I masturbate by manipulating my clitoris in a side to side massaging manner, starting gently and increasing in intensity of pressure. I use my finger (one hand). The motion is slightly circular combined with side to side, mainly. The other hand is manipulating the nipple of the left breast (the larger and more sensitive one). Legs are apart. I don't move much, in terms of body movements, until orgasm, when there is a raising of the buttocks (whole pelvic area) and a total kind of stiffening of the body, but especially the legs and feet."

"I make circles with my hand until I almost climax then fierce, hard, up and down motions around my clitoris. My legs are apart and straight and I don't move much."

"I use my right index finger and press around in clockwise circles, near my clitoris. I only start moving when I am about to come. It's inadvertent, my body just gets excited sort of like it likes what's going to happen and wants to help it along."

"I masturbate lying in bed at night. First I take my nightclothes off and just relax. I like to touch my breasts softly and stimulate them, then use my finger to stimulate my clitoris in circular and slow motions and then faster. I like to touch myself very lightly. As my body tenses, my legs close and I don't move much. I just concentrate on my feelings in the area that I'm masturbating."

"I just apply steady, fast, side to side motion to the clitoral area while I fantasize, and eventually I come. It helps if my legs are apart, but it's not absolutely necessary. I don't move much at all."

"I masturbate in bed with the door shut (four roommates!). First, I lean a pillow against my bed and sit in a reading position. I put a dab of Vaseline on my clitoris, and get some pornographic literature (maybe a questionnaire!), and then I spread my legs a little and begin to gently rub back and forth on my clitoris with my index finger. I become excited, stop reading and turn out the light, take off my glasses. Then I return to more rapid back and forth rubbing on my clitoris and fantasize, then I orgasm. I continue to rub my clitoris until it is over. Usually my knees are bent up with my left hand gripping the edge of the mattress as pelvic thrusts increase in intensity, sometimes closing my legs on my hand and rolling onto my side and rubbing my clitoris."

"Yes, I enjoy masturbation, and occasionally plan it and look forward to it. But it is for physical reasons, these days, and also during periods when my lover would be away. At present, I am getting old (age sixty), and I masturbate as a matter of course when I feel the need of it. I have tried many ways of masturbation, especially in these latter years, but I have sort of settled down to the vibrator-on-the-clitoris technique, turning it off just as I reach climax. With the finger, I use my middle finger. Also, pencil erasers when I was very young were nice, since they kind of fit into the clitoris. I can remember when I used a picking-up motion of the clitoris."

"My best 'quickie, one-minute special' is standing up with my vibrator, on my toes, totally tensed, dropping my pants to mid-thigh, and pulling up my top to uncover my breasts, with the vibrator tip against the clitoris and holding the body of the vibrator out, so it looks like a penis—in front of the mirror. I get turned on by my image doing this and come in a minute!"

"I am very faithful to one way: on my back usually lying down (in taxis or public places I can be seated or standing up), I touch my clitoral area with my right hand's knuckles (hand in a fist), actually, vibrating my hand over my clitoral area or the mound just above it, meanwhile pressing my legs together rhythmically, sort of pumping up to orgasm. Thinking sexy thoughts!"

"I usually lie down, with my legs apart, maybe my knees up. I touch myself very gently, especially the inside of my thighs, then proceed to manipulate my clitoris directly with the middle finger of my right hand. I start slowly around my clitoris, and lubricate it with saliva or soap if necessary (soap if in a bathtub). I make my whole body 'vibrate' by tensing my arm and moving it back and forth as fast as possible. I stop every so often, especially if I'm near climax, so I can enjoy the period of arousal. My whole body moves rapidly upon reaching orgasm, and my pelvic area moves spasmodically up and down. Otherwise I lie quite still except for my hand moving."

"I used to use my electric shaver—i.e., I held the side of it to the side of my clitoris. Since I've stopped shaving, I don't use it any more. (I'm not liberated enough to have the world, at least my roommates, know when I'm masturbating!) Generally, I begin with clitoral stimulation, usually with my right third finger. My left hand stimulates my breasts sometimes, but usually just massages my body. I think about someone I would like to be with sexually and generally just continue this until I reach orgasm. I don't move or utter very much sound. Legs are far apart, except at orgasm, then they are clamped together. I generally use a circular motion, but as excitement builds, up and down movements stimulates me better."

"I spread my legs, knees bent up (or else I do it standing up in the shower). I rub my clitoris with the middle finger of my right hand, pressing down, moving it in a circular motion. Sometimes, I squeeze my right nipple with my left hand. It feels strange to write this! I seem to get more and more tense all over, with both voluntary and involuntary squeezing together of vaginal muscles, until the tension in the vagina breaks into spasms and relaxation, and contractions of my whole body."

"I just rub with my fingers, up and down, usually using my left hand (I'm left-handed). I go for my clitoris and don't worry about my legs. I move some—but not enough to disturb my husband in bed beside me. He complains if I do."

"I masturbate usually after seeing an X-rated movie or reading erotic material. I can mentally recall the act and proceed to massage my body with a fur thing or sometimes just my hands. Then I moisten my fingertips with my tongue and lightly touch my breasts as if a tongue were licking them. The same with the clitoris. I hold my legs together and crossed at the ankles."

"I usually start out patting my clitoris, then after it starts to throb a little, I start an up and down type of motion, then finally a circular type motion where at times I press the labia against it (my clitoris) to make a sort of covering. Usually my legs are apart. My movements vary from being very still to jerk-type movements."

"I caress my breasts and stomach lightly. I spread my legs (very important) and rub my clitoris in circular motions with my hand or first two fingers. As I get aroused my body trembles and my hips jerk forward. It takes me maybe fifteen to twenty minutes to get to orgasm."

"Masturbation tends to be very functional; clitoral stimulation (squeezing and rubbing) by hand only. The use of jelly avoids irritation. My legs are wide apart. I touch my clitoris and squeeze it between the labia, continually rubbing the area."

"I have masturbated using my hand in circular motions, with my legs held tightly together. I have also used a vibrator, during which it is not necessary to have my legs crossed but I do find it necessary to keep them together."

"It depends. If I want it to be very pleasurable, I usually begin with *some* clothes on. Touching of the breasts and genitals through clothing is very exciting to me. As my body begins to respond, I go inside the clothing and touch my breasts gently, then move to a gentle caressing of the pubic area, moving slowly to the clitoris. I stroke it in a circular fashion, usually, and as the excitement increases, so does the tempo, so that as I approach climax, the stroking is almost a vibration, very rapid agitation until, like a starburst, I orgasm and all too quickly the climax recedes."

"I begin by stimulating my nipples with my fingers or sometimes with an object, anything that provides stimulation. An ash tray, pencil, book of matches, comb, whatever is handy. I used to have a feather which I used for this purpose, but got rid of it because of guilty feelings. Then I start to fantasize and do just this, no bodily stimulation at all. When I am ready to have an orgasm, I touch my clitoris usually applying firm pressure with my finger (or object) and moving it slightly up and down, while still touching it. I climax almost immediately. My legs have to be together tightly. I cannot reach orgasm if they are not, either with myself or partner. No, I do not move very much. I feel that it is possible for me to have an orgasm just through fantasy, without even touching my clitoris. This has happened once or twice, I believe, but it is more pleasurable to touch. I could reach orgasms very quickly if I touched my clitoris sooner, but I like to prolong it as long as possible."

"I use a simple battery-operated vibrator. I usually apply it to the right side of my clitoris, using a slight circular motion. I start with my legs apart, but they usually come together involuntarily and a thrusting motion takes over—quite involuntary. I really think what goes on in my mind (just who I am fantasizing I am with) is more important than the mechanical aspects."

"I have more intense orgasms with a hand-mounted vibrator, but more fulfilling orgasms with my fingers. I prefer a circular motion. The base of my clitoris is better to touch than the tip, which is too sensitive. I prefer my legs together. I usually squirm rather than move violently."

"I masturbate with my two hands, rather, my fingers, on or around my clitoris, up and down. Sometimes I use a wet warm towel. Psychologically, it's better if my legs are apart. I move but not frantically. The best times are long and quiet."

"I lie flat on my back, with the finger next to my thumb (always my right hand) rubbing up and down around my clitoris, thinking or reading happy thoughts and bang. If being helped, I prefer to work the bottom and them the top."

"With my forefinger, I rubbed the clitoris up and down. I use the past tense because I haven't had occasion to masturbate in thirty-three years."

"I use my second and mostly third finger in circular motions, or side to side, up and down. I do this mostly on the top (opposite from where the hole is), the very top. I start off with the legs in the middle between being together and apart, and then gradually I spread them."

"I use my middle finger and usually use a circular motion, but once in a while I'll use an up and down or side to side. Sometimes, I use a very fast motion (side to side) almost like a vibrator effect and I start up where my labia begins (right below where the pubic hair ends) and slowly masturbate around that area to build up subtle excitement, and eventually move closer and closer toward my clitoris, building more intense excitement the closer I get. I try to make this procedure last long, but sometimes it's hard to not get carried away real fast. Finally, I usually climax during direct contact around the clitoral area. I suppose it would work with my legs together, but it's easier for me with my legs apart. I don't move very much (sometimes I move my pelvis up and down); but usually my abdominal area jerks up and down once or a few times while I am climaxing."

"I lie down and begin to fantasize in my mind my

favourite fantasy, which is a party where everyone is nude and engaging in group sex, lovely, lovely sex, all positions, kissing, caressing, cunnilingus, and intercourse. After about five minutes of this I am ready, very lubricated. I lift one knee slightly and move my leg to one side, put my middle finger on or around the clitoris and gently massage in a circular motion. Then I dream of being invited to this party and all those delicious things are happening to me. I try to hold out as long as possible, but in just a minute or two I have an orgasm. It is very simple, all in the mind. After the first orgasm I do not fantasize any longer, but concentrate entirely on the delicious feeling in my vagina and surrounding areas, continuing the same movement of my finger, but slightly faster and in about one minute I have another orgasm. I am very quiet, but do moan some during each orgasm. After several orgasms in this manner I start thinking of what's for dinner and the party is over."

"I masturbate with my hand. I usually lie on my back but sometimes on my stomach. I borrowed a friend's vibrator once but I don't think it can come up to the sensitivity of the hands. I have many different movements. Flat of hand sideways across the entire mons area, fingers alongside of the clitoris and then up and down or sideways, circular movement with hand or fingers. The movement is not so important as that a rhythm be maintained and that the pressure be firm and increasing in firmness until orgasm. I usually leave my legs closed. I do not move very much, perhaps only to raise my hips. I'm not really conscious of what the other hand is doing. Probably holding on tight. I concentrate on the clitoris and do not stroke or pet myself except sometimes the vaginal area. I guess I really want to get down to business."

"Usually, when I have a period of time alone, I love to masturbate. I usually use my fingers and rub in a circular motion. Sometimes for variety I use objects to rub my clitoris, such as the rounded handle of my hairbrush, any object I have on hand at the moment, but I don't usually do that. I like my legs to be very apart. And I've never used a vibrator, although I'd love to."

"I press my thighs together, and press my fingers downward from the top of the genital hair into the outer lips."

"I use my index finger and the middle finger of my right hand, gently rubbing the hair above the lips, then the lips, then my clitoris. The motion is circular, with a kneading motion. My left hand rests on the pubic area. My legs are together, my buttocks tense. I move very little. I learned to do it this way when I was in college, so my roommate wouldn't know what I was doing."

"I use my right hand, the second finger on my clitoris moving in a circular pattern. My left arm is stiff, legs are slightly apart. I don't move, scarcely breathing, staring blankly."

"I usually do it when I'm reclining or lying down. I like to be reading (or talking on the telephone with my lover). I use my right hand and rub my clitoris along the shaft or round and round the tip of it. I also like to fondle my breasts and pull my legs up and in. Sometimes I scratch the folds of flesh (labia minora) and smell and lick the wetness on my fingers. When the pleasure becomes very intense my hips move back and forth and then to orgasm. I like to masturbate best when I'm wearing close-fitting pants. Sometimes I want to lick myself and I do lick my own breasts."

"I prefer masturbation to 90 per cent of my sexual experiences. I use both hands, usually in the tub or in bed. I kiss my own shoulders and caress my own breasts and watch the nipples erect, which increases vaginal lubrication. Then I use a circular motion on my clitoris."

"I usually use the middle finger of the right hand on my clitoris, with a circular, up and down, firm, vibrating motion that gets faster. I usually have to stiffen my body and hold my breath. Usually I keep the other hand at my side, but sometimes when I'm coming I place it under my ass."

"I prefer to be wearing tight blue jeans and pulling so that the seam presses against the tip of the clitoris. Otherwise I use my fingers to provide gentle press-release pressure to the top of the clitoris. My legs are usually together, and I move very little. I can even do it in public without being observed, I think, with the tight blue jeans method."

"I masturbate with one finger in a circular motion, usually with my legs together. I don't move much. Touching myself through my pants is usually better because the material spreads the vibrations over a greater area. Stopping a few seconds just before orgasm and then rubbing again intensifies the climax."

"I begin by stroking the clitoral area, then stiffen my legs and vibrate the skin around my clitoris rapidly with my fingers."

"Masturbation never worked until I got a vibrator—a large one with several attachments and heat. With two hands, I hold it steady or use a slight circular motion. My legs are apart, and I hold it on my clitoris. Involuntary jerking or spasmodic movements indicate I will orgasm."

"I masturbate with a vibrator, my legs together, the sheets clutched in my left hand. Then I hunt for where it feels the best around my clitoris, moving either the vibrator or my hips back and forth gently. At orgasm I hold it quite still."

"Would you believe I'm not really sure how I do it?! That is, I had to do it while thinking about it to be able to write this. I place three or four fingers in between my large lips, the tips on the area above my clitoris, and start rubbing slowly in a circular motion, while fantasizing. I rub faster and faster until I then explode into orgasm. Sometimes I try to stave off orgasm for as long as possible, but this can be a mistake because sometimes I lose it or it's not as intense."

"I masturbate on my back, with my legs spread apart, knees bent, the index finger of my right hand stroking my clitoris and sometimes my lips. My left hand strokes my anus, not penetrating, just feeling around the opening, slightly lifting my left hip. Lately I've been turning over on my stomach, massaging my clitoris with my right hand, my knees pulled up."

"I fully enjoy masturbation—both with a partner and without. The intensity varies, but it is different without a partner than with one. I am able to reach orgasm much more quickly by myself and usually have three or four orgasms within five to ten minutes. I start by lying on my left side with my legs crossed, and slowly rhythmically massaging my clitoris with the index finger of my right hand. I move my legs, bending them at the knee, and increasing pressure on the clitoris until orgasm."

"I lie in bed on my back or side, with my legs apart, and apply the vibrator to the top and then to the left side of my clitoris. When I feel myself start to 'rise,' I slack off and then build up again. Sometimes I put the vibrator on the bed and spread my legs and then, well, 'sit' on it sort of!"

"When I masturbate, I begin by massaging the area of my clitoris with my whole hand. The massaging is usually soft to begin with, and it gets harder as I get more and more excited. I usually rub my fingertips back and forth over the sides of my clitoris because when I rub the tip of my clitoris the sensations are so strong that they are almost painful. I prefer that the rhythm of these movements be fairly constant, but I like to speed them up or slow them down as I desire. When I am having sex with a partner, I try to get him to duplicate these methods that I use when I masturbate."

"I masturbate in a sitting position as much as I do lying down. I prefer circular or up and down movements with my whole hand and fingertips. I usually use my other hand to stimulate my breasts and nipples. As I said above, my legs are only slightly spread when I begin, but I spread them more and more as I go along. I also wiggle them back and forth. While I am stimulating my clitoral area with one hand, I like to stimulate my breasts with my other hand. Thus, I am usually gently bouncing and massaging my breast with my fingertips while I rub my thumb back and forth over my nipple."

"If I am dressed I usually take off all of my clothes, or I open and undo my clothes enough to have access to the areas of my body that I want to touch. Sometimes I begin to massage my clitoral area with my panties and/or pantyhose still in place and then, when I am ready, I will remove them, pull them down, or reach inside them. While I am starting to massage my clitoral area, I will also begin to caress my breasts."

"I enjoy masturbation immensely, but only in private. I usually pick out a fantasy, get into the role emotionally, then start by exciting the nipples, then working down to my clitoris. I like a fast tickling motion of the same speed on nipples and clitoris. I usually have a dildo at hand, but come before using it— just the fact that it's *there* turns me on!"

"I masturbate in many ways. I can lie flat on the bed, couch, floor, or in the tub and explore my whole body—breasts, belly, legs, ass, vagina, and clitoris. I love to rub my clitoris between my fingers, to grasp my whole vagina in one or two hands, to insert my finger in my vagina, to play with my huge breasts and beautiful nipples. I like to fantasize while doing this. I also like to do the same while using a vibrator."

"How I do it: if I'm bored, it's easiest to describe. I stimulate my clitoris with the third finger of my right hand (I find it very difficult to do it with any other finger) until I begin to feel excited. Then I use my left hand to stimulate my nipples at the same time. I hardly ever come without simultaneous nipple stimulation. I guess that's the way I do it when I'm not bored, also, except that I begin breast stimulation immediately—sometimes even just playing with my breasts alone in the beginning to titillate myself. Once I used a long ruler to be able to stimulate both nipples at once (with one hand), passing the ruler back and forth over my erect nipples. I find that if I am not in the mood for sex, my nipples and clitoris are relatively insensitive, whereas if I am excited, they are very sensitive. For my clitoris, I usually use circular or back and forth motions—very rarely patting motions—for a short while. I often find that I have to stop at intervals—as though the clitoris had become desensitized by the friction, and I have to let it build up sensitivity for a few seconds. Also, I alternate with my nipples for the same reason. It seems that I must have my legs wide apart (usually knees bent out) and I have found that, if I can arch my back (including having my head flat on the bed rather than bent forward on a pillow), I am much more sensitive. I don't move when I do it, except when I'm coming, at which time my hips raise and my back makes the reverse of an arching motion, sort of bending inwards. I think moving would simply be distracting."

IA direct

A small number of women (4 per cent) stimulate the clitoris more directly. They generally hold the skin or lips stretched tight around the clitoral area, then stimulate the clitoris *itself* directly with the other hand. Many of these women mentioned that lubrication of some sort is necessary and that after one orgasm the clitoris was too sensitive to touch for a while.

"I use my third finger, moistened, to stroke and rub on and around my clitoris. My other hand pulls back the lips, keeping a gentle tension on the clitoral area. I alternate the rapid clitoral rubbing with a slower rub of the vaginal entrance. (Actually, 'rub' is hardly the right word, since it is a very light touch until just before orgasm, by which time I am very wet.) My legs are wide apart, my knees up—not much torso motion until orgasm, when there are strong muscle spasms in my torso and pelvis."

"I masturbate with one hand only—mostly around the head of my clitoris, then gradually switching onto the head—always with a rubbing, back and forth motion. My other hand helps to hold the skin so firm contact can be gained. I alternately have my legs together and apart."

"I lie on my back with my legs together tightly. I use my left hand to pull the top of my genitals tight and apart so I can use my right hand to stroke my clitoris. I use a circular motion starting slow with a light pressure, and then increase the pressure until I start to come. Then I slow down according to the sensation I wish until the orgasm is completed. If I want to come again I start over."

"I masturbate with an electric toothbrush. I put a dampened washcloth over the toothbrush and lubricate my clitoris with lotion. I lie on my back with my legs spread. With my left hand, I spread the labia to expose the clitoris, and I hold the vibrator with my right hand and gently press it on my clitoris. Sometimes I move it up and down, sometimes I leave it in one spot, depending on what feels good. But I never really get excited until I start fantasizing. I do not move my hips. The action is all with the hand/vibrator and my clitoris."

"I use my fingers only. My left hand holds the outer lips of my vagina open, and my right forefinger and seeond finger rubs the right side of my clitoris. Sometimes I rub up and down, but usually I rub in slow circular motions. My legs are closed, strained and straight out. Sometimes I will do this lying on my stomach, but not usually. It's a lot harder—I usually do that after I've masturbated a few times and I'm still frustrated. I don't move very much, in contrast with having orgasm with a partner, and I also make much less noise.

"I use my fingers, usually holding the labia apart from the clitoris with one hand, while with the other hand I flick my clitoris with one finger, and/or rub lightly, pinch and pull it between my thumb and index finger. Sometimes I fondle my nipples, and also like to feel my pubic hair. Legs are sometimes closed, and sometimes comfortably apart. I don't move much, just lie back and enjoy."

"Mostly I masturbate when feeling very good about myself, or mildly aroused. I use one hand in a light, circular back and forth stroking motion, while separating the labia with the other hand—usually sitting or reclining. Mostly the stroking is on the clitoris, but also near the vagina with an occasional thrust into the vaginal opening. Tightening the crotch muscle hastens orgasm. Also, occasionally I use mirrors to heighten the pleasure. My legs are apart until orgasm, then crossed firmly at the thighs."

Variations on type IA: IA_1–IA_5

There are many variations of the basic IA type (stimulation by hand of the clitoral area) all of which involve varying amounts of vaginal entry while clitoral stimulation continues:

%	Type	Description
5%	IA_1	Women who, during *some* of the times they masturbate, enter their vaginas.
5%	IA_2	Women who *always* enter their vaginas during masturbation.
1%	IA_3	Women who enter their vaginas at the moment of orgasm.
1%	IA_4	Women who use one hand for simultaneous clitoral/vulval stimulation and vaginal penetration: keeping the palm on the clitoral area, while a finger or fingers are inside the vagina.
1%	IA_5	Women who occasionally enter their vaginas to obtain lubrication.*

*The reason for the separation of all these varieties of vaginal entry or penetration will become apparent in the orgasm chapter, when the sensation of orgasm with or without vaginal penetration is discussed. The separation was important for statistical purposes.

IA$_1$

Type IA$_1$ is the basic type, IA, with the occasional addition of a finger or something else in the vagina. Five per cent of women who masturbated indicated they sometimes entered their vaginas, but not always.

"I usually masturbate by gentle stroking of the clitoral region, not the clitoris directly, but on the skin above and around it; then I place the fingers around the clitoris and move them back and forth rhythmically and with a bit of pressure. Thus, to achieve orgasm, pressure is one factor, rhythmic movement is another, and protection of the clitoris from direct stimulation is another. This last one is achieved by using the surrounding skin to stimulate the clitoris. Finally, tightening my asshole and concentrating on having an orgasm helps bring it on. Sometimes I stick my finger in my vagina as this seems to stabilize the clitoris and is a bit exciting. My legs are apart. I don't move very much."

"I usually start out rubbing my clitoris on the side of it, with my finger. Sometimes I use a mirror and watch—I used to stand up in front of a large mirror. Then, usually because my finger doesn't really turn me on much, I get out the vibrator. Sometimes I read pornography, sometimes I fantasize. Sometimes I get out the baby oil and rub my breasts and stomach. I move the vibrator up and down along the slit between my legs. One leg is usually with the knee in the air, the other, opened, on the bed. I move my lower body up to meet the downward motion of the vibrator. Sometimes I lick my fingers and wet my tit, and just manipulate it, shake it around, etc. Sometimes I stick the vibrator in and out of my vagina, like screwing."

"I use my fingers rubbing back and forth on my clitoris, with the other hand massaging my nipples and/or sometimes inserting several fingers in my vagina. My legs are together (it's better that way because everything is tighter). Usually I move up and down, whether lying down or standing up. Now this always leads to orgasm, but it took me quite a while to learn what stimulated me quickly or slowly to an orgasm."

"One of my hands plays with the clitoral area, the other is in my vagina or playing with my anus. I touch all over first, then my more sensuous zones. I play in every way and position until I reach orgasm. Dancing nude and sexy is a good way of exciting yourself, and legs spread gives more room to move."

"I masturbate different ways at different times, sometimes beginning in the clitoral area, sometimes on my breasts. I use circular motions in both cases, often using two hands, one on my breast, one on my clitoris; or one on clitoris, one in vagina, or at its entrance. I achieve very large orgasms by running my finger between clitoris and vagina (in that channel) to stop orgasm before reaching it and then begin again until I cannot stop it any longer, all the while spreading my legs further and further apart. Except for raising my lower body up, up, up, my body *per se* does not move very much."

"To masturbate, I almost always need to be turned on by something like pornographic literature (and believe me it's hard to find anything even halfway decent). I lie in bed, on my back, slide out of my panties or pyjama bottoms because I like to be free to move. I rub my two middle fingers up and down and around the clitoral area. Sometimes I put two fingers of my other hand into my vagina. I rub for a few seconds and tense up my body. I can usually feel a definite fuzzy feeling when I know the orgasm is coming on and then I rub harder, mostly up and down. My legs are apart. The vaginal area is usually moistened as a result of my pornographic reading, otherwise I use spit or, very rarely, cold cream. I usually arch my back slightly when I am really turned on, at which point I take the fingers of my other hand out of my vagina and I push down on the uterine area just above the pubis."

"My earliest masturbation was with tub water, and

later with my hand, which is what I still do. I use the middle finger of my right hand in vigorous up and down motions which speed me up even more towards climax. Sometimes I put a finger deep inside my vagina, with my thumb maintaining clitoral contact. Recently, since reading the literature, I have tried contracting my vaginal muscles, which does seem to enhance the act. Sometimes I thrust my whole body up, moving with my feet under my behind, ending up with my chest and torso and sexual area pushing up and facing the sky. My greatest release is with my legs pushed way apart to give the sensation of the greatest opening. I once tried a cucumber, and also a vibrator, but that gave me the feeling I was out of myself a little—not just me, that is."

"There are a variety of ways, but usually I put my fingers together and rub them back and forth fast over my clitoris. That much friction of the tender skin is uncomfortable, so I usually do it over my underpants. Sometimes I don't have on pants and I put a finger in my vagina, thumb remaining on my clitoris, and squeeze them (the two fingers) towards each other. This way I fantasize and sometimes get vaginal spasms, but it's milder than the first (just fingers on my clitoris). But sexier. In childhood and through my twenties, I used to put things in my vagina, from ice cubes to lipsticks, whatever—and once my mother found me asleep with the flashlight on between my legs. The warmth was nice."

"I have several moods and modes of masturbation. First is the quickest, when I have clitoral discomfort from lack of sexual satisfaction. A few seconds with the electric toothbrush, my Water Pik, or vibrator and I am up and away. But when I want to give myself more full-bodied sexual satisfaction, I make more of a time-sensual body thing out of it. I get out my dildo and sometimes my pot pipe and really let myself go on memories and fantasies of beautiful sex and people experienced thus. I can give myself an hour or two free-flow body sensuality this way."

IA$_2$

Type IA$_2$ is the basic method of manual/clitoral stimulation, but *always* with some form of vaginal penetration. Five per cent of the women who said how they masturbated did it in this way.

"I put one finger on my clitoris and with the other hand I move a bottle in and out of my vagina (a plastic bottle). I have my legs apart at first until I orgasm, and then I put them together. First I rub my clitoris and then insert the bottle. When I come I close my legs with the bottle in me as far as it will go."

"I use my fingers first to penetrate my vagina, for purposes of enlarging the sensation in the general area, but then for orgasm I lightly and then more firmly rub my clitoris in circular or up and down motions. With my other hand (left hand), I'm generally turning the pages of the pornography book I'm reading. Yes, it's awkward. Legs apart."

"I fantasize first until I am lubricated. Often I tease myself and hold off touching until I am quite aroused. Sometimes I rub my whole body on the bed, lying on my stomach, and occasionally come that way, but usually I am on my back. First I caress the outer labia, then around the clitoris, using a circular motion, then I insert a finger in my vagina, while lying on my back or side, and move with it. I can come very quickly if my legs are together, but there is a better orgasm when my legs are apart and I work harder for it."

"My husband works a dildo in and out of my vagina while I press a vibrator to my clitoris. I do not touch myself because I am holding the vibrator. My legs are usually slightly apart, but sometimes together."

"I hold a vibrating dildo on my clitoris, with the nozzle of a douche bulb deeply in my vagina. This brings me intense pleasure and orgasm in thirty seconds. I just rotate my hips and move the vibrator, with my legs alternately apart and together."

"I begin with manual stimulation of my clitoris.

Then simultaneous stimulation of both clitoris and vagina. Sometimes I use the finger/fingers (first and second or just second) of the other hand for vaginal stimulation. Sometimes I use an object—usually the nicely rounded, smooth handle of my hair brush (no spiked dildos for me, thank you) for vaginal stimulation. I am defensive about mentioning that I use something other than my hand. Among all my associates there seems to be an unspoken taboo against all such 'unnatural' things. I have no object fetishes. I am not into hurting myself. It's just easier—it's hard to reach inside one's own vagina. My wrist gets tired, especially if I'm slow in coming. Also I guess I find needing vaginal stimulation is also unfashionable and I'm somewhat sensitive about that too."

"I wet my clitoral area (saliva or Vaseline) and use an electric vibrator, the kind with attachments. I like to use my other hand with the fingers against the vibrator, so I get the sensation from both the vibrator and my hand. I like to have something (smooth bottom end of a candle, or a bottle) moved in and out of my vagina at the same time the vibrator is rubbing the clitoral area. I keep my legs apart. Sometimes I hold the vibrator still and move against it, sometimes I move very little and let the vibrator move. Lately I've pulled the skin under my pubic hair up toward my stomach so I can see my clitoris as I'm masturbating. Super exciting! Occasionally I use a mirror so I can see myself."

IA₃

A few women (1 per cent) inserted a finger or fingers at the moment of orgasm.

"When I was a child, I would masturbate by holding both hands between my legs very tightly and gently bouncing my whole body. Now I usually use my fingers to rub the whole genital area in a circular movement. Then I usually put one or two fingers inside my vagina before orgasm to feel the contractions."

"Just after I climax I often put a few fingers just inside the mouth of my vagina to feel the contractions—not just to see if they happen; it is very satisfying sexually."

IA$_4$

Type IA$_4$ (1 per cent) is basically just a certain hand position: the palm is on the pubic area (clitoral area), and the fingers reach around into the vaginal entrance, making a kind of semi-circular shape of the hand. The motion most women mentioned here seemed to describe a very rapid movement of the entire, rigid hand "a rapid slapping in and out, also circular," "very rapid patting." Generally, the inserted finger(s) was kept near the vaginal mouth to increase the sensation caused by pulling around the opening. This method seemed to provide good generalized sensation.

"I hold my hand palm flat on the clitoral area, and fingers inserted in my vagina about one inch or so, and just massage gently."

"I begin stroking the vaginal opening, then insert two fingers in my vagina and stimulate my clitoris with the palm of my hand with very rapid patting motions. My legs are together."

"I use one hand and clutch the mons, vibrate my hand over it until I get a warm feeling, then open my labia with a finger, and make it wet up and down, then insert a finger into my vagina and move it up and down very fast while the palm vibrates the mons. My legs are wide apart."

"I caress my nipples to get started, and look at pornography. Then I gently massage my mound until I am generally aroused, then insert my fingers into the vagina and at the same time rub my clitoris with my palm. Sometimes I suck on a rubber penis."

"My legs are apart, my middle finger is inserted deep into the vagina, with the palm of my hand making a circular motion over my clitoris."

"I use the heel of my hand and arm against the clitoris, and three fingers inside against the preliminary ridges of the vaginal wall—*not deep.* Legs apart always. I massage the external area and clitoris. I once used a carrot internally."

"My palm is against the fleshy mound toward the top front of my genital area, and one or two fingers are inserted in my vagina. I make very rapid slapping in and out and circular motions. Sometimes I rub the exterior of my anus simultaneously with the other hand."

IA₅

The final variation is the basic IA accompanied by a momentary entry into the vagina (1 per cent) for the purpose of increasing lubrication.

"I start out squeezing my outer vaginal lips together and sort of rubbing my clitoris in a circular way through them. After a while I stick my forefinger into my vagina to get it wet and then rub the hood around my clitoris lightly in a forward and backward motion, which gradually gets a little more circular. I like to feel all around my whole vulva, but concentrate on the clitoral area. I always try to prolong the arousal state by moving very slowly, but I never can resist speeding up. I vary the pressure a great deal, but gradually rubbing harder as I get more turned on. Sometimes I feel my breasts with my other hand. I play with my hair. Sometimes I put my other hand in an 'innocent' position that doesn't appear to be involved in any way, because one of my favourite masturbation fantasies is that I have to appear as if nothing were happening at all, whereas secretly . . . sometimes my finger gets tired and I switch hands, but my left hand is always so much more awkward that I always switch back. When I'm just on the brink of coming I stop for a few seconds, if I have any self-control at that point, and wait till I calm down a little before starting again. I do this as many times as I can stand it (three or four) because I like to be so hot that my heart is pounding and shaking my whole body by the time I come. When I come, I thrash all over the mattress and gasp a lot; but if my partner's asleep I try to control it and not make too much noise. If he's awake, he usually gets into watching me, but for some reason the idea of waking him up by coming is too embarrassing for me to handle, unless I told him before he went to sleep that I was going to masturbate. I retain more guilt about masturbation than I do about any other sexual practice I engage in, and I don't know why that is, unless it's a fear of being self-sufficient. I seem to be feeling less guilty about it as I become more independent and self-assertive in other areas of my life, so maybe that's a good sign."

"I lie on the bed with my legs open, and run my hands over my body, massaging my breasts and feeling the sensations inside and outside my skin. My right hand rubs over my genital areas and my left presses my inner thigh and rubs my outer labia. I use my index finger to rub the labia, while my middle fingers rub the clitoris in circles. One finger moves down to my vagina and stirs around the inner folds, feeling the satin-like skin and bringing moisture back up to my clitoris, which I gently rub up and around and down. Meanwhile my left hand drifts around, massaging my breasts and thighs."

IA with anal penetration

A few women in all these types also occasionally penetrated themselves anally:

"Upon thinking certain sexy thoughts my blood pressure feels like it's increasing, my heartbeat instantly becomes quick and hard. My clitoris tickles and within a few seconds my vagina gets slippery. I rub my clitoris with my left index finger. I penetrate my vagina and/or rectum with the index and/or middle finger of my right hand and move them in and out at whatever speed I wish. My genitals reach two or three stages of tickling intensity—each tickling more than the one before. I rub my clitoris in a back and forth motion. Sometimes I use household items which have the shape of a penis for penetration."

"I masturbate in a darkened room. I sometimes read erotic literature, especially anal-oriented. I stimulate myself with lubricated fingers or a vaginal foam applicator or douche or enema tip. I usually make circular motions on my pubic area with one hand and touch my anus with the other hand, sometimes inserting my finger or an object in my rectum. It does not matter if my legs are together or apart. I move very little."

"Sometimes I use my fingers on my clitoris with one inside the vagina, one on the anal area, or just on the clitoris. Usually I use one of two sizes of vibrators—a small one for my anus and a large one for my vagina. One hand is used for the clitoris, the other holds the two vibrators in place. Legs are usually apart. Circular motions."

Type IB

Type IB involves a kind of masturbation in which it is important to stimulate not only the clitoris but also the other parts of the vulva (external genitals). The stimulation in this type seems to be a more generalized rubbing and massaging of the whole vulval area. Almost 9 per cent of the women answering masturbate in this way, with approximately a sixth of them occasionally also inserting something into their vaginas.

"Dig this. I use the side of my electric women's razor to masturbate. I rub up and down and sideways and usually use the other hand to stimulate the rim of my vagina meanwhile."

"I use my fingers primarily. I begin by softly caressing my body and breasts, and genital organs. Sometimes I use two hands on my genitals, but not always. I try to wait until I feel moist before touching

myself, because if I am not moist I usually have
difficulty in achieving orgasm. So I rub and stroke my
external organs, gently, and then I raise my legs into the
air (wide apart) and then rub a little more vigorously—
which leads to orgasm or orgasms. It seems necessary to
raise my legs or I don't come. I often wonder if other
women are the same."

"Slow light finger pressure below the clitoris and
back and forth, sliding to below the vaginal opening. A
slight pause, then up, then down, etc., pressing in just a
little at the lowest point, while my mind's eye sees and
feels all that is happening. I use one hand (the middle
and two adjoining fingers for the lips), with the other
hand propping up one leg as I lie on one side. There are
definite rhythmic motions of the pelvis. After a while in
this position, I turn over to my back and raise my legs
enough to achieve tension, still pressing my entire vulval
area up and down, sometimes with my middle finger in
my vagina. Intensity varies with my degree of physical
well-being, but this orgasm is long, sweet, and intense."

"I use my fingers and hands, circularly on my
abdomen, and up and down on my vulva. My legs are
stretched out and apart, with the knees bent. I touch my
abdomen, mound, hair especially, thighs, clitoral area,
and around my vagina. I start by lying down and
playing with my nipples. Just for the record, I've found
that a circular massage of the lower abdominal muscles,
pushing toward the hand, then starting from the
mound, up and out to the abdomen, helps alleviate
menstrual cramps, plus is generally comforting and
relaxing. Anyway, I cover and stroke my vulva and
mound with the palm of my hand or with two hands
until I am warm. Then, keeping one hand on the
mound for continued calmness, I stroke the whole
vulval area with my fingers (other hand), gradually
narrowing down to the clitoral area only, increasing the
speed and hardness of friction. I use two or three fingers
(index and the one or two next to it) on my clitoral area,

with other fingers spread around my vulva. As I near orgasm, I stretch my legs up and out and raise my torso, at the same time removing my hand from my mound."

Type II

Masturbating in Type I means lying on your back, and using your hands, fingers, or vibrator; Type II is very similar, except it means lying on your stomach instead of your back. Five point five per cent (plus an additional 1.5 per cent who could also masturbate in other ways) of the women who answered masturbated on their stomachs, using a hand or a vibrator, and of course Type II also contains all the variations discussed in conjunction with Type I. However, the pressure of the body seems to make an important difference; some women felt this increased their stimulation, while other women said they could not orgasm at all on their stomachs, or only with difficulty.

Some women of Type II move their bodies against their hands, while others move only their hands and not their bodies; generally, however, they move both.

An interesting sidelight of Type II is that a much higher percentage of women hold their legs together than in Type I. This will be discussed in detail later in the chapter. Only one fourth of the women who described the position of their legs held them apart—an unusually low percentage.

Type IIA

"I use my forefinger. I lie on my stomach and hug a pillow with my other hand. I use a circular and up and down motion on my clitoris and usually keep my legs a little apart, but as I get closer to orgasm, I bring them tight together. Sometimes I move a lot and other times just a little."

"I masturbate mainly on my stomach and use my right hand to stimulate my clitoris in a hard up and down movement, using my middle finger, index, and ring fingers. My left hand fondles my breasts. I move a lot in a rotating motion and up and down. I mmmmm a lot and say 'fuck.' I keep my legs open in the beginning and as I feel myself coming to an orgasm I close my legs and pull my body up off the floor, bed, whatever. Sometimes I masturbate standing up and use the same motion and move quite a bit. Occasionally I masturbate on my back and I find it hard to reach orgasm that way."

"When masturbating, I lie on my stomach with my legs slightly apart, using both hands, the knuckles of the right hand providing the direct pressure to the mons, with the left hand adding more pressure to the right hand. The motion of a moderately rapid front to back movement provides the clitoral friction I need."

"Sequence: I put a towel on the bed, put the vibrator on the towel with the pulsator pointed up (the pulsator has a rubber cup of about 1 inch in diameter). I usually wet the pulsator before starting. Then I lie completely quiet on my stomach with my arms and legs making a wide V, with the pulsator working the mons area. I don't use any hands until orgasm approaches, when I move the vibrator slightly with the left hand so that it is at exactly the right place. Just before orgasm, my hands and neck become rigid and my hands rise into the air a bit just before I move my left one to manipulate the vibrator at the critical time."

"I masturbate on my stomach with my right hand between my legs and gently and circularly massage my clitoris. I rarely touch my breasts or the rest of my body because I've found that physically that does little for me."

"I can only achieve orgasm through masturbation myself. I *must* lie on my stomach—legs together. I hold a small towel over my hand. The edge of my right hand below the thumb toward the wrist manipulates the clitoris, while my left hand in a fist forces my right hand against the pubic area. I accompany a rhythmic movement of the right hand with pelvic movements.

I've done this in exactly the same way since fourth grade (I'm twenty-five now), and nothing else will do it. Sometimes when masturbating I must take all my clothes off and perhaps rub my breasts on some rough material. Sometimes I jam something up the vagina and accompany this by a masochistic fantasy involvement.

Sometimes I arouse myself by laying a hot water bottle over my genitals. I must repeat that with me orgasm is *impossible* without an appropriate fantasy. Sometimes I cannot reach orgasm, and must cast around in my mind for the right one."

"It is fastest lying on my stomach with both hands under me, thumbs inside, next to one another, rubbing myself in a circular motion or up and down. It is also fastest with my legs together because then I constrict the muscles at the same time, which applies pressure."

"I lie on my stomach, elevating my ass, using one finger of my right hand, rotating it on my clitoris directly. I move a lot."

"Usually I'm on my stomach gently touching my entire genital area with my left hand. My right hand is stimulating my right nipple. When I'm particularly horny, I manage to put my nipple in my own mouth. Sometimes I use a circular motion around my clitoris. My legs are usually together. I do not move very much."

"The middle finger of my right hand is my strongest and most important stimulator. First I stimulate my clitoris by patting, and tickling, and then I move my whole hand in a circular motion, then I tease my vagina with my middle finger by patting or an up and down motion across the outer opening. (I never put anything inside because of infection.) I always lie face down on the bed, to get maximum pressure on the clitoris. Usually I move my hips around and up and down. I become greatly stimulated with my legs apart but have to have them together in order to orgasm. When I am ready to come, I increase hand stimulation till I am on the brink, then press down hard and enjoy. After, I quickly remove my hand and lie there relaxing."

"I masturbate by lying face down, putting both hands over my pubic area, with my legs together; while rotating my hips, I put pressure in an upward direction (sort of pulling the skin toward the heels of my hands) rhythmically—mostly with the index finger of my right hand and the second and third fingers of my left hand. My leg muscles are all tensed up. In short, I put my legs together, get a good clutching grip on my pubic area through whatever clothes I have on, start a sort of thrusting motion with my pelvis while applying rhythmic pressure with my hands, and orgasm."

"I lie on my stomach, my arm around the pillow, my other hand between my legs touching my clitoris with my forefinger. After five minutes, my body starts to move so that I'm all in motion. As I come closer to orgasm, my legs come closer together. The massaging of my finger on my clitoris must be constant and monotonous so that I can come."

Some Type IIs depend mostly on body movements, rather than hand movements:

"I lie face down on the bed with my arms underneath me, both hands over my genital area. Sometimes I need a soft substance between my hands and my genitals, as I move my body, not my hands. I have my legs together, with my ankles crossed. Oftentimes I cannot come when someone else is stimulating me clitorally because they don't know I need something soft there."

And Type IIs have all the variations of Type Is.

IIA₁—clitoral stimulation, sometimes with vaginal entry

"I masturbate on my stomach with my legs together, pressing on my clitoris with the fingers of both hands (index and middle fingers), one on top of the other. Sometimes I fondle my breasts or buttocks with one hand, or insert my fingers into my vagina, but not usually. I move much less than in intercourse."

"I am on my stomach lying with a pillow between my legs, either rubbing against the pillow or also using my fingers. My body is rigid and stiff as I rub my clitoris in a circular motion. My other hand is on my nipple, squeezing it, and sometimes I have a vibrator in either my vagina or ass. Legs vary."

IIA₂—clitoral stimulation, always including vaginal entry

"I lie on my stomach with my legs as far apart as possible and put about three pillows under me to further arch my back. I massage my body at the genital region and insert the middle finger of one hand up my vagina and press my other hand hard against it, at the region of my clitoris. This way I can strongly stimulate both my clitoris and my cervix (which is often sensitive, but not as much as the clitoris). My breath becomes short and gasping and my body starts pulsating and contracting violently, as my body comes down on the finger and the hand behind it. I have tried using two or three fingers, but this had the disadvantages that then it doesn't extend up as far as one finger."

"I use my hands beginning with a general overall rubbing of myself to warm my hands and my body. Then I move to my crotch and slowly apply pressure with the tips of all four fingers. Then I turn onto my stomach. I begin to use a circular motion with two fingers on my clitoris and occasionally an up and down motion with my clitoris between my fingers. With my right hand I check to see if my vagina is wet, and fantasize. I continue to stimulate my clitoris with my left hand and then insert two fingers into my vagina. I love the folds and crevices. It is amazing to feel the inside of oneself. I also sometimes stimulate the opening of the urethra, but that can be painful. My legs are usually closed, but sometimes open. If I haven't orgasmed by then, then I flex all my muscles in my legs and ass, and sometimes begin to move my whole body up and down, or maybe just move my hands. I often enjoy having my ass out from under the covers—cool air stimulates it or perhaps it's a desire to be exposed, I really can't say. Anyhow, turning on my stomach really improves my ability to reach my fingers deep into my vagina."

Type IIB—clitoral/vulval stimulation

"On my stomach with both hands (one over the other) cupping my outer genital area, lips remaining closed. I gently squeeze the area with a finger pushing up against the back curve of the lips and the palm of my hand pushing pressure on the front and the pubic bone. Legs together. I have been doing this every day since I was four or five. When my partner joins me he simply lies on my back and helps me squeeze."

"I use the curved plastic back, not the pad, of a small vibrator. I prefer this because I very seldom have long enough periods of time alone to use the manual methods, which I find too slow and not as interesting and more fatiguing. I kind of hold the vibrator more or less steady under me as I lie face down, and move my body on and around it. I use it pretty exclusively against my clitoris and vaginal lips. I like my legs together. That way, with my ankles crossed, I can use my legs to control the amount of contact with the vibrator. Sometimes I move a great deal, sometimes very little. The more aroused, the more movement."

"I lie on my stomach with a pillow between my legs starting at my waist and kinda bunched up in the middle. My hands are under the pillow just under the clitoral region, and I hump the pillow rhythmically. Then I put my vibrator just above my clitoris, and while it remains stationary, I rub against it for a few moments, until I am so gluttonous I have to turn it on, at which time my left hand steadies it or plays with my clitoris or my vaginal area. Anyway its mere presence is erotic. It is important that my right hand keep it from vibrating too much (the reason for the pillow). Sometimes the vibrator points towards the left, sometimes towards the anus. My legs are tight together, and I fantasize. Sometimes I tap the muffled vibrator in a special way."

IIB$_1$—clitoral/vulval stimulation, sometimes with vaginal entry

"I place my vibrator on my clitoris and labia minora and vaginal entrance, plus sometimes a candle in my vagina. Legs together is easier, especially with ankles crossed (it makes muscular tension greater and satisfies a reflex desire to press my knees together). I used to touch my breasts and stomach, but it seemed redundant. And I used to move my hands more than me, now I move me more."

Type III

Type III means masturbating by thrusting into a pillow or other soft object. Four per cent of the women masturbated in this way, plus an additional 1.2 per cent who could also masturbate in other ways. Type III is similar to Type II because it is done on the stomach, in the face-down position, but different because no hands are used. It involves thrusting or grinding the pelvis, especially the pubic area, against the bed, some pillows, or a clump of clothing, or perhaps moving one's body in pressing movements against the bed. Legs are usually together, and often there are some sheets of fabric wadded up and held between the legs. Thus stimulation is spread over a rather wide area in an indirect way. Six of the Type IIIs are unusual, and four of these quotes will be found at the end of this section.

"When I masturbate, I usually lie face down on the bed with some cloth, like a blanket or spread, pulled together so there is a mound I rub back and forth on."

"I lie on my stomach with some material pulled firmly between my thighs and pressing against my entire mons area, then bounce gently until orgasm."

"Yes, I enjoy masturbation. I have masturbated since babyhood and I don't see any reason to stop ever. However, I prefer sex with a partner because I like company. I always have an orgasm and usually several of them, depending on the mood I'm in. I don't masturbate like anybody else I ever heard of. I make a clump in the bedding about the size of a fist (I used to use the head of my poor teddy bear, but since I became too old to sleep with a teddy bear, a wad of the sheets has to suffice) and then lie on my stomach on top of it so that it exerts pressure on my clitoris. I then move my hips in a circular motion until I climax—very simple. It works with legs apart or together—either one, although when I am in a particularly frenzied state, together sometimes feels better. I usually end up sort of with my weight on my knees and elbows, so I can't do too much else with my hands."

"I cross my legs, thrust my pelvis against a soft object (a pillow is best) and fantasize. This is the tried and true way. I do enjoy touching myself, but it's just not as good as this. I really move very little; only when ready for orgasm do I get into any real action."

"Masturbation: I usually 'hump' a pillow or a rolled-up robe or even a laundry bag—I ride it like a horse, pressing down and easing up repeatedly—pressing harder and harder. With or without clothes on."

"I lie on top of a firm pillow and push a lump in it, then move up and down against it, my weight being on my elbows and groin. At orgasm, I embrace the pillow, close my eyes, faint and moan with delight."

"I move up and down along someone's leg to stimulate my clitoris. I move slowly and then more rapidly, but still with long, exaggerated movements."

"First I use my hands to excite my clitoris and genitals, then I use the pressure of several large pillows against my chest, abdomen, pelvis, and clitoris to increase arousal. Underpants keep the pressure generalized and allow a slippery sensation so it doesn't become painful. I move my body, especially my pelvis, against the pillows. The movement takes the form of several extended pelvic thrusts with all my weight on the pillow."

"For me, masturbation is an active process. I lie on my stomach, place a pillow between my legs, with my legs slightly spread, and rock back and forth."

"I have experienced masturbatory activities through several methods, but the way in which I achieve the deepest, most intense series of orgasms, although it is physically exhausting, is lying on a bed face down, stimulating my clitoris by pressing against the bed in a thrusting action."

"I use a towel rolled up and rub myself against it in an up and down motion. I never use my hands. This method seems to arouse some sensations that the hand cannot reach."

"I don't masturbate. Well, a little rubbing against the sheets maybe."

"Generally, I straddle a pillow (lie over a pillow between my legs), and rotate my hips with the pressure of the pillow against my clitoris."

"Usually I masturbate on the corner of a chair or something similar with a pillow between my legs. I hump up and down with my legs together. I discovered this method by accident as a child of four, having no idea what I was doing; it just felt good and I've been doing it ever since—up until about a year ago, when I had very strong guilt feelings about it, but now I don't anymore—but I still don't think I'd tell anyone about it."

III—with vaginal entry

"Lying on my stomach with something small (like a Tampax) in my vagina and a pillow clamped between my legs, I move up and down slowly, then faster and harder. The sequence is like this—I insert the object, roll over on the pillow, then move rhythmically to orgasm."

Another variation
The final version of Type III, referred to earlier in this section as unusual, involves holding yourself off the ground with your arms, and rubbing the pubic area against something while suspended:

"I stand on a chair with a protruding but low wing back and rub first against it, then raise myself so I am above it, and stroking downwards. This method allows much freedom of movement for my body, which I like. I first learned it as a child while playing on a chair my mother had."

"I draw myself up slowly against a bathroom sink, and press my mons against it very hard. The sink is stimulating because it is cold. Sometimes I revolve my legs to press harder, and sometimes 'flap' them to vibrate the vulva."

"I usually suspend myself against a piece of furniture and rub myself against it in an up and down, slow, circular motion. I never heard of it being done like this before, and I don't know where I picked it up, but at an early age it gave me a quick orgasm, or several. It's a good way, only it gives you calluses on the palms of your hands."

"When I was eleven years old I was playing around our swimming pool near the ladder. I leaned across the top of the ladder and felt a wonderful sensation in my genitals. I had no idea what it was, but I learned I could reproduce the same feeling if I leaned on the back of a chair. I continued this for years. I didn't know I was having orgasms until I was fifteen, but I knew that it was something special to me and that it wasn't some thing to advertise around the neighbourhood, because this was something happening near or in my vagina, and that was a no-no to talk about. Anyway, I still masturbate this way, only now I've advanced to sinks! If I go into the bathroom and straddle the corner of the sink, and rock back and forth I can have wonderful orgasms! I have tried to stimulate myself while I'm in bed, but it's futile. This upsets me, because my lover (he doesn't know about my masturbating—yet!) can't make me come either. I can be stimulated, but not to orgasm. An interesting note to add—throughout my teenage years (I am now twenty) I used to hop on the back of my desk chair and put a book in front of me on the desk and read and have orgasms for as long as I wanted! I went through *In Cold Blood* in total bliss!"

Type IV

Type IV is a way of masturbating in which you cross your legs very tightly and squeeze rhythmically. You can be sitting, or lying down, or on your side, just strongly tensing and untensing your legs, especially the upper thigh muscles. Sometimes there is a pillow between the legs, which can help to centre *and* generalize the stimulation.

Most of the 3 per cent of women who masturbated this way (plus the additional 9 per cent who could also masturbate in other ways) simply squeezed their thighs together or contracted their muscles:

"I lie on my back, with my legs together, and move quite a bit until right before I come; then I am pretty rigid, squeezing my vagina on the inside, moving slowly. But it's the clitoral stimulation and squeezing inside that make me come. I squeeze the whole pelvic area that way and the cheeks of my ass are very tight."

"I masturbate by rubbing my thighs together, usually lying down, but it can be done sitting up (in an office, on a bus, etc.). I rub them rhythmically, putting subtle pressure on the clitoris. The tension gradually builds to an orgasm."

"I lie flat on the bed, lock my ankles together, rhythmically squeezing my thighs together, fantasize and occasionally touch my nipples if I have difficulty reaching orgasm by thigh-squeezing alone."

"I cross my legs twice—that is, cross them and tuck an ankle around the other leg, which creates a pressure on the clitoral area. I never use hands or touch myself— don't have to. I squeeze my legs until I achieve orgasm, moving only slightly. I have very easy orgasms."

"I lie down (mostly when I bathe) and cross my legs; I caress my breasts and lightly bounce up and down as the stimulation builds. I keep squeezing my breasts and then I have an orgasm."

"I can rarely take much direct clitoral stimulation. Therefore I am more inclined to tense and release vaginal muscles in my upper thigh area. Crossing legs helps. Occasionally tapping the clitoris helps, but I do this very rarely."

"When I'm sitting (like in school), I cross my legs and contract my leg muscles together—a technique my lover (a woman) showed me."

"When I masturbate, I sit up in a chair or on the bed, cross my legs right over left at the knees and use the pressure of my inner thighs, exerting all the energy in my body and centring it in my genitals."

"I either read a sexually explicit passage in a book (keep several on my night table) or run through a sexual encounter mentally, and with ankles crossed press my thighs together—no manual contact. Have tried vibrator or manual stimulation, but usually don't bother. I first masturbated to orgasm accidentally by this method and have so continued. I saw no reason to change ever."

Some women who masturbated this way also held something—usually a pillow or towel—between their legs.

"Initially, I get stimulated either from the outside, or I tell myself stories or I fantasize, then I lie down and put my right arm through my crotch with my wrist or lower arm on my labia and clitoris (I can be either clothed or naked) and my hand on my ankle or calf, and close my thighs on my arm. My left hand may support me (if I lie on my side), or else play with my nipples. I rock my hips or pelvis for friction. Occasionally I use my fingers or hand for my labia, on my clitoris, or up my vagina."

"I bunch up a blanket or sheet, place part of it between my legs, which are tightly pressed together, and then I rub the sheet into and on my cunt, especially my clitoris, using no hands, just hip and leg movements. I begin to fantasize a situation and come in minutes."

"My legs are crossed as I tightly squeeze some object which touches my clitoris and the entrance to my vagina—like any slightly elongated object. Usually I keep it on the outside of my underwear. I rarely use my hands, I just press my uppermost thighs together against the labia. My masturbation is just basically the placing of objects and rocking of my pelvic region, with pressure on my uppermost thighs against the labia."

"When I masturbate, I usually press my legs hard together (or wind them around each other) and use a towel, pulling it against my clitoris rhythmically until I come."

"I use a pillow or some other object that is firm but soft. I hold it between my legs and rub it up and down or squeeze it with my thighs. I can get stimulated somewhat by rubbing my fingers directly on my genitals, but can't touch my clitoris, as it is too sensitive. In fact, I'm better off wearing pants so I don't become too directly stimulated. My legs have to be clasped on the pillow; they can't be apart. I move quite a lot but don't need to if my fantasy is strong enough. I need lots of air, so therefore I prefer it out of the covers, with my ass and feet, especially, exposed."

"I masturbate on my side, squeezing a quilt between my thighs, moving up and down. This is the way I did it the first time orgasm happened to me, and I've had no reason to change, although at times I've thought I should practise lying on my back to learn to please men."

"I lie in bed on my stomach, my arms around my pillow, fantasizing. Then I put a soft pillow between my legs, and push it against myself with my legs together tightly around it. By moving up and down, I orgasm within five minutes in a really beautiful way."

"I put a blanket between my legs, stuffing as much as I can of it between them, and then close them together tightly. I push the blanket especially against my clitoris and move up and down rhythmically, tightening and releasing my thighs at the same time. And sometimes I put one finger of the other hand inside my vagina or anus, from behind."

"I lie on my stomach and pull one or two pillows between my legs. I press against them with my pubic area, while pushing with my hands in the front of the pillow (both hands). My legs are apart and moving as in a butterfly stroke in swimming—like a butterfly! A few times I have used the hose of a hair dryer to blow warm air on my vagina for initial stimulation, as a kind of 'foreplay.' I also push pillows against my breasts."

"I use a small pillow between my legs and use both hands on it to apply pressure to my clitoris. I move up and down until orgasm, which takes half a minute."

"I am sixteen and have no boyfriend. I have hardly ever 'fooled around,' so all of my orgasms have resulted from masturbation. I have at least one orgasm every time I masturbate. I enjoy masturbation physically. I masturbate very often, from once to six times daily. Usually in school or in public I just cross my legs and press my thighs together, then relax, then press. By myself I do one of three things: 1) lying down on my back or side, I cross my legs and press my thighs, then uncross my legs when at the height of tension and raise hips off the bed; 2) lie on my stomach with some material (or a nightgown or something) pulled firmly between my thighs and pressing against the entire mons area, then bounce gently until orgasm; 3) or rub my clitoris with my finger, legs apart."

"In my teens I branched out into public masturbation in boring classes and during the sermon when I was a member of the choir. All I did was cross my legs and squeeze the thigh muscles together repeatedly for two or three minutes. But even with the utmost control it was impossible to avoid a slight convulsion at the moment of orgasm, which I would disguise by a coughing fit or having to lean over and scratch my leg. Must have been pretty horny."

"I get completely naked and lie on the floor. I place a towel between my legs so it's in contact with my clitoris. Inside my vagina is some object like a penis, and the towel is also in contact with the tip of this. I put my legs together tightly and rotate my hips. Sometimes I read pornography first."

A few women also described another highly unusual variation similar to one mentioned at the end of Type III. Here again the whole body is off the ground, although there is no outside pressure on the pubic area as in Type III.

"I masturbate by tightening (clenching) my vaginal muscles. I don't usually touch my clitoris at all, but can do it just with my muscles. I can do it sitting up and pressing myself up with my hands or arms, i.e., sitting at a desk I can lean on my arms, raise my pelvis and tense my muscles and have a great orgasm."

Type V

Type V (water massage) is masturbating by running water (usually warm) over the genitals to orgasm. Two per cent of the women who masturbated (plus another 2 per cent who also masturbated in other ways) used this method. The most common way of doing it is to turn on the faucet with a strong, hard flow, lie on your back with your legs up on the wall and your clitoris positioned under the rushing water. Legs are usually apart.

"I masturbate with shower water only. I aim it at my

clitoris, legs spread apart. Sometimes I hook up a hose and sit on the side of the tub, and use a nice steady stream of water. Or I lie down in the tub, and let the shower water strike my clitoris if it is hard enough."

"I lie in the tub on my back with a stream of very warm water on my vagina, mons, and clitoris. The harder the pressure and hotter the water, the quicker the orgasm."

"I remove the head from my shower to allow a steady stream of water to come out. I open the vaginal lips, exposing my clitoris. The water can be slightly hot for more stimulation, and hips can be moved slightly to tantalize and prolong the enjoyment. I usually do it standing up. Lying down is more beautiful, but you get your hair and face wet. This orgasm tops them all for me, and can be multiple."

"I masturbate with water, preferably a half-inch stream that is arched so my butt does not stop the drain. My feet are braced on the wall about two feet apart, and I am lying on my back."

"Occasionally I bring myself to orgasm in the bathtub. First I excite myself with fingers, then I turn the water on and get into an acrobatic position so my vagina is directly under the faucet. I start with the water warm or cool and at a low pressure on my clitoris. When I have gotten excited I run the water harder and I lift myself closer to the water and let it pound into my vagina and then I come and it's the most fantastic feeling."

"For masturbation, I have used a vibrator, but I usually masturbate when I take my bath by letting the gush of warm water run over my genitals. My legs are apart and the water usually hits right on my clitoris, until I go into orgasm."

"I use the hand shower (very efficient). I regulate the flow and the heat and pat my clitoris up and down with water. My legs are almost closed, otherwise it hurts. I do not move my body. I almost always come this way. When no hand shower is available I use an object, but then it takes a very long time for an orgasm to come, if any."

"I get in the tub without water (usually this occurs immediately following a shower) and turn on the faucet only part way, adjusting the water to warm. Then I manoeuvre my buttocks as close to the running water as possible, arranging my body so the water strikes directly on the clitoris. Sometimes I 'rock' to and fro just slightly. I always come in a few minutes."

"I regularly have orgasm in the bathtub by allowing the water from the tap to flow over my clitoris and labia, and moving my body so that the flow 'strokes' the area. In this way I can achieve orgasm rapidly and fully, and feel quite satisfied after. I turn the water on, lie under it, adjust it for the right pressure and temperature (I like it slightly hotter than body temperature). Then I lie on my back, directly stimulating my clitoris and labial area with the water flow from the tap, and moving my body—sometimes a little, sometimes a lot. I like to spread my legs apart when I do it, and to cry out or moan with pleasure when I have the impulse to. As the sensation becomes stronger I move faster and faster until orgasm occurs. I lie there a few moments after, then sit up and wash myself."

"With the hose in the shower was how I masturbated for eight years at home and then when I moved to the place I have now, my dear old landlord (eighty-nine years old), gave me a hose you hook onto the shower (I have no bath). If he only knew. I first put the nozzle of an intense spray right against my clitoris, spreading the vulva area apart with my fingers of the other hand a little. At the same time I would stand, sometimes inserting the two tubes from my vaginal foam in my rectum and vagina. This was a little difficult because it's hard to relax while standing up and holding the tubes in me at the same time. It also gave me helpless feelings of great pleasure, standing there and reaching an orgasm. Finally I tried sitting down on the cold floor with my legs out in front of me. This is much better because I can brace my feet against the wall and relax better. It doesn't take very much pressure before I get the aching feeling and then I come. It's pretty hard to get up and take a shower after that."

Type VI

Of all the women who described how they masturbated, only 1.5 per cent masturbated only by vaginal insertion, plus another 0.4 per cent who used this method sometimes. Over half of these women stimulated their clitoral areas first manually.

What was inserted?

candle	=	5 women
fingers	=	13 women
one finger	=	4 women
vibrator	=	6 women
dildo	=	3 women

"I usually masturbate with my finger and touch my breasts with my other hand, but not always. Sometimes when I'm lying in the sun in my bathing suit and I'll start to feel sexy, I end up going inside to masturbate (when I'm alone in the house). I usually use a back and forth movement in my vagina, or just hold my fingers there for a while. My legs are quite wide apart with my knees up near me. Sometimes I move a lot, depending on the intensity of my feeling at the time."

Leg position

An interesting and important, but as yet unanswered puzzle about female orgasm is why some women need to have their legs apart for orgasm while others must have them together; still others prefer to have them bent at the knees or up in the air. Just as different women need different kinds of stimulation for orgasm (the masturbation types we have just seen) they also *need* different leg positions to orgasm.

Unfortunately, many women did not answer this final part of the masturbation question, probably due to the length of the question, and because they assumed their leg position was the same as everyone else's. However, most of the women who did answer usually had their legs apart. Still, a significant number of women in all the masturbation types did hold their legs together.

Reasons women gave for keeping their legs together included the following.

"I like my legs together because then everything (the whole genital area) is tighter and the vibrations travel better."

"If I have my legs *apart,* I feel almost nothing, no matter what I do!"

"Legs *together* intensifies orgasm—to have everything as tight and tense as possible is best, like a drum."

"When I masturbate I tense my legs up real tight and squeeze them together in order to come. It is almost impossible unless I do this 'tense and squeeze.' Then for the few seconds I am releasing I feel out of this world."

"It is much stronger if my legs are together and I contract my pelvic area and hold my whole body tight."

"Legs together is better, easier, quicker."

On the other hand, some women could feel nothing with their legs *together.*

"I prefer to be on my back with my legs raised and open wide. There is such a strong feeling in my legs accompanying orgasm that if my weight is resting on my legs the orgasm is different."

"My body is still, I think—my face is 'distorted' (as though in ecstasy). And my legs must be apart and straight up in the air."

Some women who liked their legs apart also liked their knees bent.

"My legs are apart, either with my knees bent while my feet are flat on the bed, or with my knees at right angles and my feet together. I can masturbate sitting also, and standing, but I prefer lying down in this position."

"I prefer to be on my back with my legs somewhat apart and bent and holding quite stiff. My movement is like a gradual increased vibration."

"Legs apart, knees bent, sometimes touching my chest. I move very little, as this stillness seems to heighten my pleasure."

"Legs bent up and somewhat apart. It helps to have the pubic area pulled up taut."

"I lie on my back, knees bent, legs up and apart. Then I move the bottom half of my body a lot in a sort of pumping motion."

Some women moved their legs together for orgasm, as the feeling intensified, after having them apart during stimulation (and a very small number did the opposite).

"As my body begins to tense, I put my legs tightly together."

"I like my legs far apart when direct stimulation begins, but it is torture for me to try to keep them this way as the 'good vibes' heighten."

"I have my legs apart first then grip them together later on."

"I lie on my back, legs apart at first, then put them tightly together near orgasm. I move very little except to tense and relax my body."

Some women also moved their legs alternately together and apart, perhaps increasing the stimulation by "pumping" the genital lips and interior bulbs.

"I prefer to lie quite still; then, when the orgasm starts to happen, I get into this rhythm thing, usually lifting one leg, then the other."

"As I'm building up to orgasm, I sort of pump my

legs back and forth slightly, especially my upper legs. Each time they come together I feel a spark of the orgasm feeling, then I go apart (a few inches) to build it up more and after about ten times, wow! It's beautiful!"

Most women had only one basic leg position that worked best for them, but a few women found leg positions interchangeable.

"I hold my legs together or apart depending on the type of fantasy I am using."

"My muscles usually tense up, and then right before orgasm my hips start moving back and forth. My legs are the tensest of all, usually bent at the knees, one up and one sideways when I'm by myself. With a partner, there are other considerations that determine what I do with my legs—sometimes they stiffen out straight."

The reason for the importance of different leg positions to different women is still a mystery. Does it depend on how the woman first learned how to orgasm? Or does the anatomy of our genitals (both interior and exterior) vary just enough from woman to woman to make different positions necessary for different individuals? Answers to these questions are simply not known.

2 Orgasm

Is orgasm important?

"Orgasm feels great! Like a combination of intense pleasurable sensations plus an ecstatic frenzy of love, energy, and emotion, all mixed together."

"Orgasms are a renewal of all my senses, an awakening of life, spring, refreshing, sparkling, exciting, and complete relief of everyday boredom."

"They make me incredibly happy, everything on the way to orgasm is heavenly. An orgasm cancels out all rage and longing for at least forty-eight hours, and the day an orgasm bores me, I think I'll commit suicide."

"A marvellous happiness, comparable to no other."

"Orgasm is the *ultimate* pleasure—which women often deny themselves, but men never do."

"Orgasm. The most fantastic sensation I've ever experienced."

"At best, an organ-moving cataclysm: my ovaries, uterus, breasts, and brain become one singing dark pulsating sea of the most exquisite feeling."

"Whoever said orgasm wasn't important for a woman was undoubtedly a man."

Are orgasms important to women? Although the answer would seem clearly to be yes, it has often been said, and written, that women do not *need* orgasms, at least in the same way men do. One woman answered these claims perfectly when she said, "Whoever said orgasm wasn't important for a woman was undoubtedly a man. Good sex expresses love, relaxation, and letting go, plus pure body pleasure."

Most women agreed:

"Only physicians and clergymen tell women we

should comfort and pleasure our husbands, and to 'stop chasing rainbows' when our turn comes around."

"The idea that it doesn't matter if women have orgasms or not is an absurd lie women tell themselves."

"I am entitled to orgasms. If I have to masturbate to get them, then my man should also have to masturbate for his and that does not mean masturbating in my vagina—i.e., intercourse when he's the only one who has orgasm."

"I can't imagine having sex without orgasm. Maybe that's because I like having sex with a woman, and I've read that women with women have many more orgasms than a woman with a man. I mean, how could a woman who has any kind of intelligence not have an orgasm during sex? I would not like to have sex without orgasm—and can't see why I should."

"I love having orgasm, there's no question about this, I can tell you! But I don't like it when I feel like: now you have to come, now's the time, and I am expected to do it like to demonstrate that I am enjoying it or something. Today now that men are supposed to know how to give me an orgasm, it has become part of the whole thing, that moment when you can feel they are watching to see if you do."

Women are now under great pressure to perform by having orgasms, especially during intercourse.
It does seem clear that women should have a right to orgasms during sex as part of the natural course of things. However, now that the idea has become popular that women should enjoy sex "too," this new "right" has sometimes turned into an oppression. Women can be made to feel that they must have orgasms more to please the man than to please themselves.

"It is only fair to him, and makes him feel 'as a man' and successful."

"I 'perform' and boost his ego and confidence and love for me with an orgasm. I do not *like* to think of myself as a performer, but I feel judged, and also judge myself, when I don't have an orgasm."

"There's this pressure there is something psychologically wrong with you if you don't have an orgasm."

"Yes, alas, I still feel I must have an orgasm to make him feel, er, macho."

"An orgasm is not necessary to make you 'normal,' but men do expect it so I often force myself, especially because he enjoys watching. Besides, it's better for him to feel a contracting vagina, but you can also do that at will if you practise."

"Yes, I feel the need to perform orgasmically, competitively, with other women at large in the community. I wish I didn't. It really got started when I used to feel pressure from my former partner, because if I didn't come, it proved he wasn't a 'real man.' But I'm not a star or a two-ring circus."

"I'm very wary about telling new partners I don't have orgasms because then they make it a contest to see if *they* can be the one to make me come. I really resent being expected to come, and almost *forced* if I don't."

"Sometimes I have felt that reaching orgasm was more a matter of satisfying my partner's desire to satisfy me than my own need for orgasm."

"You're supposed to be uninhibited and have orgasms, and when I do it makes him feel confident and secure. Orgasm is important, but not as important as *he* thinks: my orgasm is actually more important to my husband than to me!"

"Yes, I must have an orgasm. Otherwise, I'm not a real person and it'll make him feel bad and maybe he'll abandon me. Men enjoy making love more to women who have orgasms."

"I would enjoy sex with no orgasm at times, if I felt other people weren't uptight about it, and if the reasons were my own. Maybe sex would be better if we'd never heard of orgasm."

"I'm afraid that new partners will think that I'm weird and not as sexy as other women if I don't have orgasms—or that I'm selfish and aggressive if I do!"

"I wish orgasms didn't exist. Then maybe sex would be fun."

There is also a social pressure that says a woman who has an orgasm is more of a woman, a "real" woman.

"I don't think orgasms are that important; the literature has given women another burden. But I'm ashamed to admit, because of the myth, I feel 'good' having an orgasm—like I'm a *real woman!* Arrgh . . ."

"I can enjoy sex without orgasm, but psychologically I feel like I'm a failure, like a not totally functioning woman."

"Orgasms are continually talked about. Therefore if I don't have one, I feel inadequate."

"The idea of having orgasms is important to me, but I can certainly enjoy sex without having them. Worse than not having the orgasm is the feeling that I've failed or that I'm frigid or unsexy. I feel a lot of pressure, both from men and from women's liberation, to have orgasms or insist on having an orgasm. I don't have sex in order to have an orgasm—I suppose part of me wonders whether I will 'this time'—but generally I have sex because I want to have a loving fucking tenderness with that person. Or because it seems like a good idea at the time. Or because I want to possess them in some way for a while."

"Orgasm is great and I can have them easily—except in one circumstance: when I am getting really passionate and acting hot, if the man moans something like 'oh what a devil of a woman you are', then this turns me right off and I can't do it."

"Yes, orgasms are important, but the symbol of 'Orgasm' has probably been exaggerated as a symbol of being 'sexy,' 'fiery,' 'passionate,' 'alive,' etc."

"All the publicity about orgasm is making me nervous."

"It's a big credential to have orgasms—I feel sort of commended when I do."

"Having an orgasm unlocks the door to my being a full woman."

"When I have an orgasm, I show open, clear womanness."

"My mate says I look and 'perform' like a woman, so I'm not bothered about whether or not I have an orgasm. However, I must admit the old myth of being 'less of a woman' lingers in the back of my mind."

"Orgasms are important, but I don't know if it's because of their own sake or because I think I ought to have them. I rarely feel I *need* one."

"Now there is so much emphasis on orgasm, a person would feel abnormal not having one."

A few women reacted strongly against this pressure to perform.

"Once in a while a desire to impress someone with my 'tremendous sexuality' appeals to me, but usually I am just very happy to have lots of orgasms. Basically I'm too selfish to bother to prove anything to my partners—and especially, too intelligent to want to do *anything* to prove I'm a real woman! Bullshit on that!"

"I only want to have orgasms for my own pleasure, not for his appraisal of my womanliness!"

On the other hand, not having an orgasm with a man could be frustrating too, because you could wind up feeling left out and cheated watching him have his.

"I want to have orgasm, not so much for the feeling of the orgasm itself as for the frustration and anger I feel when I don't."

"When I see my partner having one, I feel I should enjoy one too."

"It's rarely that I have an altruistic, non-orgasmic

intercourse. Without orgasm I feel robbed."

"I *always* felt cheated when he had orgasm and I didn't."

"Having sex without an orgasm makes me feel like I was along for the ride, but why? (Except when I'm really emotionally involved.)"

"Consciously, I don't care, but perhaps I resent the absence of orgasms on a more unconscious level."

"Yes, when having sex with someone I become furious if I don't have at least one orgasm. I don't enjoy sex without them because I get terribly built up. I wouldn't even bother with sex without orgasm."

"Orgasm is important to me for two reasons: 1) physically and 2) I feel cheated when I do not experience one. I feel many times my sexuality is not important to certain men."

"*Never* having orgasms would be indicative of something being wrong with 'our' sex life. He always has one, so why shouldn't I?"

"If I am engaging in sexual activity with the same partner repeatedly, never achieving an orgasm, I become very angry and frustrated and increasingly frigid—really turning off on things that would normally turn me on."

"I *deserve* a climax after working him up to one. He has one so why shouldn't I? No matter how long it takes I make him rub my clitoris until I orgasm."

"I regard orgasm as a natural end to sexual experiences—when I kiss passionately I want and expect to go on to intercourse and orgasm. When the man doesn't seem to notice or care or try to help me to have one, I become *infuriated.*"

"My situation is that I like sex with my mate a lot, we have been together for four years and he is the sexiest thing alive, really turns me on, but I often don't come with him. Why? I don't know, maybe I'm still shy or insecure, I'm so crazy about him. I know this is wrong, but I'm working on it. Anyway, often I do come, though I have to stop 'being in the moment' with him and focus on myself. I don't like doing that so much, but otherwise I feel left alone after he comes and he feels relaxed and I'm still up there."

"Intercourse is okay sometimes for the emotional and physical warmth of the sharing, but it's better with orgasm and I interpret a man's understanding of my desire for orgasm both as an indication of his sincerity and of his caring."

"Because I never orgasm during intercourse, I still enjoy intercourse but sometimes I do feel cheated and angry when he has his orgasm because I can't orgasm."

"Orgasm is important—especially if my partner has one."

"If I don't orgasm, when intercourse is over I am left frustrated and unfulfilled and bitter/guilty. The more orgasms the better."

"Always watching the joy of my partner would be intolerable."

"I prefer no sex to bad sex, which to me means sex with a fumbler or a male chauvinist pig, who doesn't let me have an orgasm."

"Before we settled into a pattern of clitoral stimulation to orgasm and then intercourse, I sometimes enjoyed sex a lot without orgasm. But usually I felt very frustrated and pissed off, especially if I almost had orgasm but then didn't. Unfortunately, I was and still am too inhibited to masturbate in a situation like that."

"There is no reason for sex unless I orgasm too, otherwise I get mean."

"Sometimes I feel slighted if my partner doesn't bother to give me one, and just goes on and enjoys his own and then falls asleep."

"Why would a woman want sex without them? Sick!"

"Sex play with no orgasm is lovely sometimes, but not intercourse where he does orgasm—it makes me feel short-changed and inadequate."

"Sometimes I get hung up on the thought that I

could have had an orgasm when *he* did."

"We have had lots of sex without *me* orgasming— sometimes it's very frustrating and I'm upset but I love him and I keep trying."

"I feel cheated and in pain and angry—so frustrated that I am seriously considering getting a divorce."

"I must have an orgasm, or I climb a wall. I have to go somewhere private and masturbate. Before I knew about orgasms, I loved to be aroused, and just come down naturally after the man had his. I would go to sleep just pleasantly horny but not disturbed. Now I can't and I won't."

"The rare times when sex was a tool for healing, or emotional relating when extra warmth and intimacy were needed, orgasm was unnecessary. Also, before I learned how to have an orgasm, sex was a service of intimacy to my partner. Still I always enjoy it more with one, and usually it's not fair if he does and I don't, do you think?"

"If he comes and I don't, I feel short-changed and like crying and like I don't want to have sex ever. But once in a while I feel satisfied and warm and cuddly."

"It is okay without orgasms if my partner isn't being selfish, or taking advantage, and if he is tender and considerate—but inside I still feel kind of pissed off."

"I feel confused and cheated when I don't have an orgasm and I lie there watching him have his."

"Sometimes I tell my husband I don't *need* to come to enjoy sex, but I think that's *bullshit* on my part."

"How would a man feel if he made love and never achieved orgasm?"

"I must orgasm because sex is supposed to be an exchange. If I'm going to serve his physical needs, he has to serve mine. Also, orgasm is such a great experience, I like to let a man share it with me. I think men should get used to giving this pleasure to women. I don't like just getting fucked."

Sometimes women focused on the man's orgasm as a surrogate for their own.

"I guess I get very tied up in how he is feeling also, and so when I can make him climax, I feel as though I have also, so that I don't need to any more."

"Sometimes I can have mental orgasms helping my partner reach an orgasm—and find it just as stimulating."

"Sometimes it's more fulfilling without orgasm because it's possible to experience my partner's orgasm more completely."

"I think sometimes it's okay not having orgasm during intercourse, but perhaps I am too concerned with making the sexual experience whatever he wants."

"Giving is more important than taking, therefore if there is a choice between my partner's and my orgasm, I take theirs."

Some women came to the conclusion that orgasm during sex was not important.

"Orgasms are exceedingly pleasurable and as I haven't given up masturbation, I guess you could say they're 'important' to me. But that's exactly the point of something else—I totally associate orgasm with masturbation. *I don't have to come,* and often when he comes, it's the peak of sex for me."

"To me orgasms have nothing to do with regular male/female sex. Orgasm is not necessary because I can give them to myself in masturbation."

"Since I don't have orgasm during intercourse, therefore I enjoy it without."

"Personally, I don't mind very much if I don't have one with a man. I don't expect to."

"Orgasm is something I am able to give myself any time—so it's no big deal not to have one. Cuddling and touching is more important to get from my partner."

"I think orgasms are over-rated. When I masturbate, it is to achieve orgasm, but with my lover I really don't care if I do or not. I just want to feel warm and close."

"Orgasm is not always necessary during intercourse. It's still okay because of the warmth and comfort and just to let someone know you accept their physicality."

"Orgasms are only important in context. If all I wanted was orgasm, I'd masturbate. If someone wants to give me an orgasm, and it is an act of love and affection and consideration, then that is important."

"It's okay not having an orgasm if you love your partner and there is lots of affection and caring. If I love my partner, I get emotional satisfaction even without orgasm."

In a sense these women were *right*: to experience sex as a race for orgasm is a narrow and unimaginative view. However, most women are not speaking from a position of strength in this regard. We are not always *having* orgasms during sex, and *then* saying they are not important. To bring our sexuality up from underground, we must bring our own orgasms (and the stimulation and body positions necessary to have those orgasms) out of hiding, and feel free to make them a natural, comfortable part of sexual relations.

The right to orgasm is a political question for women. Although there is nothing wrong with not having orgasms, and nothing wrong with empathizing with and sharing another person's pleasure, there *is* something wrong when this becomes a pattern where the man is *always* having an orgasm and the woman isn't. If we make it easy and pleasurable for men to have an orgasm, and don't use as much energy starting activities that lead to ours, so that we have orgasm ourselves, aren't we just "servicing" men? If we *know* how to have orgasms, but are unable to make this a part of a sexual relationship with another person, then we are not in control of *choosing* whether or not we have an orgasm.

This is the sexual version of the traditional female role—watching and nurturing, always acting as a helpmate in the lives of others. Isn't not expressing our means of orgasm part of the same sense of martyrdom and self-sacrifice that women have always shown in other aspects of personal and family relations? We are the sensitive and understanding ones, while men are the physical and mechanical experts who "get things done." In sex, supposedly, men know what to do: they initiate and carry out the main activities. We "respond" to them. Fortunately, women today are becoming more and more physically active—in sports and in sex—and this has only just begun to change the shape of what we call "female sexuality."

What do the stages of orgasm feel like?

Arousal

What does arousal feel like?

Judging from the rapturous descriptions of feelings during arousal, its pleasures would seem definitely to rival those of orgasm itself. *No one* disliked arousal; there wasn't a single negative description of how it felt. Words used to describe it often included "tingly," "alive," "warm," "happy," feelings of wanting to touch and be touched. Most women felt the sensations all over the body; few mentioned genitals. And in these descriptions most seemed to be describing their experiences during sex with another person—emotional terms were abundantly used.

"I feel (without touching them) my skin, breasts and legs and hands and neck. It's like my body has expanded and wants frictional warm-type contact."

"There is an exquisite tension, an ache, a hunger— and my breasts get tight and feel as if they must be touched."

"I have a sort of fainting type feeling—tingling warmth, fullness, dampness, energy."

"Blood pressure rising . . . every part of my body feels each and every touch made on it—I am hypersensitive, in heaven."

"A sense of well-being, I am radiant, like a gradual awakening."

"A feeling of being loved and wanted. Exhilarating."

"A crawly feeling all over; I want to get closer and closer."

"My body feels poised, alive, pulsing—glowing, 'high.'"

"A quickening of all my senses."

"Urgency, an irresistible pull."

"Moderate arousal is lovely and is intoxicating in many ways; severe arousal is practically painful but *wonderful* with the final orgasm."

"I'm high—I breathe fast—also light-headed, in a dream world, sounds are distant, time suspended."

"At my best with the person, happy, and, in general, warm."

"It feels like tenderness and caring."

"Happy and joyous, tingling."

"Could go on forever—will go insane."

"Warm and good, secure, caring."

"It is a pleasure to be aroused. I become more sensitive and alive to everything."

"Great, like in good health."

"A total focus of attention, while time stands still, body alert, waiting."

"Heightened sensitivity all over; I become aware of part of me I am not usually aware of."

"Floating."

"Supreme sensitivity to touch—waves of butterflies in my stomach."

"I love it when it turns into a fiery, driving force. I become conscious of my vagina and it seems to beckon through a longing feeling."

"I am aroused by some people just by closeness and tenderness. I feel like I want to touch all my skin to all of their skin."

"Like an awakening and the beginning of life."

"Fantastic, almost unbearably ecstatic."

"Like wanting someone so close you just can't touch enough."

"The physical state of wanting—a feeling in the back of my throat, deep emotion and desire."

"Emotional well-being, affection, intimacy."

"Very free and uninhibited about my body, and very close to my partner. I want to rub my body all over his and get as physically close as possible."

"Attractive and wanted."

"Blood throbbing."

"Reckless!"

"Being aware of all parts of my body, wanting to give caring touches—in touch with my own cosmic energy, and my partner's—there is no past and no future."

"My whole body feels wide awake, *super*-stimulated."

"Wow! My whole body is alive, sensitive, fantastic, tingling, positive!"

"My body becomes soft and fluid, and completely in harmony with the universe."

"Happiness, energy, thrills, ecstasy, lying in whipped cream."

"On the edge of an earthquake."

"Warm, tingly, heady. Specific parts of the body come into focus as they are touched, and I feel loved, wanted and worthwhile."

"I feel sensual, excited—and a trifle wicked."

"I am completely sensitized."

"Hot, want to be close and touch her."

"Beautiful and *alive.*"

"A rush—hot—yearning in my breasts to be touched—a desire to kiss."

"Warm and wet inside and out, electric—open and languorous."

"Electric currents blowing through my body to my clitoris and vagina—I want to touch and hold him and want my body up against his."

"Heightened alertness, mental health, euphoria."

"I would describe arousal as an increasingly powerful beautiful tingling I always felt was the step past the shivers we gave each other in the sixth grade."

"Electricity with outward streaks, like drawn outwards from stars."

"Buzzy, like being mildly aware of every bit of my body, especially my genitals, breasts and neck, stomach, mouth and ears. Also, pretty, desirable and *good*!"

"Very emotional, completely alive, with my entire body urging towards my partner. I just can't get enough of being felt all over and would like to merge with the other person and their body."

"My whole body reacts with a feeling of aching and releases great feelings of love within me."

"A heightened sensitivity all over, a vaguely burning sensation in the clitoral area, and a sort of yearning to be touched on my breasts, stomach, ass, and vagina—great!"

"Tremendous excitement, losing control of my body, I feel desires and needs which I can't deny, and might do things which I would never do in an unexcited state. My body becomes acutely sensitized and simple touches or caresses in various places give me excruciating pleasure."

"My vulva feels still and hot and sexy—my skin feels funny."

"Joy is the only word I can use to describe the feeling with someone I love."

"Warm and loved and content and not lonely, and 'together' with the other person."

"I lose control, do things impulsively—feel shaky and weak and at the same time tense and super-sensitive all over—I have a good feeling that I can't describe because it's better than any other feeling I've ever had."

"A feeling of power, strength."

"A racing of my heart, an intense feeling of closeness, wanting to touch bodies."

"Somehow it gives me the chance to climb above myself—to wake up from the fogginess of daily existence."

"Like being outside of my body, outside of my mind, not really caring what is important to my usual self."

"Sometimes I feel aroused generally, without actually having been touched—it feels like a kind of tension, a sweet tension, and there is a dreaminess in the desire to touch and be touched. Then again, arousal from touching and being touched can be more acute, a kind of pang in my vagina; nerves stand up under my skin.

Being *too* aroused is painful."

"All touch feels exquisite and I want it to go on forever."

"It feels like freedom or power, in the cunt and gut. My body feels uninhibited and *strong.*"

"Gorgeous pleasure like baths and sun."

"Senses alert and energizing."

"Sweaty hotness all over my body."

"Like a strong emotion."

"Physical *yearning.*"

"Suffusion of delicious feelings."

"Alive everywhere."

"I am alone in the world with my partner."

"Suspended animation, like an eternity in one second. Intense communication through drinking and tasting of their body."

"Voluptuous, elegant, and sensuous."

"Eager for more!"

"A strange feeling, another dimension of myself, melting away from my anchors."

"A feeling of swelling heat, dense, engulfing, sweet."

"Warm, pulsating, dark. All over my body, an intensity of feeling."

"My whole body burns."

"Do you enjoy extended periods of arousal? Arousal for its own sake?"

Arousal is highly enjoyable. But is it pleasurable for its own sake, without an orgasm following?

Many women said that long arousal does feel good.

"No sexual experience has probably ever quite equalled those old high school days in the back seat of a parked car when arousal was an end in itself."

"I wish making love were more sensuous touchings and less direct genital activity. My most exciting times were the hours I used to spend just touching my best friend, and she me."

"Arousal is the ultimate part of sex. During a stage of heightened arousal, I prefer *not* to have orgasm. (It brings me down off it.)"

"I don't remember, as my sexual experiences in the last eight years always led to bed. But as a teenager, getting hot was always neat."

"I often find I like the period of lengthy arousal better than the relatively brief orgasm. After two or three hours of it, I'm as exhausted as if I had had an orgasm."

"When I am with someone I love, sometimes being close and not going for an orgasm can be beautiful."

"I have often enjoyed just passionate kissing and then lost interest when more involved sex followed."

"I like the 'befores' better than intercourse."

"Yes, I like arousal, but I've been conditioned *not* to, so when I get really aroused, I cop out and turn it into intercourse."

"A very intense state can be achieved and maintained—I call it skimming."

"Yes, arousal is more important than orgasm. It was this that sustained me through all the sexual encounters I had that didn't end in orgasm."

"Yes, I am so ungenitally oriented that I find it difficult to make it with my lover. I just tend to caress and be loving rather than get directly involved genitally. Sex is the only legitimate way to get enough skin contact."

"Plain old-fashioned necking and petting can go on for hours as far as I'm concerned, including touching, kissing, nuzzling and rubbing."

"If I had to choose, I would give up orgasms rather than this feeling."

"I like to keep this state for as long as possible. It just feels very alive and responsive. And it removes the loneliness and isolation more than anything else."

In other words, women really loved the feelings of arousal and being together physically with someone. Many of them would like to see the imaginative mix of activities expanded and revalued—not always necessarily aimed so mechanically at orgasm.

But some women complained that men wouldn't wait for long periods of arousal.

"I like to prolong my states of arousal until the desire for orgasm is irresistible. Unfortunately, many men are too impatient to allow this."

"I never reach this state with a man. They are much too uptight."

"Yes, I love long arousal, especially if it is clear we are not going to have intercourse. I had one of the best times ever last summer necking with a man for several hours. But I haven't found anyone to do this kind of thing within a situation of possible intercourse. It's always cut short and I guess I haven't yet been able to say, 'I want to do this and I don't intend to do anything else.'"

"I like long arousals but it usually doesn't last as long as I need because he is rushing me to move along toward orgasm."

"It makes me sad I have to control my actions and miss so much of this because my partner is still conditioned to want intercourse practically whenever we touch."

"A long period of arousal is very important to me, and sometimes I'm disappointed if my partner becomes too excited to continue."

"Sometimes when I'm having sex, the guy comes just as I'm beginning to be turned on. I don't like it. It's disappointing."

"I like long periods of arousal. That's why my husband I are not too compatible—I talk to him and he's sensitive for five minutes, then it's 'business as usual.'"

"Who has such choices? Not me!"

"I like it prolonged, but I know very few males who can or are interested in doing so."

And arousal is not so much fun when the man goes on to orgasm, leaving the woman aroused with no orgasm.

Many women have often had sex without orgasm, and feel resentful that men almost always do orgasm. Thus they made it clear that although arousal is enjoyable, they expect to have an orgasm too.

"I enjoy simple touching just for its own sake without overtones of 'this has to conclude in intercourse.' But getting me aroused so that the man can be satisfied—that is a sexual rip-off as far as I am concerned."

"It's pleasurable to be caressed extensively, but I don't want any man getting off on me if he isn't willing to work to get me off too."

"I generally find men unable to accept arousal alone. They demand fulfilment, their *own,* of course—but rarely mine!"

"It's like a big let-down and makes me very quiet and sad when I don't orgasm, and he is already lying there quiet and happy and not interested any more."

"If I see I'm not going to have an orgasm, I feel resentful, bored and frustrated."

"If it doesn't lead to orgasm, I have a feeling of being cheated and a lot of anger."

"Sex for me until recently was a long series of one-nighters, and I never felt that I had plenty of time to be physically satisfied. Usually the man would just hop on and pump away and suddenly it was all over. I resented it more and more each time it happened, and now I never let it happen."

"If I'm with a man I'm sure will satisfy me eventually, I enjoy prolonging it. But if I'm doubtful, I have to try to 'get mine' before I lose the chance."

Other women pointed out that long arousal without orgasm at some point is extremely frustrating—especially when it becomes a pattern.

"It is very frustrating to *repeatedly* become aroused and then not orgasm. Now I refuse to let myself become aroused in this situation."

"It can become painful both physically and psychologically. I guess I resent non-orgasmic stimulation because I associate it with the years I couldn't come, and would hate myself and the men I was with."

"After a certain point, non-orgasmic sex, even just non-genital sex, dragged out over a period of months, makes me lose interest."

"Yes, but if it happens continually without a release it soon makes me ill. I'm on edge all the time and feel sluggish and congested. Teasing is fun—for a while."

"Heightened sensitivity and sensual experiences are great especially when shared. But genital arousal without orgasm is frustrating."

"The longer the better, up to a point. I feel like I plateau at several levels, but then must finish."

"When orgasm is in doubt, I have conflicting feelings about arousal. It is pleasurable for itself, but after a certain point I am left tense and angry and disappointed and . . . depressed. Ultimately I have to come and know I will enjoy it."

There were no mixed feelings about how it felt to be on the edge of orgasm, and then have the stimulation that brought you there changed or withdrawn: it felt terrible.

Questionnaire III asked, "If you are just about to have an orgasm and then don't because of withdrawal of stimulation or some similar reason, do you feel frustrated?":

"If my husband comes before I have a chance, I am left shaken and sick to my stomach and resentful and angry."

"Men often have orgasm and roll over and go to sleep, leaving me in a state of high excitement but no orgasm. This is mentally infuriating and has a terrible psychological effect on me. They can be trained to satisfy me but most men seem to assume that women don't need orgasm like men."

"At first I think, oh, it doesn't matter, it was pretty good while it lasted, and then I think, *no*! why should I settle for that?"

"Frustrated and angry, and potentially violent. It usually happens when my husband decides that his method of stimulating me is not working fast enough and so changes it—without asking first."

"I feel extremely frustrated. I'm almost doubled over in pain and I'm furious, and would like to kill my partner."

"I feel frustrated and disappointed and a little hurt and resentful that his work (the next day) should take precedence over me."

"Frustrated, cheated, angry. Usually he comes too quickly. I sometimes think my husband only cares about his release, like he doesn't think I need one."

"Yes, very frustrated and sad, and sometimes I cry."

"Damn, yes. I feel sad, let down, that something is wrong with me."

"Yes, I feel furious and insist my partner continue. It is the ultimate in frustration. It makes me feel like I could commit murder."

"I feel frustrated and disappointed and sometimes physically ill, and hurt and rejected emotionally. However, I usually hold my emotions together by trying to reason with myself."

"If the stimulation has been sufficiently long and strong, I feel a discomfort in my genitals and down the back of my legs. Then I'm uncomfortable for hours."

"This happened repeatedly during the early part of my marriage before I turned myself completely off as a means of survival. Now I'm somewhat resigned that this is what happens with men, and don't expect to climax. So it's not too bad. I haven't gotten to that 'just about to' point for a long time."

"No orgasm is frustrating and worse than no sex at all. It makes me feel depressed and discouraged. I would give up a partner I didn't orgasm with."

"If I am really aroused, and don't have an orgasm, I am frustrated to tears."

"It's okay without sometimes when I am mentally into it. Otherwise, not having an orgasm is disastrous, disgusting, and depressing."

"I feel a great frustration when I don't have an orgasm, which destroys all other pleasure for me. Especially if I am very aroused, and still don't have an orgasm, I often cry as an alternate form of release."

"Not having orgasm *hurts.*"

"In the beginning of my sexual experiences I didn't mind, but after a while, after a few experiences with guys who just cared about their orgasms, or were ignorant enough to believe all women would just come at the sight of their penis, I got disgusted, and now it makes me feel extremely frustrated. I hate the man and will never see him again."

"Yes, frustrated, angry, frightened, insecure, and humiliated."

"Frustration comes in the form of abdominal cramps, I don't know whether in the uterus, ovaries or where, but around there, and also involves bitchiness, irritability, nervousness, depression, pessimism, self-doubt, and lack of energy to accomplish anything."

"I feel slightly frustrated, mostly inadequate and greatly disappointed at *myself* for being too slow or perhaps incompetent."

"I feel frustrated, tense, bitter, scrappy, resentful, and guilty for feeling bitter and resentful."

"It feels like someone is trying to kill me, like God hates me by not letting me be gratified."

Orgasm

Suddenly, after the period of arousal, which can vary greatly in time from a minute or so to hours, with appropriate stimulation, there is a sudden, intense sensation known as orgasm, climax, "coming." What does this, the moment just *before* the contractions, feel like?

"There are a few faint sparks, coming up to orgasm, and then I suddenly realize that it is going to catch fire, and then I concentrate all my energies, both physical and mental, to quickly bring on the climax—which turns out to be a moment suspended in time, a hot rush—a sudden breath-taking dousing of all the nerves of my body in Pleasure—I try to make the moment last—disappointment when it doesn't."

"Before, I feel a tremendous surge of tension and a kind of delicious feeling I can't describe. Then orgasm is like the excitement and stimulation I have been feeling, increased, for an *instant,* a hundred-fold."

"It starts down deep, somewhere in the 'core,' gets bigger, stronger, better, and more beautiful, until I'm just four square inches of ecstatic crotch area!!"

"The physical sensation is beautifully excruciating. It begins in the clitoris, and also surges into my whole vaginal area."

"It's a peak of almost, almost, ALMOST, ALMOSTTTT. The only way I can describe it is to say it is like riding the 'Tilt-a-Whirl,' at the amusement park."

"Just before orgasm, the area around my clitoris suddenly comes alive and, I can't think of any better description, seems to sparkle and send bright dancing sensations all around. Then it becomes focused like a point of intense light. Like a bright blip on a radar screen, and that's the orgasm."

"There is an almost frantic itch-pain-pleasure in my vagina and clitoral area that seems almost insatiable, it is also extremely hot and I lose control of everything, then there is an explosion of unbelievable warmth and relief to the itch-pain-pleasure! It is really indescribable and what I've just written doesn't explain it at all!!! WORDS!"

"I can't answer this question. The charm of an orgasm is that, when it's there, all your concentration is on it, until a feeling of intense relief encompasses your whole body and mind—then when it's over, it's impossible to describe it accurately or catch any remnant of the feeling. So you go at it again and it seems all fresh and new again, but then the moment it's over it's as elusive as ever: pure *amnesia* seems to set in the minute you try to explain it."

Perhaps slightly easier to verbalize is exactly where this orgasmic sensation, this rush, is felt—although subjective perceptions such as these are notoriously tricky.

"Just before orgasm, my clitoris is burning and tingling and vibrating until there is a sudden orgasmic gush of heat and burning into the vagina also, that followed all too suddenly by my contractions, the clapping of the walls together."

"It begins with great pressure and tightness in the clitoris, like the organ itself will explode. Then it grabs my pelvis and vagina."

"The clitoral area builds up the tension, with the release being in the vagina. Arguments over vaginal versus clitoral are irrelevant. They work together."

"It starts at the clitoris and surrounds the vagina like a hoop."

"It goes spreading from the clitoral region descending to deep in the vagina and makes me want penetration."

"It begins with an incredible throbbing in my clitoris and then progresses upward including my vagina and belly and finally my head."

"During masturbation or cunnilingus, there is a strong feeling of the clitoris expanding and filling and becoming unbearably pleasurable, after which, at about the moment of orgasm, there is some shift to the vaginal area and then strong contractions of the vagina, with me trembling and swooning."

"Orgasm starts as a pressure from within and a tingling tension near the clitoris, which spreads to the vagina inside my abdomen. There is a general stretching tension throughout until orgasm breaks."

In other words, clitoral area stimulation (direct or indirect) is necessary to have an orgasm, but the orgasm itself is felt in an indeterminable area around the clitoris and vagina, often including the upper part of the vagina. Similarly, men need stimulation on the tip of the penis to orgasm, but feel the orgasm itself inside their bodies.

Some women described the feeling in the vagina at this time.

"I feel it in the depths of the vagina. I have a strong urge to be penetrated, which, if I allow before I've begun coming, makes orgasm virtually impossible."

"It feels like a balloon in the abdomen filling up and then exploding rapidly through my body."

"I feel a tense tightness for several seconds midway in my vagina."

"I feel it at the base of the vagina—a burning, tingling feeling, then I feel like jumping and screaming."

"There is a burning, aching feeling in my vagina, and the feeling that the rest of my body will follow."

"I have burning warm feelings in the upper opening of the vagina."

"I am unaware of my body except for a centre core deep inside my vagina."

"It comes as a sort of bearing down/opening feeling in the mouth of the womb."

"It is a hard pulling throbbing sensation. The harder the orgasm, the further 'up' or 'back' it feels—that is, from the clitoris on back or up towards the uterus."

What does your body look like during orgasm?

Picture book and pornography examples of female orgasmic passion often show women writhing and arching like wild horses during orgasm. This is more accurate as a depiction of passionate arousal than as a picture of a woman during orgasm. During orgasm, women (and men) become rigid and tense—and for most women this means lying stiff and still. (If movement continues, it tends to have a spastic quality.*) Women who continue moving are often the same women who masturbate by moving their entire bodies and not just their hands.

"I stiffen into a long hard teeth-gritting stretch that seems to bear down on my orgasm and squeeze every marvellous feeling out of it."

"During the orgasm, every muscle (that I'm aware of) tenses completely. Sometimes my stomach buckles up and afterwards I convulse with what may look like the 'dry heaves.' I kind of shudder and shake spasmodically as the muscles in my vagina contract."

"Just before orgasm my whole body clenches and becomes completely rigid, with a kind of intense trembling. It is completed when I feel a rush of heat up my body."

"My legs stiffen and point out. My eyes automatically shut, and my lower body becomes sort of spastic."

"I feel sort of epileptic—veins in my neck stand out, my face is red, I am rigid and mostly motionless, but the motion that does take place is spastic. It sounds awful, but it feels great!"

"I always feel a hot flush just before orgasm. My body is tense and fairly rigid. My legs are usually spread apart but not always. I don't know my facial expression."

"My actions get very spasmodic. My body becomes rigid and often shakes and vibrates with the tension."

*Kinsey has pointed out the similarity between epileptic movements and the movements both during and after orgasm.

"I gasp, breathe heavily, grip him tightly, then dissolve, during which there is a regular rhythmic pulsating of my vagina."

"I breathe heavier and heavier, gasp, have rigid and frenzied pelvic movements, my face contorts, I go rigid, and then I relax dramatically."

"I flush, my vaginal muscles tighten and loosen repeatedly, I moan, and at the peak, my body tightens to the point where I'm paralysed and I usually say something like, 'Don't stop!'"

"Tense, legs straight out, back arched and body in convulsions. I imagine my face looks like it is in pain."

"My body is usually tense, with legs straight out, my pelvis thrusting erratically. I think my facial expression is a bit pained—brows knit, eyes closed, mouth open."

"I get a sex rash, usually have my legs extremely wide, around the man, and my pelvis is very tilted; I move uncontrollably up and down across the man's pubis."

"I move some, especially my hips, but I do not writhe or twist. I think my face must remain fairly expressionless. What's happening goes on primarily inside. I'm told that I give few indications of what's happening."

"When I am having an orgasm, in my experience, men have trouble knowing what is going on—I guess because I don't move that much and I tend to have my legs together. (Usually I really come when they have been rubbing my pubis with their hand while we're rolling around—the 'warm-up'—and then I put my hand there and really take over to make myself come. They are surprised, but try to act cool, like 'oh, this happens with every woman, I'm a cool dude, I've seen it all before.')"

For women who don't move their whole bodies against the point of stimulation, this stillness at orgasm can be misinterpreted by a partner to mean lack of interest!*

*Many primate researchers seem to have been confused by the very same stillness as they are frequently unclear as to whether the female primates they observed had orgasmed or not.

"Does your partner realize you are having an orgasm when you do?"

45	usually
226	my regular partner, yes; others, almost never
51	yes, because I tell them
50	yes, if the partner is experienced
40	no
9	"I think so"
13	"I don't know"
42	yes, because I cry out, and utter moans and sighs
3	"I hope so"

479

Some women did show physical signs.

"Yes. I'm vibrating and spastic and probably moaning. I *hope* he notices!"

"Yes, probably. Other than vocal heights, I get a rocking motion in the pelvic area and my thighs begin to really squeeze together. Since he's between my legs, he soon knows I'm coming. I also sometimes experience shudders for up to five minutes after orgasm."

"Usually he knows unless he's in the middle of orgasm himself. I moan and groan and lose control of my pelvis. With my hands I grab my partner's buttocks and guide him in his movements if he isn't already doing what I want."

"Yes, I show the same signs as for faking: rapid breathing and interior contractions, wilful or not."

"With intercourse, he can feel the contractions, but clitorally, I have to tell him just before."

But most women did not show signs—or, that is, not the mythical signs of writhing and arching, etc.

"This is one of my hang-ups. I have a tendency to grow suddenly passive just before orgasm, and it bothers me. I wish I knew if other women have felt this. I feel like I am waiting for something. The stillness of it bothers me. Why can't I accept it?"

"Up until my early thirties, I didn't know if I was, or wasn't, having an orgasm, since the type of orgasm I *thought* I was supposed to have was not what my *partners thought* I should have. And to this day I haven't come across one man who knows *when* or *how* a woman has an orgasm. They all think it is the same as theirs, with thrusting, ejaculation, etc. And, of course, only one orgasm."

"Before orgasm, I am absolutely motionless myself, almost not breathing, for a while, while he's stimulating me. They get turned off by this lack of motion and response."

"A lot of my partners think I'm strange because I'm very quiet and I get very much into my head when I have an orgasm. They think because I don't pant, scream, and claw I haven't had one."

"I used to go out of my way to offer all the mythical Hollywood signs of female orgasms, but now I offer only some subdued signs or sounds."

"No, he doesn't. I hold on tighter, but I don't show the signs you're supposed to."

"I wish I could show him more, but I get so high during orgasm I don't speak or even hardly move."

"Women always can; men never could. They don't know what a real flesh-and-blood woman is like—all they know is *their* own image of us."

"Nope. Sometimes when I'm groaning and shaking they think I'm coming but I'm not. When I really come, I'm stiff and rigid and epileptic."

"I am surprised when they are not aware. Sometimes they mistake when I am just getting very aroused or excited, and think *that's* it."

"They only think I orgasm when I fake it."

"They keep telling me that I don't come, because I don't thrust and writhe and scream."

"I don't move convulsively the way women in books do. I don't know if anyone does. I guess I just hold on tight. Sometimes it bothers me when a man hasn't been able to tell that I climaxed."

"Sometimes—but I don't think I show much different responses when I'm really excited from when I come; only after several orgasms do I relax my whole body."

"I guess not, since he usually asks. But it is hardly mistakable—I go into simulated rigor mortis."

"It is not always obvious when a woman has an orgasm. I suppose the main indicator would be my body stops moving."

"My partner thinks I do when I show signs, like special hard breathing and body movements. But I never have orgasms—*never.*"

"My body lies very quietly while it happens. I don't seem to show any vivid signs. But the different type of movement and feeling of the body should be evident to any sensitive partner."

"Usually not. Sometimes they ask, and sometimes they assume I do, or else couldn't care less."

"When I masturbate, I'm constantly amazed at how I managed to fool so many men in the past about whether or not I had an orgasm. After all, I have intense vaginal spasms and involuntary pelvic convulsions."

"Are you shy about having orgasms with a partner? Only with new partners, or always?"

Some women move a lot at orgasm, while others don't move at all; it all depends on how you're getting the stimulation. But even women who move usually move in a spastic, rigid way at orgasm, with the whole body tense and stiff. Women, aware of this, are sometimes concerned that they might look strange and unattractive to their partners, and this fear has inhibited some women from having orgasm.

"I am a thirty-six-year-old lesbian woman working in telephone sales in North England (that place Tony Blair tells us is not economically underprivileged). I am proud of my life, or I thought I was until I realised that, although I am Out with my colleagues I'm working with (they know I'm gay), my actual sex life is rather traditional. I know that's an odd thing to say, maybe, but what I mean is that I have lots of fantasies that I love acting out. I like to be in the top or bottom spot, kiss her bottom or have her kiss mine (with the appropriate story line), but I'm . . . I have trouble admitting this, I think of myself as really heavy duty, but orgasm is not always part of the picture when I have sex. Maybe somewhere down deep I just feel less in control and I don't want to show this vulnerability (the real me?) with a mate."

Although the majority were not shy with their regular partners, quite a few women did express these feelings.

"Yes, so I am very non-communicative about letting it be known when I have orgasm."

"Well yes, sometimes all that feeling seems out of place, overwhelming."

"Yes, but it helps me to remember that he will enjoy any contractions my vagina might make. But I still fear I will become only an animal and he will get all messed up."

"Yes, his watching me while I'm out of control seems undignified, embarrassing. I'm also embarrassed when he does."

"Yes, with all my partners. I'm afraid they'll think I'm doing something weird."

"I haven't orgasmed with a partner yet because I'm afraid they will find it offensive. I feel another person would be turned off to see me like that."

"Yes, I am, because I need to hold him, open to him, cry out for more, and make noises that sound almost desperate. I feel it's too heavy and I'm afraid of sounding animal."

"I just don't like my face on full view when I'm experiencing orgasm. I notice the same is true with my husband."

"Yes, I'm shy because I don't like the way my face and body *look* when I'm feeling that way."

"Yes, but maybe it's because we're taught that convulsive movements and loss of control are unattractive. Whereas maybe, theoretically, they *are* attractive."

"Yes, I'm even shy about expressing appreciation for anything my partner might do for me. And I'm especially shy about asking for the *amount* of stimulation I need to have an orgasm."

"With new partners it's a problem all right—letting them know what they have to do and taking the time to do it."

"Yes, with a new partner. I worry because I don't feel they really want to satisfy me—and perhaps it takes me longer than other women?"

"I'm afraid that new partners will think I'm weird and not as sexy as other women if I don't have an orgasm or that I'm selfish, or aggressive, if I do!"

"Yes, I'm especially shy with new partners because I'm ashamed I don't have orgasms during intercourse."

"Yes, I am with new partners because maybe he will think of me as oversexed if I achieve a strong orgasm."

"With a new partner I'm shy because I have to explain the masturbation business (clitoral stimulation). About the orgasm itself I have no fears. The thing is so damned powerful, it can't fail to boost his ego about four miles."

"With new partners, especially. I turn off all the lights, but it still isn't dark enough."

"Well, with new partners I tend to be quieter. But also, I feel proud to have come with a partner—"There, I did it, it's my accomplishment, I got what I wanted out of this.'"

"No, I used to be, then I said fuck it! I'm not going to be such a product of society that I can't even enjoy my own body!"

Contractions

The intense feeling of orgasm lasts for only a second, and is followed by contractions. The peak itself is so brief that many women didn't separate the two concepts.

What do the contractions feel like?*

"I feel a spasm starting inside my cunt (a regular pulse beat) but also extending down my legs and through my body."

"There is an intense sensation in my vagina and clitoris (orgasm), and then intense pulsations close to pain."

"My clitoris vibrates at some unbelievable speed, and the muscles in my vagina and further back contract intensely, my head seems de-burdened, my toes curl, my abdomen feels strong—and my whole body pulsates along with my clitoris and vagina."

"I feel pulsating white lines of intense pleasure with a lovely throbbing in my vaginal area."

"My body runs itself, with no thinking on my part. I feel a rhythm in my vaginal canal, a throbbing or muscle contraction, and my upper legs are very tense."

"Waves of muscles in my vagina are pulsating, tingling, alive."

"Vaginal contractions radiate out over my body in waves."

"After the big blinding light or flash, then come the after-flashes in waves. Each time I feel the same feeling of the first massive big light flash, like a pulsing, with each pulse (like two hands clapping together) less, receding, receding, fading . . . until I lie quietly for a few minutes, until I feel a new desire creeping up inside me."

*It is interesting to find that *"no part of the vagina itself produces the orgasmic contractions*. The muscular contractions engendering the actual sensation of orgasm are produced by the extravaginal muscles contracting, not against the vaginal wall directly but against the circumvaginal venous chambers. The lower vaginal wall is passively pushed in and out by these contractions."[1]

"Orgasm occurs to me like an intense tickling in the front of my vagina, with a sudden release through rolling pulses inside my vagina."

"I feel involuntary highly pleasant spasms in my clitoris, vagina, and anal areas. Sometimes my whole body seems to be in spasm. The pleasure is basically in my genital area, but my whole body does react."

"I experience a series of profound contractions in my vagina with immediate reactions of sweating, hyperventilation and *release.*"

"I feel vaginal contractions at the moment of release, and in a strong orgasm, uterine contractions also. (Sometimes my whole body jerks, but I'm not sure how involuntary that is.)"

"The sensation of orgasm feels to me like fantastic excitation of my clitoris and a general explosion through my entire body. There are definite contractions of the uterus and vagina, which were most apparent to me when I was a good deal pregnant."

"I feel the muscles in my vagina rippling open and shut, sometimes powerfully, sometimes lightly. A few times it has been so intense that I felt brief cramps in my uterus."

Although a *slightly* arched position may be natural during arousal, and the moments up to and just including orgasm, during the contractions the hips tend to move forward somewhat, as does the head, in a kind of bending inward.

"I arch back before orgasm, then during the contractions my hips raise and my back makes the reverse of an arch, sort of bending inwards—almost a foetal position."

"During the orgasmic contractions, I convulse towards the direction of my stomach, like doubling over."

This bending inward sometimes takes the form of whole body spasms, reflecting the uterine spasms that often accompany orgasm.

"During the arousal period (build-up), my whole body's muscles tense, and my limbs may jerk. Then the release is accomplished in about four vaginal spasms, during which my upper body sort of lurches forward slightly, either simultaneously or sometimes after."

How did women describe the whole orgasm, from arousal to contractions?

Finally, to sum up and get the complete picture of how orgasm feels to women, following are some complete descriptions of orgasm from some very articulate women.

"At a certain point, I know I'm on my way, but it's hard to put into words. Physically my breathing is faster, my body tenses and strains to make my clitoris as open and vulnerable as possible. My vaginal and clitoral area gets absolutely hot and I seem to switch into a pelvic rhythm over which I have no conscious control; every contact with my clitoris at this point is a miniature orgasm which becomes more frequent until it is one huge muscle spasm!"

"To begin with there is increasing heat and pleasure focused in my clitoris and genitals. Then a piercing localized pleasure, a feeling of inevitability which grows until there is a rapid, skyrocket-like burst of piercing pleasure, beginning clitorally then radiating to my whole groin. It only lasts a minute, then there is some trembling, diminishing shudders, some residual heat, breathlessness and some residual piercing-like pleasure. Then I rest."

"First, various parts of my body tingle and feel strange, then at different times there is the feeling of an orgasm but only for a split second, then all of this becomes more and more frequent until orgasm comes like waves. At that time all else is non-existent. Orgasm is centred in my clitoris releasing waves to my vagina, and ends after an intense but brief amount of time, very slowly again emitting the split-second sensations for a few minutes, getting more and more infrequent and less intense."

"Orgasm is a feeling of warmth, first, all over me. In fact, my general mood and the atmosphere around me before sexual activity begins is a great part of the build-up of this warm or excited feeling. After the general warmth comes tension in my legs (particularly thighs), my abdomen, and, of course, my breasts and genitals. My clitoris feels very 'tingly.' I feel very strong just before the orgasm and my 'insides' seem to be alive and powerful. The moistness, heat and strength are all very satisfying. Sometimes my buttocks and pelvis feel the need to be very frenzied and move a lot, and sometimes I feel more like pushing strongly against something with my pelvis and legs. The orgasm itself reminds me of a dam breaking. I can feel contractions inside me and a very liquid sensation. The best part is the continuing waves of build-up and release during multiple orgasms."

"It starts out feeling like a sweet, good, slightly intense feeling. This feeling occurs every now and then, then it increases in intensity and more often; the time lapse between each feeling gets shorter. Just before orgasm the feeling is very intense and almost all the time, with glowing good feelings radiating on the inside of my thighs. During the climax, it feels like everything around me stops existing and I am fully concentrated on this good feeling which seems to intensely buzz for a while. Sometimes I am aware of twitching or contractions in my vagina, especially around the opening. Afterwards, my genitals are very touchy and just seem to glow with the same slightly intense 'sweet' feeling that I started with. This feeling I have been describing is also an aching feeling that is centred at the top of my vagina. When my clitoris is being stimulated, I am also aware of that feeling in my clitoris, but when orgasm occurs, somehow the two feelings (vaginal and clitoral) get together and become one."

"Orgasm is the greatest physical pleasure, by far, of any in life. The greatest pleasure is just *before* the first contraction. At first, sexual tension is localized in the genitals but as the orgasm starts, pleasure spreads through the entire middle part of my body and down into the legs. Then when the contractions start, they feel like what they are—contractions of the uterus and cervix and perhaps the circular muscles around the cervix end of the vagina."

"Orgasm feels like an intense drawing together sensation, located in my genital area (I can't differentiate in feeling between my clitoris and vagina at that point), then my whole body tenses and the sensation is one of total involvement without any 'will' or thought involved. 'It' takes over completely. The physiological sensation is best described by the word 'outrageous' in terms of its devastating total effect. It's over within seconds, but fantastic when it occurs. The only awareness I can state is a certain stiffening all over, in addition to the intense 'implosion' in the undifferentiable genital area."

"I don't have orgasms like they describe in books. (Not skyrockets or total relaxation, etc.) What I have starts as a diffuse 'good feeling,' most strongly genital, but all over my body. This feeling gets more and more genitally focused, and I can predict the quality of the climax—if it is *too* focused, it's not as good an orgasm: the best climaxes seem to involve more of my body. The quality of the orgasm can vary from almost a frustration (the climax coming somehow before the build-up is completed) to a total release—-waves of relief involving my whole body."

"My thoughts tend to focus on myself—moving and positioning, so that I can feel the greatest stimulation. I become aware of pulsating sensitivity in the area of my vagina. I have some anxiety about whether I can climax or not and so attention is focused on completing the sexual act and not being 'left hanging.' Then there is a convulsive muscle activity, occurring in a wave-like rhythmic cadence, which lasts about four to five seconds. Then, generally, a lot of muscle relaxation and frequently I feel very tender towards my partner."

"First, tension builds in my body and head, my heart beats, then I strain against my lover, and then there is a second or two of absolute stillness, non-breathing, during which I know orgasm will come in the next second or two. Then waves, and I rock against my partner and cannot hold him tight enough. It's all over my body, but especially in my abdomen and gut. Afterwards, I feel suffused with warmth and love and absolute happiness."

"There is a gradual tensing of my body which reaches a sharp peak then hits a thrilling plateau, a kind of screeching, sliding across a plane, then lets go in five to six fluttering convulsions, at first sharp and quick, then duller, slower and smoother."

"I feel it beginning with intense pressure and tightness in the clitoris, like the organ itself will explode. Then it grabs my vagina and pelvis. I feel hot, usually sweaty, my head buzzes, everything blocks out but the excitement—it's like being one big, hard clitoris."

"Before it begins, I feel a vibrant pulsing in my clitoris and pent-up tension in my vagina, then the tension explodes and I feel my vagina contracting, my heart pounding, my body moaning, and my voice going 'oh, oh ohohoh.' There is a feeling of intense pleasure when it starts, then disappointment that it cannot be sustained. Then my husband becomes a person again, and I am very aware of him and the feeling of closeness."

After orgasm

How did women feel after orgasm? Did they feel "satisfied" and "fulfilled"? Ready for sleep? Relaxed?

It is now widely accepted in sex research that women can have many orgasms in a brief period of time, and that orgasm does not return women physiologically to an unaroused state but rather to pre-orgasmic levels of arousal, which recede only slowly. Mary Jane Sherfey has made an important contribution to our understanding of this capacity. As her point of departure, Dr Sherfey quotes Masters and Johnson:

> *If a female who is capable of having regular orgasms is properly stimulated within a short period after her first climax, she will in most instances be capable of having a second, third, fourth, and even a fifth and sixth orgasm before she is fully satisfied. As contrasted with the male's usual inability to have more than one orgasm in a short period, many females, especially when clitorally stimulated, can regularly have five or six full orgasms within a matter of minutes.[2]*

Sherfey goes on to explain, in more detail than anyone else has ever done, the physiology behind this capacity:

> *. . . the popular idea that a woman should have one intense orgasm which should bring "full satisfaction," act as a strong sedative, and alleviate sexual tension for several days to come is simply fallacious . . . Each orgasm is followed promptly by refilling of the venous erectile chambers, distension creates engorgement and oedema, which create more tissue tension, etc. The supply of blood and oedema*

fluid to the pelvis is inexhaustible.

Consequently, the more orgasms a woman has, the stronger they become; the more orgasms she has, the more she can *have. To all intents and purposes, the* human female is sexually insatiable in the presence of the highest degrees of sexual satisfaction.[3]

Sherfey adds:

I must stress that this condition does not mean a woman is always consciously unsatisfied. There is a great difference between satisfaction and satiation. A woman may be emotionally satisfied to the full in the absence of any orgasmic expression (although such a state would rarely persist through years of frequent arousal and coitus without some kind of physical or emotional reaction formation). Satiation-in-insatiation is well illustrated by Masters' statement, "A woman will usually *be satisfied with 3–5 orgasms . . ." I believe it would rarely be said, "A man will usually be satisfied with three to five ejaculations." The* man *is satisfied. The woman usually wills herself to be satisfied because she is simply unaware of the extent of her orgasmic capacity. However, I predict that this hypothesis will come as no great shock to many women who consciously realize, or intuitively sense, their lack of satiation.[4]*

Helen Kaplan, in her book *The New Sex Therapy,* puts it this way:

. . . apart from the fact that he often feels placid and sleepy after intercourse, the male returns to his pre-aroused resting state, both psychically and physically, rather rapidly. In contrast, the woman returns to the non-sexual state much more slowly. If she has achieved orgasm the woman can experience profound and prolonged sensuous pleasure during the resolution stage and, as mentioned above, can be brought to orgasm again at any point during this period, if she is open to this.[5]

Most women in this study did not seem acquainted with these facts, the great majority reporting a desire for only one orgasm,* and being unaware of how many they might be capable of.† It is possible that the phrasing of the question—"Is one orgasm sexually satisfying to you?"—may have been somewhat responsible for eliciting "yes" answers, plus the cultural pressure to see "one" as the norm. Or perhaps, as Dr Sherfey suggests, one may be satisfying, although not satiating. A larger number of women did indicate that they were less inclined to be satisfied with only one orgasm during masturbation than during sex with a partner.

Here one woman describes the pleasure she has with several orgasms:

"Riding the waves, or what was the song? By the sea, by the sea, by the beautiful sea—well that's me all over. I like coming and coming, can't stop myself. Of course I have to play with myself again to make myself come two minutes after I just came, but if I don't I feel more frustrated than when I started! I can come about four to eight times, then I get to feeling better."

How do you feel after orgasm?

Although women in general indicated satisfaction with one orgasm, when asked how they felt after orgasm, they did *not* indicate a return to a state of a relative lack of sensitivity. There were two basic kinds of feelings described:

Feeling tender and loving, wanting to be close.

"It varies, but the instant my consciousness returns to my head (after the contractions) I feel this overwhelming passionate love for my lover, sometimes to the point of crying."

*There was no correlation found between women's desire for more orgasms, and their age, amount of experience, or number of children.
†In response to: "How many orgasms are you capable of?" many women replied that they did not know.

"A feeling of closeness and relief, and *intense* affection for my sex partner."

"A feeling of crazy friendliness, sometimes unfounded."

"My orgasm subsides into a warm glow of well-being. This afterglow is short if I am not emotionally close to my partner. Otherwise, it is long and rich and almost the best part."

"I want to 'hold' my partner, a sort of tightening time that is my arm and vaginal muscles and emotions wanting to hold my partner tight, and then there is a gradual loosening and lessening of this 'holding action.'"

"I feel deep spasms, several in a row. Then I always cry and feel a fierce tenderness."

"I am more aroused after an orgasm, more loving, needing."

Feeling strong and wide awake, energetic and alive.

"I feel the most alive of any time except after vigorous exercise. A feeling of well-being, feeling beautiful."

"There is a prolonged energy release during the following hours—in other words, a desire to do and be physically active."

"After, I feel exhausted and totally relaxed, with a feeling of well-being, then either sleepy or recharged with energy."

"Fulfilled. I could conquer anything."

"I feel exhaustion, for a few minutes, lying around sleepy, and then a lot of energy, more aware than to begin with and usually in a more positive state of mind."

"I experience a warm burning tingling—a supreme sense of health, vitality and even power immediately after."

"It varies. Some leave me exhausted, some light and bouncy and I *receive* energy."

"I like best this feeling of my own muscular *strength* at orgasm."

"I used to masturbate before I got up in the morning, and I felt like singing, optimistic, friendly, generous. I always marvelled how nice people seemed to me at those times."

"Orgasm is *magnificent*—it is the absence of all thought or thinking for me, sheer body sensations—tingling, tension, tremendous heat and strength—my body feels *alive* and *powerful!*"

Both of these reactions represent continued arousal. *The descriptions of arousal earlier in this chapter are very similar to these descriptions of feelings after orgasm.* It seems to be only a matter of perception as to whether we interpret what we are feeling as driving us on towards orgasm or as just general good body feelings. Of course there are many degrees of arousal, and some do point more strongly towards orgasm than others. To repeat Dr Kaplan, "If she has achieved orgasm the woman can experience profound and prolonged sensuous pleasure during the resolution stage [or] . . . can be brought to orgasm again at any point during this period, if she is open to this." Of course there is no need to interpret arousal as a need for orgasm, whether it occurs before or after an orgasm.

Women who are very physically active in obtaining orgasm may also feel more satisfied physically after orgasm. According to one woman: "There is a sense of physical relief after orgasm, but the degree of satisfaction depends on how strenuous the sex has been, and how long." Orgasm and physical exercise have much in common in terms of release of tension. Vigorous sex may be the most strenuous exercise many women get, and this may also account for some women's emphasis on the pleasurable feelings of body strength and well-being during and after orgasm.

The truth is that all women *are* capable of many orgasms *if* they want them. However, this does not mean that more are necessarily better, or that women who don't have or want more are not "performing" correctly. The point is that women seem unaware of their capacity, and in that way limit themselves. The decision to have more than one orgasm must be based on the knowledge that there is a choice, and on the freedom to act on that knowledge.

Multiple orgasms

Why don't many women realize their capacity for orgasms? Why don't they perceive their arousal as continuing?

There often seemed to be an unconscious rejection of the possibility of having more than one orgasm.
If men can only have one, perhaps it seems greedy or aggressive, challenging, to want more when with a man; perhaps a woman who does is "unnatural" or a "nymphomaniac." We are told, by inference, that one *should* satisfy us. Even during masturbation, some women (although less than during sex with a partner) felt guilty or self-conscious about wanting more than one.

"It's hard for me to indicate I want more than a single orgasm in love-making, and I almost always leave it to my lover to take the initiative. Continued caressing now satisfies me as much as another orgasm."

"I've never felt that I couldn't come again with pleasure, but am hesitant to pursue it."

"Although I've often felt vaguely unsatisfied with one orgasm, I've never attempted to have more."

"One, so far, is just great, and then I concentrate on *his.*"

"I think I could have several if he used his tongue, but I don't like to make him stay down there that long."

"One never is enough, two sometimes (rarely) is, but I usually 'need' about five once I have the first one. (The five is for masturbation. On the rare occasions in the past when I came during sex with my partner, two or three was 'enough'—i.e., I couldn't admit to the man I wanted more . . .)"

"I have at least three during masturbation. But my male partners usually stop after I have come once."

"I get worried about his exhaustion, and that inhibits me during clitoral stimulation."

"I feel like I want twenty. However, because my

husband seems to want only one I have had to adjust to his pattern."

"With a partner, I feel lucky if I even get one, and usually, I wouldn't attempt even *wanting* more. Usually I get 'none' and feel starved!"

"One orgasm is usual for me, via clitoral manipulation (cunnilingus or manual stimulation). I *have* had five or six orgasms due to self-manipulation and fantasy. With men, I have never had more than one. I have had the uniform feeling that men, no matter how much they talk about 'taking you higher and higher,' aren't really interested in your capacity for many orgasms."

"One orgasm is usually satisfying to me because I'm so damned lazy. I usually wait until I'm stoned or so tired that one orgasm leaves me without any energy and I fall asleep. As far as I know, however, I'm capable of going on indefinitely when I'm wide awake. In the past, my partner has generally gotten worn out before I'm ready to quit. During masturbation, I usually come two or three times, depending on how worked up I was before I started. When I was little, and before I started having sex with men, I used to spend half the night masturbating over and over and over again."

"I found with women—after having sex with men for years—that I wanted and could enjoy many orgasms, and continue love-making for a much longer time. Men, because they only had one and then collapsed, assumed that I was satisfied and I told them I was. The truth is, I was still aroused after orgasm—even more than before."

Some women didn't even know it was possible to have more than one, and confused the idea with multiple orgasm.

This made answers to the question "How many orgasms do you want?" even more confusing to interpret. Few women really seemed to know what multiple orgasm is; and several wondered if each contraction was one orgasm, and four to five contractions "multiple orgasms."

"I am not sure whether I have one long orgasm or several shorter ones."

"I have a lot of contractions grouped together. Is that one orgasm?"

"I wish I could have a continuous orgasm for a long time—say one half hour. Is that possible?"

"Last night I masturbated. I've always never been quite sure if I have 'multiple orgasms' or not. But last night I felt I did. Or was it just multiple 'contractions' or 'convulsions,' or is that the same thing? This was in the space of less than a minute, and whatever it was happened maybe four to five times, the first one being the strongest."

"Yes, one is fine. I usually feel so content and exhausted, actually, that I don't have any desire for another. However, having heard about 'multiple orgasms,' I wanted to know what it was like, but actually find it uncomfortable to continue clitoral stimulation immediately following an orgasm. My orgasms are usually so prolonged that I wonder if they may represent 'multiple orgasm.' I don't know how many I'm capable of."

What is multiple orgasm? Sequential orgasm?

Multiple orgasm is *not* the same thing as restimulating yourself every few minutes to have another orgasm—which we will call *sequential orgasms*. Multiple orgasms, which are much rarer, are several orgasms with no break in between (with the stimulation continuing, of course). Sequential orgasms can be continued indefinitely by many women. To have a sequence of orgasms, *you must wait for a few minutes after each orgasm, until you feel the return of the focus of sensation, and desire for another orgasm.* Then, when the feeling is centred again, stimulation of that spot should bring the second orgasm very quickly. Restimulating yourself too quickly, before sensation refocuses, could diffuse and dull the feeling and make another orgasm impossible. Sometimes subsequent orgasms increase arousal, and so you may feel the spot that is sensitive moving lower, deeper into your genitals.

Unfortunately, the whole concept of being able to have more than one orgasm, and multiple orgasm, has taken on a competitive ring, as in "Am I a 'complete' woman? If other women are having multiple orgasms, why can't I?" and so on. The Orgasm Olympics, as one woman called it.

"I have read that one woman had fifty orgasms within an hour—I struggle to have one mini one a week. How jealous I am!"

"I can't believe this multi-orgasm business. I once had two about five minutes apart. It was a pretty grubby affair, and the second one was weak. By grubby I mean I had to work awfully hard, and had a desperate feeling. Afterwards I felt totally wasted. I only want one. Like the average man, I could get it up again, but why?"

Once again, merely discussing women's capacity for orgasms does not imply that we would necessarily always want many orgasms. The point is that we must become aware of and acquainted with our bodies' potential, so that *we* are in control of defining ourselves and making our own choices—not the people around us, or our lack of information. And, after all, many orgasms can feel very good.

Many women mentioned that one orgasm (or none) could be emotionally satisfying.

"Yes, one—but as I've described it, with its after-shocks. I don't know how many I'm capable of. I haven't experimented. It seems to me, though I may be wrong, that there is an emotional quality to the experience and that immediate repetitions of that aspect of it probably aren't possible. At least not for me."

"Depends on what has gone before, whether or not he is having his. Generally, I am satisfied by his orgasm, regardless of how many I have had or not had. My body is capable of an indefinite number, really limited only by how energetic I am at the time. I couldn't answer 'How many do you usually want?' It seems somehow inapplicable."

"One orgasm is always sexually satisfying for me. I don't know how many I'm capable of because I never want to go beyond just one. I think I reach such a high, such a state of ecstasy that to go beyond it would take away from that peak. It takes a while for my body to feel normal afterwards anyway."

Also many women felt that their arousal was physically diffused and "satisfied" by intercourse. This will be discussed later in the chapter.

Some women stated that they could not have more than one orgasm because their clitoris became too sensitive to touch after orgasm.

"I'm incredibly aroused before orgasm. After I come I feel like I can't move, very very satisfied, but also as if I could do it ten times over. I can't though—when I am touched again it feels irritating. I like to lie there and flex my vaginal muscles because it gives me a curious electric tingling sensation on the soles of my feet, believe it or not. I feel content and full of love for my lover. We usually talk about how our orgasms felt and laugh a lot."

"I've often wondered about 'multiple orgasms,' but I never go on, for being so sensitive—sensitive is a better word than hurt."

"Afterwards I can't bear to be touched directly. Usually I feel a return to gentle lapping accompanied by the pleasurable sensations that precede orgasm, but I just can't do anything about it."

"After orgasm I am relaxed, drowsy and contented, and my clitoris is hypersensitive and touch is irritating—I only want to cuddle."

"One is satisfactory—after which I'm extremely sensitive and ticklish for at least twenty minutes. I could go on all day with pauses after each orgasm, but seldom have the opportunity."

"One is fine. I had three once, but never more. I had two with masturbation, but had to wait fifteen minutes between them. My clitoris was so sensitive I couldn't touch it for a while."

It is possible that in many cases this problem is caused by "too direct" stimulation of the clitoris (for example, masturbation type IA direct), perhaps in combination with a build-up of something appealingly called "smegma," under the clitoral hood. It is important every so often to pull back the foreskin or hood of the clitoris, and using your fingertip or fingernail, remove the partially hardened (harmless) whitish deposits that tend to collect there. This can be slightly painful to do, but these deposits can lessen the flexibility of your clitoris. In any case, these deposits would probably not interfere with your capacity to enjoy renewed stimulation unless you stimulate your clitoris very directly, more directly than most women do.

Other women did prefer more than one orgasm.
"The first orgasm is just the beginning. I find that I become more aroused generally (not just in the genital area) after the first couple of orgasms. I arouse slowly, but once aroused, the feeling grows larger and more intense and sweet, engulfing me."

"One is okay, but many are nice too. I have had as many as six within a half hour; I prefer one at a time, with time in between to relax and enjoy it, and then being restimulated."

"I prefer half a dozen smaller ones, building into a crescendo."

"One orgasm is enough, but I can usually have several after the first one, and very quickly—everything builds!"

"During cunnilingus I can achieve up to five orgasms if vaginal and clitoral stimulation are alternated."

"I find I am still aroused after one orgasm and am able to have several. Then I am still not satisfied. I still feel localized arousal in the clitoral area, but I am tired and I stop and wait for the feeling to subside."

"During my period I am very excitable and the more I masturbate and have orgasms the more my clitoris tickles and after ten orgasms my clitoris sort of itches and can be insatiable—it'll tickle more and more and instead of relieving the tickling the orgasm makes it tickle more."

"The first orgasm is hard, but after that it's easy. Once I'm really going, I can enjoy six or seven."

"One good one. It's nice to orgasm from clitoral stimulation first, then intercourse. When I have all day, several times is great. I always want to come a million more times."

"After the first orgasm I want to be aroused and have another almost right away. I am capable of several in one session but how many depends on the partner, my mood, how we make love, etc. and I think it would be silly to set any definite figure."

"One is intense, but I usually want more, usually two. If manual stimulation is going on, I can have five or six, but sometimes this is even more frustrating, because then I have a hard time coming down—which is not true with just one orgasm, because I haven't really gotten going yet."

"The more the better. Each one is deeper and more stimulating and I get less inhibited with each one."

"I like a few in a row after one gets going. It's nice to orgasm from clitoral stimulation first, then again from intercourse."

"One is just a warm-up and the best is to go on until I drop from exhaustion. They just keep getting better and better."

"The more the better—but also, to be satisfied, I have to feel that communication has occurred."

"Sometimes one's okay, but other times I could go on until I can't move."

"The more the better. Once I start having orgasms, it

is one long series of orgasms."

"In masturbation, two to three, sometimes five to six; with a partner, it's too much work and I just make it once."

"Yes and no—an orgasm from intercourse is tiring, and feels as though my pubic bone is getting pulverized—so one is okay that way. But I want more if I am masturbating or am being masturbated. Usually two but I also like three to five."

"Males I have been with tell me my sex drive is unusually strong and sometimes make me feel like a freak. I'm very interested to hear if other women have had similar experiences. According to Masters and Johnson, women are capable of having sex the entire night, while men are not. Although many men I've known think they're liberated, they're not. They don't grasp the significance of this idea about women's sex drives."

Do subsequent orgasms feel different?

"Each subsequent orgasm is stronger than the preceding."

"Orgasm is a sharp explosive feeling followed by a series of contractions. After several consecutive orgasms, the feeling becomes more like a 'melting sensation.'"

"When highly aroused for a long period of time, my feet tingle, and my clitoris responds readily. After several orgasms, it is very sweet to be still and allow the sensation of heightened sexuality to suffuse the body, vagina, lips, etc."

"In a good situation, orgasms keep going and going and getting stronger (as long as restimulation is continued) until when I am finally finished, I cry to release the tension or whatever it is—leave my body and fly!"

"My orgasms get more intense the longer I stimulate myself."

"My first orgasm seems to involve a definite generalized excitement—i.e., a metallic taste in my throat or my clitoris expands, etc., then a feeling of wanting to have a penis inserted, then a rapid rise to intense bodily shaking with my legs thrown up, then rapid vaginal contractions, then a lessening of tension but not a complete release—for which I need three or four orgasms. The first orgasm does not involve a great deal of vaginal sensitivity, which generally develops with continued intercourse or a return to sex play or whatever. Second, third, or fourth orgasms are more likely to involve changes of consciousness where I do not seem to hear or be aware of what is going on around me but feel inside a vast inner space."

"Each orgasm brings its own exquisite sensations, each different and sweeter than the last . . ."

"At the best times, I reach frenetic peaks over and over in rapid succession."

"One orgasm is almost never enough. Successive orgasms become stronger and usually deeper, more satisfying. I don't know how many I might be capable of. In fact, I often feel frustrated and a bit scared by this multi-orgasmic capacity. I've rarely had 'sessions' where I've felt like I really had enough. I get tired by myself and I haven't been with many men who can sustain a long enough period of arousal in themselves. So, too often, my reaction when I feel horny is 'oh, no.'"

"Each level of orgasmic satisfaction only seems to open a new level of frustration. So, most often, I avoid getting aroused—not always successfully. I find myself wishing something would zap away the frustration, but not the desire or pleasure. I would love advice on this."

"I am sixteen, living at home and a lesbian. For me, sex is a beautiful experience and important in showing my love to my lady and feeling my *sexual* love I have to hide so often. Orgasms are a part of my sexual life and important to it. My lover satisfies me because both of us can continue in bed having orgasms over and over again and never really coming down off them."

"Years ago I tried a couple of times to see how many orgasms I could have and reached about fifteen. Up to about eight they were very strong and then they started to weaken. I have slept with other women a few times and they all had a similar pattern of enjoying loving and caressing by the hour, but after one orgasm they did not want to continue. I always felt they were ashamed to try for more. The most thrilling thing for me was a woman in my arms during her orgasm, hearing her moaning."

"Each orgasm is deeper and more stimulating and I get less inhibited with each one."

Does orgasm feel different with or without intercourse?

Even after the well-known work of Masters and Johnson has conclusively proved that all orgasms in women are caused by clitoral stimulation (whether direct or indirect), there is still enormous confusion over the terms "clitoral orgasm" and "vaginal orgasm." Why does this confusion continue? There are several reasons: the first is that we lack complete understanding of our anatomy, mainly because most of our sexual organs, unlike those of men, are located inside our bodies. The following description of our sexual anatomy will try to give a fundamental picture of the basic underlying structures.

Anatomy

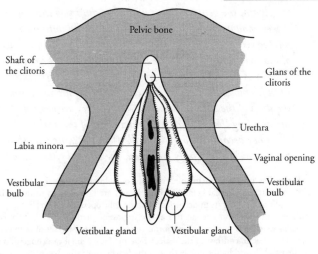

The vestibular bulbs and the circumvaginal plexus (a network of nerves, veins, and arteries) constitute the major erectile bodies in women. These underlying structures are homologous to, and about the same size as, the penis of a man.

Redrawn by Charlotte Staub from *Atlas der deskriptiven Anatomie des Menschen* by J. Sobotta, Berlin: Urban and Schwarzenberg, 1948.

Sherfey's book *The Nature and Evolution of Female Sexuality* is, although technical, definitely the best and most complete explanation available of the female anatomy, and worth the time a thorough reading requires. Here we will quote from Edward Brecher's analysis of her main points, in *The Sex Researchers*.

> *The truth is . . . that the glans and shaft of the human clitoris are merely the superficially visible or palpable manifestations of an underlying* clitoral system *which is at least as large, as impressive, and as functionally responsive as the penis—and which responds as a unit to sexual stimulation in much the same way that the penis does.*
>
> *The penis, for example, has two roots known as* crura *which play an essential role in its functioning. During sexual excitation these crura become engorged with blood and contribute to erection of the penis. The clitoris, too, has two broad roots, of approximately the same size as in the male. The clitoral crura, too, become engorged with blood early in the woman's sexual excitation.*
>
> *Again, the penis contains within its shaft two caverns or spaces known as* corpora cavernosa, *which fill with blood during sexual excitation, and contribute to the expanded size of the erect penis. The female clitoral system has a precisely analogous pair of bulbous* corpora cavernosa, *which similarly fill with blood during sexual excitation. They are not inside the shaft of the clitoris, however. Rather, they are located surrounding the vestibule and outer third of the vagina.* *
>
> *They become engorged (swollen) in the same way that a penis does.* † *When fully engorged, the clitoral system as a*

---

*Sherfey has provided an imaginative way of helping us visualize this: "We may say that the external genitalia of the female are homologous to the entire penis split open along its undersurface and the split-open scrotal sac."[6]

†Masters and Johnson refer to this as the "orgasmic platform." Helen Kaplan explains that "local vasocongestion forms the basis of the responses of both genders. However, in contrast to the male, where the local genital vasocongestion is limited and shaped by the penile sheath, the female congestive response is more diffuse . . . The thickening of the orgasmic platform results from this general distention of the blood vessels surrounding the vaginal barrel and the 'bulbs of the vestibule.' These structures, which are located deep within the labia and surrounding the vagina, are analogous to the cavernous bodies of the penis."

whole is roughly thirty times as large as the external clitoral
glans and shaft—what we commonly know as the "clitoris."

Our sex organs, though internal and not as easily visible
as men's, expand during arousal to approximately the same
volume as an erect penis. The next time you are aroused,
notice how swollen your vulva and labia majora become;
this reflects the swelling of the vestibular bulbs and other
tissues, which lie just below this area.

In short, the only real difference between men's and
women's erections is that men's are on the outside of their
bodies, while women's are on the inside. Think of your
clitoris as just the tip *of your "penis," the rest of which lies*
underneath the surface of your vulva—or think of a penis
as just the externalization of a woman's interior bulbs and
clitoral network.

(They are therefore known as the vestibular bulbs.) The
spongelike body (corpus spongiosum) *inside the penis is*
paralleled by a similar spongelike structure in the clitoral
system which functions in the same way.

The penis [Dr Sherfey continues] *is associated with*
sets of muscles which help to erect it during sexual
excitation. The clitoris is associated with precisely
homologous sets of muscles which serve to retract it, too—
though, as Masters and Johnson have shown, at a somewhat
later stage in the sex act. Other male muscles contract
during orgasm, forcing the ejaculation of semen. Precisely
homologous muscles function during the female orgasm,
causing a rhythmic contraction of the outer third of the
vagina. Indeed, as Masters and Johnson have also shown,
the male and female sets of muscles respond in the same
rhythm—one contraction every four-fifths of a second.

There are also differences [Dr Sherfey concedes]
between the penis and the clitoral system—but the
differences, astonishing as it may seem to readers brought up
in a male-dominated society, are in favour of the clitoral
system. That system, for example, includes at least three
(and possibly four or five) networks of veins called venous
plexi, *which extend diffusely throughout the female pelvic*

arc—but especially through the regions immediately to the left and right of the vagina. These networks are also [Dr Sherfey reports] a part of the clitoral system; and in addition they merge with the venous networks of the vaginal system. Together the clitoral and vaginal networks become engorged with blood during female sexual excitation.* Thus the clitoris itself, far from being a vestigial or rudimentary organ, is merely the visible tip and harbinger of a vast anatomical array of sexually responsive female tissue. When fully engaged, the clitoral system as a whole overshadows the clitoral glans and shaft in the ratio of almost thirty to one.*

The total blood-vessel engorgement of the clitoral system during sexual excitation may actually exceed the more obvious engorgement of the male.[8]

As Barbara Seaman has explained in *Free and Female,* our sexual structures expand as much or more during arousal as men's; the only difference is that male erection (engorgement) takes place outside the body, and is therefore more visible, while ours takes place underneath the surface— under the vaginal lips. The total size of our engorgement is no smaller than the size of an erect penis.

Helen Kaplan, in *The New Sex Therapy,* explains a further anatomical cause of the continuing confusion between "clitoral" and "vaginal" orgasm:

> *. . . it is now believed by many authorities that all female orgasms are physiologically identical. They are triggered by stimulation of the clitoris and expressed by vaginal contractions. Accordingly, regardless of how friction is applied to the clitoris, i.e., by the tongue, by the woman's*

---

*Ruth Herschberger has made some pointed comments about terminology in her chapter of *Adam's Rib*, "Society Writes Biology": "The partriarchal biologist employs *erection* in regard to male organs and *congestion* for female. Erection of tissue is equivalent to the filling of the local blood vessels, or congestion; but erection is too aggressive-sounding for women. Congestion, being associated with the rushing of blood to areas that have been infected or injured, appears to scientists to be a more adequate characterization of female response."[7]

finger or her partner's, by a vibrator, or by coitus, female orgasm is probably almost always evoked by clitoral stimulation. However, *it is always expressed by* circumvaginal *muscle discharge.*

Apparently, it is this dichotomy—on the one hand, the location of orgasmic spasms in and around the vagina *and concomitant perception of orgasmic sensation in the general vaginal and deep pelvic region; on the other hand, the location of the primary area of stimulation in the clitoris— which has served to perpetuate the myth that the female is capable of two distinct types of orgasms, and has also given rise to the incredibly stupid controversy surrounding female orgasm. The orgasm is, after all, a reflex and as such has a sensory and a motor component. There is little argument over the fact that the motor expression of this reflex is "vaginal"* . . .

The entire argument really only revolves around the location of the sensory arm of the reflex. Is orgasm normally triggered by stimulating the vagina with the penis? Or is it produced by tactile friction applied to the clitoris? The clinical evidence reviewed above clearly points to the clitoris." [9]

In other words, clitoral stimulation evokes female orgasm, which takes place deeper in the body, around the vagina and other structures, just as stimulation of the tip of the male penis evokes male orgasm, which takes place inside the lower body of the male.

The clitoral—vaginal controversy

"Do orgasms with the presence of a penis (intercourse) feel different from those without? In what way?"

Another reason the clitoral–vaginal controversy remains with us is that the mystique of orgasm during intercourse is still very strong. The idea is that orgasm during intercourse ("vaginal orgasm") feels much better than orgasm without intercourse ("clitoral orgasm"). It is this idea which will be examined here. The fundamental question is: Does orgasm with a penis inside feel different from orgasm without a penis inside? Have women who orgasm during intercourse, by whatever means, defined their orgasms in any way that is different from the general definition of orgasm? And what comparisons have they made when asked if orgasm felt different with or without the presence of a penis during intercourse?

Most women felt that orgasms during intercourse were more diffuse, while orgasms without intercourse were more intense.

"I feel they are different, but it's difficult to say how. With a clitoral orgasm* the feelings seem centred, right there, while an orgasm with penetration seems more to pervade the body."

"Yes, they are different, but I'm not sure how. Non-penetration orgasms are more intense, almost disturbing in intensity. Penetration ones are usually lighter, almost fleeting."

"With penetration they are less sharp."

"Penetration orgasm is softer, more diffuse."

"Yes, with vaginal penetration, there is a lesser sense of your own orgasm."

"Intercourse involves the whole body, not just the genitals."

"Intercourse orgasm involves the musculature of the abdomen more, gives more of a feeling of being shaken (like an earthquake) than being electrified, as clitoral does."

"Clitoral are sharper but lonelier."

"Clitoral orgasms are more intense, longer; intercourse orgasms are dull, no edge, very short."

*"Clitoral orgasm" in these replies refers to orgasm without a penis inside, while "vaginal orgasm" refers to orgasm with a penis. This is true for all the quotes in this chapter.

"Clitoral orgasms are stronger, more definite."

"Clitoral orgasm is higher, more exciting, the peak of sensitivity."

"Masturbatory orgasms are stronger, but I prefer the diffusion and variety of intercourse and the warmth and pressure of a man's body and the sounds and smells of two people."

"Clitoral is stronger and more localized. Intercourse is more total body."

"Clitoral are specifically located and very intense. Intercourse are more whole body, stronger, longer lasting, and more satisfying."

"Clitoral are stronger; intercourse is weak and unsatisfying and extremely frustrating!"

"Masturbation orgasm is stronger, more erotic."

"Clitoral is stronger and more physically satisfying. However, during intercourse, the emotional closeness of being together is also extremely satisfying."

"My most satisfying ones, both physically and psychologically, are those during intercourse. My most *intense* ones are those from masturbation."

"During intercourse, the sensation of orgasm is more diffuse because of the presence of the penis inside me."

"Clitoral orgasm is more piercing, intercourse orgasm more deep, widening, pulsating—the difference between sharp and dull pain."

"I can tell when I have a clitoral orgasm when I masturbate, because it's such a distinct climax, but sometimes when I'm with a man, I can't always tell if I've had an orgasm—I just sort of heat up and die away."

"Orgasm can't be felt with penetration and seems more like a state of mind. I *wish* I could have the same kind of orgasm as I have during masturbation then."

"Orgasm without penetration is sharp, well-defined, spasmodic—goes on almost unbearably—orgasm after orgasm until I could scream—and do—vaginal penetration is softer, longer, and less well-defined— different, more tender, less scary."

"I have orgasms during masturbation, by clitoral stimulation. During intercourse I sometimes have a type of "release" which may be another type of orgasm (??). It's not as intense as with the masturbation orgasm. The way I know something happens during intercourse is that sometimes I feel satisfied after intercourse and other times I feel hornier than when we started."

"I never have the same sort of violently physical orgasm with vaginal penetration with the penis as I do with direct clitoral stimulation. I'm not even sure if I come. I get a great sensation of pleasure, but it never peaks like it does the other way. I wish it did. I'd love to come right when he does without any extra attention."

"I do also have orgasms in coitus, but they are less specific as they happen. More or less just a release that makes it unnecessary to fuck any more."

"Most people (and I previously) think of orgasms as only that muscle spasm that is obvious, but I found out I have orgasms very quietly and many times I only realize afterwards that I'm relaxed and don't feel like moving for a couple of minutes."

"I have recently had my first intercourse. It was strange—I was used to the sensation of vaginal contractions, but when his penis was in me, it seemed to prevent the contractions. I still had them, but it was hard to feel them, and if he had been moving during the orgasm, I might not even have known that I had one."

"Orgasm during intercourse is more of a diffused total mental and physical trip, whereas a clitoral orgasm involves a tremendous sense of physical pleasure and tingling in the whole lower pelvic area and vaginal contractions."

"Intercourse orgasm has a deep tingly effect over my whole body; orgasm during masturbation is a concentrated extreme tingly effect in basically my pelvic area."

"Orgasm is more diffuse when I am emotionally aroused with my partner, but more specifically genital during masturbation."

"During clitoral stimulation, the unbearable pressure

is suddenly dissipated, my raw nerves stripped. During intercourse, my whole body is involved and feels tingly, especially my hands and feet, and my husband says the vaginal walls quiver."

"Masturbation is the most intense type of orgasm I have. It is centred in my genital area and upper legs. During intercourse when I am on top, there's no centre of feeling, but my whole body, especially my arms, hands and face, feel a very intense tingling."

"I have two types of orgasm: clitoral (during masturbation or oral sex) in which I feel warmth and pressure in the genitals, my muscles become tense, and then there is a fantastic rush from my toes to my head, then an explosion in my clitoris. Afterwards I feel high for a half hour or more. It is very intense. During intercourse, it is not as intense. I feel the deep thrusts, then a general rush from toes to head, and after, I'm numb in my arms and legs."

"During masturbation, I experience a clitoral orgasm that approximates my idea of male orgasm—a build-up of overall sensation in the general area of my clitoris, and a 'muscle spasm' feeling. A vaginal orgasm is a more pervasive sensation through the whole body, less concrete to describe—wider waves of feeling."

"A masturbation orgasm is physical and somewhat localized. It involves a building of tension in my legs and buttocks and probably my whole body. When released, there is a throbbing contraction of muscles in my anus, vagina and, if I am really with it, my whole body jerks with the contractions. Non-masturbatory orgasm is very subtle. I can build up to it like in masturbation, and then there is some sign of orgasm, or it can come upon me and even I don't know it's there until I become aware of the post-orgasm symptoms."

"Orgasms not during intercourse are usually more 'defined' due, I think, to the concentration of attention. However, I find intercourse more erotic and hence more satisfying."

"Clitoral orgasm is more explosive and intense; vaginal is a slower rise and slower decline in feeling."

"Clitoral is more intense, intercourse orgasm vague."

"During clitoral stimulation, the orgasm is so intense I can't believe it; during intercourse, it comes on by surprise, just flowing smooth and deep."

"Clitoral orgasms are more tense, but not as good an all-over feeling."

"With direct stimulation, the orgasms are stronger; without, they are often weak and unsatisfying and extremely frustrating! My orgasms when I masturbate are fantastic and make orgasm during intercourse (usually) seem awful."

"Clitoral orgasms are stronger and sharper. Sometimes during intercourse I have almost a 'missed' feeling."

"Orgasm is more locally intense by clitoral stimulation, but more diffusely satisfying through intercourse."

"I have clitoral orgasms when I masturbate and occasionally vaginal orgasms during husband–wife intercourse. I wish I could have the same type of orgasm I have during masturbation when I have intercourse with my husband."

However, some women emphasized the over-all body pleasures of orgasm during intercourse and thereby saw orgasm during intercourse as "stronger."

"Intercourse orgasms are stronger and better and satisfy my whole body rather than just the genital area, the way direct stimulation does."

"Masturbation is the fastest and most technically proficient, but the over-all and entire body effect of intercourse is the richest and longest lasting."

"Intercourse is better, because the pressure of the penis adds to the pleasure, also the weight of the body, the caresses, etc."

"Intercourse is more intense because it has more emotional impact."

"Intercourse is more emotional, abandoned, high, joyous."

"Orgasm during intercourse is more violent, muscular, rather than just that warm good feeling."

"With no penetration, orgasms seem lighter and freer."

"Clitoral orgasms involve less of the body and seem rather shallow and empty, less satisfying."

"Clitoral stimulation orgasm is more intense and wracking, but less pleasurable, slow and sexy."

"Orgasms with my vibrator are stronger and more prolonged, and not distracted by all the other stimulation. However, the pleasure and other sensuous reinforcement during intercourse make up the difference."

"Intercourse is stronger emotionally and is a better, more whole feeling. But for outright getting it done, me wanting five or more orgasms, masturbation is better."

"Clitoral contractions feel more intense and it is easier to differentiate one from the other; during intercourse, the sensation is more diffuse, and it is hard to count the contractions. The feeling is felt all over. Both types are groovy, but intercourse is better usually because I like the sensation of closeness and the pressure of my whole body, and especially my breasts, against the man's. But clitoral orgasm is more intense and sometimes gives more complete relief. Often, I have both types of climaxes in one evening."

"Masturbation orgasm is quicker and more intense physically, but there is an emptiness or isolation following."

"Clitoral orgasms are more intense and make me feel tingly all over. On the other hand, intercourse orgasm is a deeper, and more overwhelming, feeling."

"Clitoral is very intense but less deep and full; there is no qualitative difference, only a difference in richness, fullness and emotional satisfaction."

"Orgasms with penetration seem to involve my whole body and mind more. They sort of flow, whereas orgasms I have while masturbating just seem to involve satisfying my horniness."

"There is more total physical and psychological involvement during intercourse orgasm, which is less focused on my genitals."

"Vaginal orgasms are deeper, more releasing, more satisfying, better both psychologically and physically. They are like an underground volcano. A manual orgasm is sharper and more piercing, more superficial."

"Clitoral orgasms are more violent but less satisfying."

"During intercourse, it goes through my entire body; during clitoral orgasm, it is an outer body sensation."

"The direct stimulation of the clitoral area leads to a different kind of orgasm, which is less satisfying. It is stronger because it is more concentrated in one physical area, but it doesn't envelop me. There's an intense pulsating and then it's over."

"I prefer orgasms with penetration, and it is easier for me to have them that way, catalyzed by clitoral stimulation of course. This is because the closeness to my partner resulting from the penetration turns me on more. I also feel like I'm doing more for him during penetration. Orgasms during penetration are more satisfying psychologically."

Despite their seeming surface contradictions it seems clear that both of these groups of women are saying the same thing. While one group terms clitoral orgasm "more intense and focused," the other group calls it more "localized" and therefore more "limited"—in much the same way as one person will see a glass as being half full of water, while another sees it as half empty. While some women found orgasm during intercourse "more diffused" and more "whole body," and therefore not as exciting as the locally intense clitoral orgasm, other women found the "whole body" feeling during intercourse more fulfilling than the "locally intense," and "limited" clitoral orgasm.

The way you interpret these feelings is an individual matter, a question of your own individual feelings, what is going on in your life regarding another person (perhaps, especially in this case, a man), and of course cultural pressures to find intercourse more fulfilling. Whichever way you interpret the physical feelings, however, there is no argument that the sensations differ: a clitorally stimulated orgasm without intercourse feels more locally intense, while an orgasm with intercourse feels more diffused throughout the area and/or body.*

Thus, it can be concluded that the presence of a penis seems to diffuse and generalize the sensation of orgasm. This is not to say that orgasm without intercourse is "better" or to make any other value judgement, since only individuals can make those. The sole purpose here is to define the actual physical feelings as most women experience them.

The fact is that clitorally stimulated, non-intercourse orgasms—especially in masturbation—are physically stronger than orgasms during intercourse. Masters and Johnson have also reported that not only were contraction patterns stronger in masturbation orgasms than in intercourse orgasms, but also that their study subjects gave the same subjective opinions. As a matter of fact, the highest cardiac rates of all the orgasms they studied occurred during female masturbation.

A few women found deeper pleasure physically while being entered vaginally, saying it made the orgasm stronger:

"I hope Jessica does not mind that I need to have her put a candle or something inside me while I'm making myself come. Does that sound gross? There it is—I can't come otherwise. Well, I can, I don't bother when I make

*These findings are quite similar to those of Seymour Fisher's study of 300 women. Fisher wrote: "Scanning the comments the women offered, I was struck by how often clitoral stimulation is described with words like 'warm,' 'ticklish,' 'electrical,' and 'sharp,' whereas vaginal stimulation is more often referred to as 'throbbing,' 'deep,' 'soothing,' and comfortable.'"

myself come in the shower, but it feels ever so more complete if she does that. I forced myself to ask her soon after we started dating, she seemed disappointed and maybe she thought I was criticizing how she made love to me, so I explained that then the feeling spreads deeper inside me—or maybe it's just that I feel like she's inside me? So she does it now, but sometimes she goes all quiet while she's doing it. I can't tell if it really excites her or just she's doing it because she must (how awful, my fear) or if she's trying to be careful and not hurt me or what . . . I love to have orgasms this way, she inside my vagina and me playing with myself in front. Drives me crazy."

Is the feeling of orgasm weaker during intercourse because of the presence of the penis, or because of other factors?

There may, for some women, be an increased intensity in orgasm during masturbation because of being totally unselfconscious when alone.

"My orgasm is more powerful when I am alone than when I am with a partner. As I am coming, when I am alone, I usually wish someone were with me to hold me and be in me, but when someone is there, the orgasm isn't as powerful, because I'm holding back and thinking about what they are thinking of me."

"Masturbation orgasm is better, probably because of psychological factors like not having to concern myself with someone else's pleasure, or with my own feelings of fear and insecurity about their feelings about me."

But other women felt just the opposite: intercourse is more acceptable than masturbation, and therefore one can "let go" more then.

"Physically, I feel much more excited with penetration, and this affects the depth and intensity and loss of self-consciousness of my orgasms."

Also, the women in the Masters and Johnson experiments were not alone when they masturbated, and Masters and Johnson found their orgasms to be stronger during masturbation than during intercourse.

Perhaps orgasm during masturbation is stronger because you can get the stimulation more perfectly centred and coordinated, including your leg position.

"For me, the intensity seems to depend on 1) not rushing the orgasm but trying to hold on as long as possible when the peak excited stage has been reached. The longer I hold on (I can't wait longer than about 1 minute at that stage) the more intense the orgasm. The second factor is 2) letting go at just the right moment. This leads to very intense orgasms. If I let go too soon, or a little too late, I have a less intense orgasm."

"What I mean is, have you ever had that feeling that it was almost getting it, but not quite, and you wanted to say, 'Move over just a little bit'—but you didn't and you came but it wasn't just really making it?"

Another reason why orgasm without intercourse could feel stronger is the absence of body movement of the other person that is going on during intercourse.

"I'm more aware of every nuance when I'm not at the same time engaged in vigorous intercourse. My body seems more wholly responsive and involved and I can feel shock waves travelling to every extremity."

"Clitoral stimulation-orgasm is better because I am not distracted. I cannot concentrate on my orgasm when somebody is pushing themselves in and out of my vagina."

"Penetration with clitoral stimulation feels good, if the penetrating 'object' is not moving."

"If my partner is moving too fast, I don't feel the

orgasm as effectively as I would otherwise."

"Clitorally stimulated orgasm is more erotic and sensitizing, whereas, with intercourse orgasm—maybe the discomfort of the partner thumping on my body distracts me."

On the other hand, orgasms during intercourse "may feel stronger psychologically because of very real feelings for the man, or because we are culturally conditioned to feel intercourse is the highest expression of our sexuality."

"I can't answer which feels best, because conditioning has been too important a factor for me to be definite about it. Because I have striven for a vaginal orgasm, I probably attributed undue intensity to it in relation to clitoral orgasms, which I considered almost illegal."

"I feel that it is more acceptable to orgasm during intercourse, that it shows my womanness more, and so I guess I let myself revel in the sensations more."

"I guess the mystique of joining affects me. I attach a quality of transcendence to orgasm with penetration that orgasms without don't have."

Orgasms during intercourse may feel more "whole body" partially because there is usually a longer build-up period than during masturbation.

"Sometimes, if it's an orgasm that occurs early in the love-making then it's more limited to excitement and tension and a sort of explosion/relief in the clitoral area; but when the love-making is more lengthy it affects my whole body—really from head to toe."

"My second husband used to make love with a sort of massaging motion of my entire body, and this may have made me enjoy vaginal orgasms more. Orgasms were more localized in fast fucks, and more diffused in longer love-making."

However, none of the factors just mentioned changes the basic conclusion that the physical intensity of orgasm *per se* is greater for most women when intercourse is not in progress, and especially during self-stimulation.

Despite this, a majority of women stated flatly that, no matter what the difference in feeling might be, they would always prefer orgasm during intercourse because of the psychological factors of sharing with and being loved by another person, the warmth of touching all over, body to body.

"Love of another is what makes intercourse orgasm better, in its way, and self-manipulation is more intense in its way."

"Orgasm during intercourse is less intense, but more emotionally satisfying."

"With penetration I feel more whole and loved."

"I feel the contractions less during intercourse, but I enjoy the feeling of fullness, and psychologically, being seen as complete."

"Clitoral orgasms are more intense, but intercourse with love is more fulfilling."

"Clitoral orgasms are stronger, sharper, but intercourse orgasms are better, probably because I like to hold onto him. Masturbation is lonely."

"Intercourse orgasms are better. They involve my soul, while masturbation simply staves off insanity."

"During masturbation I may achieve orgasm five times and really enjoy it—but not be fulfilled; the orgasms are not as satisfying as through intercourse— they are less emotional, less deep, less meaningful."

"Vaginal ache"

There is a very specific but important question that has been saved until last—something that will be referred to throughout this book as the phenomenon of "vaginal ache"—that is often perceived as the desire for vaginal penetration. It is part of the same question just discussed, i.e., the difference in feeling between orgasm with intercourse or without. This feeling of intense desire, or "ache" (desire to be filled), comes during the build-up to orgasm, very near the moment of orgasm itself, and then spills over into the orgasmic contractions.

What happens is this: sometimes building up to and just at the moment of orgasm there is an intense pleasure/pain feeling deep inside the vagina, something like a desire to be entered or touched inside, or just an exquisite sensation of pleasure, which we call "vaginal ache." It is an almost hollow feeling, and is caused because the upper end, the deeper portion, of the vagina is ballooning out, expanding into what has theoretically been pictured as a little lake for the collection and holding of semen.

Some women perceive this feeling as hollow, empty and unpleasant, while others find it intensely pleasurable. Whether you prefer to have a penis there or not at that moment depends on your own personal preference, of course. For most women, "vaginal ache" is not felt so intensely with a penis present; the penis seems to "soothe" and diffuse the feeling, so it depends on whether you prefer to feel the sensation or not.

Without intercourse the sensation of "vaginal ache" was described like this.

"I feel an urgent yearning way deep inside to envelop and take him inside me."

"During arousal, there is a craving in my vagina—which is, by the way, disappointed if satisfied."

"I feel empty without intercourse after clitoral stimulation. My vagina throbs and is screaming to be filled."

"First I stimulate my clitoral area, pulling the skin up toward me. My vagina begins to feel open, wanting to be filled, or penetrated—but it ruins the whole thing if it occurs, maybe because it is too generalized. Maybe if the particular spot could be touched—wow! At the moment of orgasm the feeling is the most intense. But if there is penetration at that moment, I lose the whole thing."

"My vagina becomes very aroused during clitoral stimulation and I start to crave contact there (either penetration of the penis or just reaching in and touching with a finger)."

"Sometimes while masturbating, I'll feel the urge to push something up me—usually always I am disappointed with the result."

"After cunnilingus, just at the moment she reaches orgasm, she likes me to place my tongue in her vagina, as it seems to soothe the ache."

"Just at the moment when I orgasm, there is a beautiful, painful feeling in the vagina."

"Clitoral orgasm makes me want penetration. It feels like the top of the vagina is screaming for pressure."

"Vaginal orgasms are more releasing; clitoral orgasms leave you wanting the other kind."

"Clitoral orgasms make me desire intercourse."

"I can get high on clitoral stimulation, but I like intercourse after."

"Clitoral orgasm is exciting and a great prelude to penetration, while vaginal orgasm is a feeling of completeness."

"Yes, the two orgasms are different but hard to explain. Vaginal penetration is more like the storm followed by calm, whereas orgasm without penetration is still one of desire."

"My vagina feels like a 'desiring hole' just before orgasm. But then orgasm causes me intense pleasure as long as I *don't* put anything there (at least, sharper pleasure). My feelings get diffused with something there—I feel less desire for another orgasm but also less satisfaction."

"This itchy feeling can continue after a clitorally stimulated orgasm (no penis pressure) because clitoral orgasm (with no penetration) only leads to more arousal."

"I feel as if I can have orgasm after orgasm clitorally, but I am completely satiated with one or two orgasms by intercourse."

"During intercourse, there seems to be more finality and less desire to continue having more orgasms, whereas clitoral are more easily repeated."

"Orgasm during penetration gives me a deeper satisfaction, ordinarily. I think it's the hitting of his whole body against my lower legs and bottom that triggers this relaxation, in addition to the penetration. Clitoral orgasm is great as far as it goes, but I still feel quite tense, by comparison, when it's over."

Conclusion

We have seen in this section that, with the presence of a penis, the orgasm and contractions are felt less concretely, and that the "vaginal ache" as well is either soothed or not felt during intercourse. In general, then, vaginal penetration or the presence of a penis seems to have a soothing, diffusing, or blanketing effect.

There are two ways of interpreting this phenomenon. You could say either:

1. During intercourse the penis works as a pacifier—the touching and rubbing kills feeling, allows less intense contractions and sensations, and disperses and diffuses the focus of orgasm—making it less intense and less pleasurable.

2. During intercourse the penis, by soothing or quieting arousal, gives more of a feeling of peace and completeness, relaxation and satisfaction, than non-intercourse orgasm, which in many cases only leaves you a second later with continued arousal. Thus, intercourse (actually, with or without orgasm) is more "fulfilling" than orgasm without intercourse.

Whichever you prefer is a personal decision and a matter of temperament—whether you define pleasure as desire or its satisfaction. Is the greater pleasure desire (arousal), or its fulfilment?

Finally, you could prefer either sensation at different times:

"I cannot describe the difference, it is neither better nor worse, just different. Sometimes I want penetration, and other times I am happier engaging in other activities. It depends on my mood."

"Just a general thought about the relationship between the type of orgasm I have and the frequency I desire. I find that if I don't have intense orgasms due to clitoral (direct) stimulation often enough, I go through sex always thinking about that, and wanting it and focusing fantasies on it. I'm never as completely satisfied. If a week goes by without that type of orgasm, my desire and need for it builds up. When I finally do have one, it's fantastic. But if I never have penetrations, I also get hungry for that. It's important to strike a balance."

If orgasm during intercourse is vague, "more or less just a release that makes it unnecessary to fuck any more," how can you be sure you have orgasmed at all? In some cases, it was not even clear to the woman herself whether there had been an orgasm or merely high levels of arousal:

"When I'm on top, my mouth is near his right ear and I whisper what's happening in a variety of explicit ways. When I actually come, my body stops moving and I moan and sigh. Afterwards, I kiss his face all over. This whole thing varies, of course. Sometimes I think I'm coming, and then don't; sometimes it feels almost as good as if I had come. We often ask each other afterwards if there was any doubt, and describe how this time felt different from some other time."

"Now, with some experience, I can distinguish between an orgasm and it just feeling good . . . but there have been many times during intercourse when it was a draw. I guess what I'm saying is that a good fuck without an orgasm is as pleasurable as most orgasms during intercourse."

"There is a deep throbbing inside my vagina when I orgasm—but I have not always been sure whether it was my orgasm or my lover's throbbing."

"My masturbation orgasm is very intense. My stages of excitement are *very* distinct and I usually don't spend much time to do it. But there have been many times in sex with a man when I have been very excited and I have felt a rise and somewhat of a plateau, and satisfied after. Then I wonder 'did I come or didn't I?' and I honestly don't know, because I didn't feel the explosive charge and super-release. I think orgasms vary in intensity, so I sometimes think maybe I had a little one. But it frustrates me when I don't know for sure."

Probably, in many cases, no regular orgasm has occurred; perhaps at other times there was an orgasm but the sensations were dulled or diffused by the presence of the penis. Some women who think they are having orgasms during intercourse probably are not. In any case, an orgasm, with or without intercourse, although it may be perceived differently, is the same basic orgasm: orgasm is always due to clitoral stimulation in some form, and always follows the same physiological pattern. Therefore, from now on in this book, the terms "clitoral orgasm" and "vaginal orgasm" will not be used, since they carry so many confused and outdated meanings. Instead, we will refer to orgasm simply as "orgasm"—adding any other descriptive phrases that may be necessary.

Emotional orgasm

Some women who mentioned that they have a different type of orgasm during clitoral stimulation or masturbation than during intercourse meant that they have "real" orgasm during clitoral stimulation and something else during intercourse—what has often been called "vaginal orgasm." By this they did not mean they felt vaginal contractions, or intense clitoral or vaginal sensations, but that they felt an intense emotional peak (sometimes experienced as an extreme opening sensation both in the vagina and the throat)—accompanied by strong feelings of closeness, yearning or exaltation. We will call this "emotional orgasm":

"Clitoral orgasm gives me a full-blown climax. During intercourse, none of the flash sensations occur, but there is a tremendous calm and loving feeling that makes me cry—kind of like having an emotional (rather than physical) orgasm."

"With a man I care about, penetration leads to an emotional climax that has physical aspects, but not to orgasm. I tremble, sometimes overtly, sometimes psychologically. There is a feeling of direct 'communication' with another person, without defences, and expressed through the touching and vibrations of our being together, as we two become one. If it's really good, I feel an intense wanting to suck his penis into me, inside my vagina deeper and deeper."

"It's difficult not to use clichés I've heard or read, but some of them are so accurate. It is a full, warm sensation in the vagina, lips, and surrounding pubic area, that spreads out, plus a feeling of tremendous exhilaration in my chest. If the man is an important part of my life, I find myself wishing his penis could reach clear up to my neck, that he would just crawl inside of me. He can't seem to get deep enough or close enough."

"It's silly to explain what an orgasm feels like to me because it sounds so sentimental. I love my fiancé very much, to where my heart feels like it will burst. Sometimes it does and I get a feeling of great contentment. Well, when I have an orgasm it's like my whole body is consumed by this bursting forth of love that it can't contain, and I get a feeling of great inner peace. I'm usually laughing with happiness for myself and my man."

"First all feeling seems centred in the genital area and it spreads through my entire body in great waves of sensation and sensitivity. Sometimes I feel as though I want to sing, as though the sensation has travelled to my vocal cords and has set them vibrating in a key yet to be discovered."

"Penetration leads to a great and large feeling. It is difficult to describe—my body is electric all over, and I desire physical and spiritual union with the other. Sometimes I am praying to God, being one with Him, and it is ecstatic joy."

"This kind of orgasm for me is metaphysical immersion in another world, religious, ascending a mountain. It happens mostly in my mind, which is flushed with sensation, and sends me very close emotionally to the person I am with."

"Orgasm: a compelling sensation of light pouring from his head and into mine. I start pouring out light to match. My vision dissolves into brilliance behind my eyes, blinding me; my body dissolves into pure light. I see nothing but light, hear nothing at all, feel nothing that can be named—but every blood cell is dancing and every pore outpouring radiance—and the spiders in the closets and the ants on the floor must be full of joy at receiving the overflow of love."

Emotional orgasm is a feeling of love and communion with another human being that reaches a peak, a great welling up of intensity of feeling, which may be felt physically in the chest, or as a lump in the throat, or as a general opening-up sensation, a feeling of wanting deeper and deeper penetration, wanting to merge and become one person. It could be described as a complete release of emotions, what one woman called "a piercing feeling of love," or an orgasm of the heart.

Sometimes emotional orgasm was felt as the desire to conceive, to be impregnated, to keep the person there, inside you, mix the two as one in real flesh and blood:

"When I was married for sixteen years I had an all-pervading thinking that was not really fantasy about having the baby implanted in me. Especially if I really am involved with my partner, at the moment of orgasm I want his baby so much I can only think of that."

Physiologically, there are some rather remarkable parallels between childbirth and regular sexual orgasm, as pointed out by Dr Niles Newton in an article in *Psychology Today*. A few women mentioned child-bearing as another kind of orgasm: "What I consider was the biggest orgasm of my life was the birth of my first daughter—I saw her coming out of me in a mirror above me. Never, never, before or since was there anything like that."

Drs J. and I. Singer of MIT have emphasized in a paper on orgasm the physical components of the emotions felt during the emotional orgasm, especially in the throat. They quote from Doris Lessing's *Golden Notebooks* to illustrate their point:

> . . . *the response is a kind of laryngeal spasm in the throat, accompanied by tension of the diaphragm. The breath is inhaled cumulatively, each gasp adding to the amount of breath contained previously in the lungs. When the diaphragm is sufficiently tense, the breath is involuntarily held in the lungs, and the cricopharyngeus muscle tenses, drawing the larynx down and back. The feeling is one of "strangling in ecstasy." Finally the cricopharyngeus snaps back to a resting position, and the breath, simultaneously, is exhaled. The suddenness with which this occurs produces the explosiveness without which the term "orgasm" would hardly apply . . . For me, the relief from sexual tension which this cricopharyngeal orgasm brings is analogous to the relief from pent-up nervous tension which an acute sobbing spell may bring. Both involve cricopharyngeal action.*[10]

The Singers also mention that this physical reaction in the throat and the tension in the diaphragm are characteristic of a variety of emotions, including grief, surprise, fear, and joy. For example, crying can be considered another kind of orgasmic release. In fact, many women mentioned crying after sex with no orgasm, to let out the feeling of frustration: "There were times when I used to feel tremendously unsatisfied following sex without orgasm and if I were near enough, I'd begin to cry following my partner's climax as an alternate form of release."

As long as women are not pressured into using emotional orgasm as a substitute for *real* orgasms (as they have been and still are now), there is no reason why many types of releases should not be enjoyed. However, their existence should never be used to discredit the fact that women have, enjoy, and need regular physical "clitoral" orgasms:

"Without bona-fide, clitoral orgasm, sex would have no greatness about it. When I orgasm, all the tensions, emotions, and feelings that go into sex come out in the orgasm. I feel flooded with relief and also with remorse. Everything seems to come out in a strange mixture that leaves me refreshed and renewed, and happy with the world."

"Orgasm is an explosion which clears my mind, a force collected from my entire body, revitalizing and inspiring—like waves of fire, like becoming one with the rhythms that run the universe, like receiving a personal message that life is good and beautiful . . . "

Women who never orgasm

Women who have never had orgasms often felt extremely depressed, or cheated, since society glorifies orgasm so much, and, indeed, it is a great pleasure that is being missed. The purpose of this section will be to look at what these women say and to try to suggest what they might try.

Almost every woman who didn't orgasm would like to.

"I feel I'm less desirable since I don't or seldom have orgasms. I often wonder if having orgasms is partly an individual physiological response. I don't really believe that differences in this area are all psychological. I wish our culture put less emphasis on orgasm and 'tiger' lovers. It would be easier for people like me to accept ourselves."

"Half of my sex life seems to be in search of having an orgasm. It took seven years before I experienced my first orgasm and I feel like I keep falling into a negative failure pattern about it; I almost *never* have them."

"Never have and never will. I am frigid."

"It would make my lover happy. I don't really want one until he gives up. Orgasms are a big myth to me. What is an orgasm?"

"I read about orgasm and hear about it constantly. How would you like to be colourblind and keep reading about rainbows and butterflies?"

"The questionnaire is okay except it is oriented to the orgasmic woman and I have become very depressed since beginning it. I feel cheated and envious of women to whom all questions apply!"

"I need to talk with other women about sex but it is so impossible. I am embarrassed about my not having orgasms and wonder whether my friends share this problem. My best friend is highly orgasmic and I could cry when she says something because I can't share my problem with her. I felt comfortable with my male shrink and gynaecologist but feel inadequate around women—probably because I know that many women have orgasmic problems and experienced men are aware of this and of the fact that a woman can be a good sex partner and enjoy it without orgasm, but a woman, such as my best friend, thinks it must be torture not to come—that a woman must be very unhappy, tense, and screwed up and that it would destroy a marriage or relationship. I can't expose that much of myself in the face of such judgements and can't stand the pity."

"God, I feel like a whole part of me is just *shut off*. I think there are a couple of things blocking them, both concerning my head. One is some bad personal history (rapist stepfather) and the other is such a strong need to maintain control over my head that I cannot surrender it even in sex."

"I never have an orgasm and I have been having sexual partners for three years now. Can you tell me how? I waited for so many years, all during my teenage years (I'm twenty-four now), not even bringing myself to climax, because I wanted to wait and have something special and perfect with another real human being. It doesn't seem to be working."

"Orgasms escape me no matter how hard I try and God knows I've tried. I dig getting there but swear to God before I die, I'm going to orgasm at least once even if I'm eighty-five at the time!"

"If others enjoy them, I want them too. And also, my husband has trouble getting an erection, and so I usually don't have much hopes of its being completed with my having an orgasm, and so I don't get as turned on as I used to."

"It's like being the only person with cake with no

frosting—you feel you're missing something but you're not sure what."

"Not having orgasm used to matter to me. I felt a lack, an incompleteness, a yearning. I felt I was a disappointment to my husband, and also felt a deep self-hatred."

"I never really enjoy sex anymore because I'm obsessed with the possibility of having an orgasm, and disappointed for the millionth time when I don't."

"Since I'm not sure I have orgasms, they have assumed importance to me. I am ashamed of the fact that I don't seem to have any. I still enjoy sex with my husband, but I wish I had them."

"My female lover also received the questionnaire to answer, and when I asked her if she was going to complete it, she said she'd gotten through Part I and gave up—felt funny because it seemed to centre on orgasm and she had never been sure if she actually *has orgasms*. (I think she does have them, certainly reaches a peak and relief; without convulsive movements, however.) Anyway, she said she wasn't going to send in what she had, and I could not convince her to, though I suggested other women may also be confused about orgasm. She said she was defensive about it, from the questionnaire."

"I am living in friendship with my sixty-year-old husband. I *am* and always have been sexually anaesthetized and believe I always will be. I enjoy sex psychologically (closeness, intimacy, feeling feminine, meeting a man's needs, etc.) but I have no way of knowing what sex *with* orgasms would be like, to compare it to. I feel extremely unique, sexually isolated, and disgusted."

"Sometimes I feel psychologically inadequate because the feeling in the air is that modern liberated women have orgasms most or all of the time, whereas I do not seem to have the need to have orgasms. Probably I have a low sex drive. Nevertheless I resent the pressure placed on me and other women to have orgasms. Every time I read a survey that says Masters and Johnson or other researchers have found that x per cent of women almost always have orgasms, I feel psychologically inadequate. But except when I read about the expectations for women's sexual performances, I feel quite satisfied regarding my sex life."

Only two women didn't *seem* to mind not having orgasm:
"I am not interested to the point of pursuing the matter, it's not too important anyway."
"I have to consider (at this point, it seems to me) that maybe I'm just not very orgasmic, and that it's nobody's fault, including my husband's."

One woman who never orgasmed gave a description of her feelings during sex with her husband:
"At first during foreplay it is pleasurable, usually— but sometimes there is no sensation—except like rubbing—I hate that. I feel so defeated. A couple of times as I got more excited I felt as if I might urinate. It was like a welling over. Then later it feels like something is happening to my body, but I'm not always in it, sometimes it feels a little like pain. I used to never have anything or else have pain which was quite severe. It is a lovely feeling to be held and to hold my husband."

Some other women weren't sure if they were having an orgasm or not.
"For a long time I didn't know if I was having them because of verbal myths surrounding them and no means of comparison with other women."
"To tell you the truth, I'm really not sure. I have read so many descriptions and heard so many concepts of what an orgasm is and should feel like. I used to be terribly worried because I didn't think I could have one. I was expecting something really exciting and dynamic

to happen—you know, bright lights, psychedelic flashes—but they never did. Also I read, I think in Dr Reuben's book, that your back will arch and you'll have uncontrollable vibrations in the vaginal area. I never had this happen either so sometimes I would fake it and almost believe it was really happening. Now I say—whatever happens, happens. It's usually quite nice but I don't know if it's an orgasm. I always know what I'm doing and I'm always in control of my faculties."

"I get very wet, then start getting dry. I don't know what an orgasm is, and occasionally I feel slightly unhappy or cheated after sex, but if the wet/dry happens, I always feel tired, relaxed and content. Is this an orgasm?"

"Throughout this questionnaire, every question relating to orgasm finds me in somewhat of a puzzle. I'm not all that sure what it is, but if it means a very pleasant feeling of being loved (even if your mind tells you it's a one-night stand), then I guess I know what it is. But I never noticed if I have any tingling sensations or vibrations, etc. I always secrete a lot . . . even if I'm just talking to a sensual guy. So does this mean I have orgasm with my clothes on and no body contact? Oh well. It is pleasurable."

"I have had a lot of sexual experiences and still can only say that I am not sure if I have orgasms or not. If I have had, they must not have been so outstanding because I do not hold in my memory any memory of them in particular."

"I don't know, but I've heard that if you're not sure then you aren't having any."

The best way to learn to orgasm is to masturbate.
One method for helping women to learn how to orgasm is masturbation. The percentage of women in this study who never had orgasms was five times higher among women who never masturbated than among the rest of the women.

Of the women in this study 11.6 per cent never orgasmed,* and most of them also never masturbated.

Of course this may only mean that if they felt free enough to touch themselves they would feel free enough to masturbate, and so learn to orgasm. If a woman has never masturbated because she is disgusted with the whole idea, and still refuses to try on the same grounds, "treatment" would then involve getting her to overcome these feelings.

There were some women who never orgasmed but *did* masturbate, though not to orgasm.

"I enjoy masturbation while I'm doing it, but afterwards I feel bad about it. I can't get over the things my parents taught me about masturbation being bad. I used to do it once or twice a month, but I've only done it once since I got married. I've come closest to having an orgasm when I was masturbating, but I've never had one. It's more intense alone because I'd be too embarrassed to do it with anyone else around, including my husband. I've seen my husband masturbating, but he doesn't know it."

"When I am undressed, I enjoy just feeling my body. On rare occasions I become aroused enough by feeling my body that I masturbate. When I masturbate, I continue to feel my body in general, but I concentrate on my breasts. I feel them, stroke them, massage them, etc. When I get more aroused, I concentrate on my nipples, and I tickle them with the tips of my fingers. I continue to feel my body in general too, but I do not concentrate on doing that the way I concentrate on the things I do to my breasts. It never leads to orgasm, of course, since I never have, nor ever expect to have, orgasms."

"I masturbate frequently (every other night or more) but only enjoy it on a limited basis since I rarely come this way (am working on it though). I find it too lonely

*It has been estimated that approximately 10 per cent of the women in the US population do not orgasm. According to Masters and Johnson, 94.5 per cent of the women in their study who never masturbated also never orgasmed in any other way.

and even with a fantasy I miss a lover's touch."

"I've been experimenting but usually I start with a fantasy of the best lover I ever had and imagine that my hands are his and caress my body the way he would, rolling over and caressing everywhere, lightly fondling my breasts. I use different motions on my vagina—patting, circular, pressing and releasing, and up and down, while I keep one hand free to stroke my breasts. I find the insides of thighs very sensitive. Usually my legs are apart and my hips move rhythmically. I've been thinking of trying a vibrator for an aid towards more consistent orgasms."

"I've had no good feeling from hand manipulation of my vaginal area. As I said, I haven't found my clitoris yet, nor has my partner. I enjoy warm water from the shower on my pubic and rectal areas."

"I have considered this more lately than ever before in my life. I think I have a hang-up about it because when I begin to feel great doing it and become aware of impending orgasm, I always stop. I have thought about getting a vibrator to see if I could succeed with that method."

"I have never masturbated for sexual pleasure. I have at times fondled my breasts, wondering what men thought of them, but that is the extent to which I have masturbated."

"I stimulate my own breasts, sometimes my thighs, but I never put my own fingers or objects in my vagina. When I touch my breasts I feel warm and I feel psychologically okay about it. But, it's usually not for orgasm. In fact I've never done that. I do 'squeeze' my thighs and that feels good, but I've never brought it to an orgasm. I think I could if I wanted to."

"I rarely do it and only to see if my parts are still working—they don't. Nothing ever happens—I could go on for hours and only get tired. I don't discuss the subject—when my husband asks if I masturbate, I never give him a straight answer."

"I know I must have masturbated, but I don't know what it really entails. What gives me a lot of pleasure when alone is to dress myself up by draping scarves over my breasts and other places on my body and taking nude pictures of myself. Also stimulating my breasts in front of the mirror, standing up."

"I raise my legs and spread them apart and rub my clitoris with a finger or other object. Sometimes I thrust my fingers into my vagina rather forcefully like a male thrusting his penis, but I never get an orgasm."

"Usually after intercourse, I rub from my clitoris to my rectum in a circular pattern with my legs apart. Often I can get into a frenzy but cannot get an orgasm no matter what."

"I masturbate two or three times a day. I use my fingers; usually I press my middle finger against my clitoral shaft and exert and release pressure very quickly. The effect is much like a vibrator. I keep my legs pressed tightly together. Sometimes, the other hand fondles the small lips or inserts a finger into the anus, sometimes violently—but my hang-ups take over before I reach that point usually and so I never orgasm."

"I masturbate with my fingers or my husband's genitals. First I get warm feelings, then breathe faster, and feel an increasing physical response in my genital area, then it just drops off to lack of feeling. I use circular and up and down motions, move very little, and it's better with my legs slightly apart."

"I enjoy masturbation, but I feel ridiculous! Which is why I hardly ever do it. Also it never leads to orgasm, another reason I gave it up, although sometimes I get horny when alone and do it anyway. I never tried a vibrator on myself. I probably would if I had any time to myself."

Where should you stimulate yourself?

A book written in 1947 by Dr Helena Wright still has good advice to offer on getting acquainted with your anatomy:

Arrange a good light and take a mirror and identify all the parts described. To find the clitoris, the thighs must be separated widely enough for comfortable vision, then if two fingers hold apart the larger lips, the mucous membrane-covered hood will be seen immediately inside the front end of the space between the larger lips. The hood can be gently drawn backward by the finger tips and inside will be seen a small, smooth, rounded body (sometimes it is very small and only just visible), which glistens in a good light. This is the clitoris. Its root runs upward under the hood and the junction of the outer lips and extends for about an inch. The two inner lips begin in the mid line close together just under the clitoris, and extend downward and backward on each side of the smooth space in the middle, and come to an end by fading away at about the middle of the ring-shaped opening which is the entrance to the vagina.

When all external parts of the sexual equipment have been carefully and thoroughly identified, it is next necessary to prove at first hand the truth of the statement that the clitoris does possess a unique kind of sensitiveness. It is best to do this with something other than the owner's finger, because the fingertip is, naturally, itself sensitive to touch, and if it is used, there may be confusion of effect between the feeling finger and the part felt. Any small, smooth object will do, such as an uncut pencil, or a toothbrush handle. The procedure is one of comparison of response by a very light touch. One hand separates the outer labia without touching the inner ones, and the other hand, holding the chosen object, touches first one inner lip and then the other, and then the clitoris, through or under its hood. If the hand movements are watched in the mirror, it is easy to get the touches accurately in the right places, but without a mirror and a good light, it is not easy, because an inexperienced woman has practically no sense of accurate position if she tries to use a finger unguided by her eyes. The effect observed is that the instant the clitoris is touched, a peculiar and characteristic sensation is experienced which is different in essence from touches on the labia or anywhere else.

This difference has to be experienced; it cannot be described in words.[11]

Perhaps it is important here to say something about what most women mean when they say they stimulate their clitoris. In most cases they do not mean they stimulate it directly. The preceding quotation was intended basically for purposes of getting acquainted with your own anatomy. What happens for most women is that they feel around the general clitoral area until they find a spot that feels good— and actually, the "good feeling" is really stimulated by the movement of the hand, fingers, or whatever, and lies *beneath* the surface skin. Some women described it like this:

"It's a matter of exploration of your body; you hit upon a spot that tingles and you just exploit it."

"At first, I just fiddle around the entire clitoral area, looking for a good spot—then I stimulate it directly."

"I don't feel the excitement exactly at the spot I am touching, but more buried, more underneath somewhere."

"It seems to 'catch fire' about one inch inside or behind the mons area. One inch inside the clitoris."

"It comes from directly *beneath* my clitoris."

"When the rhythm and pressure is right, the sensitive spot will reach out."

"It's like when someone rubs your back, you know the spot you want them to do next, and you move your muscles around, put your back in the position where you can feel the rubbing the best, and you tense your body to feel it better—to focus the feeling. That's what I do with my legs."

To put it another way, as general stimulation continues, usually one spot begins to stand out as the focus of feeling, an almost burning sensation, which flares up on and off, as you make contact, and then you strive to make total *longer* contact with that spot. You adjust your movements to cause that feeling to continue and increase to orgasm.

Some women had learned how to have orgasms, sometimes after years of not being able to.*

"I rarely had an orgasm during the first three years after I started having sex on a regular basis. I have gradually learned how to enjoy sexual relationships and I really always do have an orgasm now. My last sentence implies that I once didn't enjoy sex, which is not true. I have always enjoyed sex. I have always become very aroused. I just didn't know enough about sex or myself to know how to climax. Having an orgasm is important to me, but I don't think that it is necessary to orgasm *every* time to have good sex, but if I didn't climax most of the time, I think it would be very frustrating. I do have orgasms by many different means. I have not yet experienced an orgasm in intercourse with a man, but I think the situation is probably due to the fact that I don't slow down and initiate the type of things needed to bring me to orgasm. I have always been too concerned with making the sexual experience whatever he wanted and was too self-conscious to let myself go enough to be able to climax. I experience orgasm generally during masturbation, oral sex, and manual sex."

"I am thirty-five years old and never experienced an orgasm until I masturbated and made myself have them!"

"I did not have an orgasm until I was twenty-one, through masturbation. I did not have one with another person until I was thirty-three, despite the fact that I was married at eighteen."

"I didn't orgasm until a year ago. Masturbation showed me the way. I discovered what stimulated me and then encouraged my lover so that he would bring me to orgasm."

"I do now. I didn't for a long time. I had to get better acquainted with me and my body—practice has made perfect."

---

*The age range of women who never orgasmed was from eighteen to seventy-seven.

"I didn't for years—six years of marriage and two before. Mostly it was inexperienced partners and at the very first it was guilt; I thought sex was 'wrong.' Later it was a reluctance to masturbate—which I later overcame."

"Unfortunately, I didn't know how to masturbate until I had been married about five years; I enjoyed sex, but I kept waiting for an orgasm I didn't know how to achieve."

"First, I read a lot about women and sexuality, sex manuals. I began to accept and appreciate myself. Then I ventured beyond my old limits, in all directions, and learned to orgasm too."

"I just started having them about one year ago. Before that, I was very interested, perhaps obsessed, about it. I came to the realization that I should learn to masturbate to orgasm, which I'd never done. I bought a vibrator, and had one the first time I touched myself with it!"

"I thought I had had orgasms but I didn't know until my partner spent a lot of time stimulating my clitoris in different ways and then all of a sudden, whammo! Orgasm! And a whole new world for me."

"I have had orgasms ever since I discovered my clitoris—which unfortunately happened after *seven* years of vaginal sex."

"For four years I was frigid—this was because of my partner's selfishness and indifference and my guilt over sex."

"I never had orgasms during my entire marriage and its aftermath. I think what cured my frigidity was becoming my own person in other ways as well, which I did through psychotherapy and a love relationship. Orgasm, for me anyway, is part of self-hood."

"I couldn't orgasm, I think, because of over-control and my inability to relax. Once I convinced myself that having orgasms was possible and beneficial to me and my husband and that I was *entitled* and deserving of them, I started having them."

"I used to not have orgasms. What started me off into having them was a great deal more confidence in myself which has been a steadily growing feature of the last several years, talking plainly about sex and the sex that we were having with my husband and experimenting with different things to do in bed."

"I went several years without orgasms. Sometimes I wanted them but I wasn't quite sure how it would be different from the sex I was having. My husband's help and patience and me knowing and accepting myself better helped free my mind. Now, as I get older, they have become easier to achieve, longer and more intense."

"I was thirty-five years old and faking orgasms with my husband since I was eighteen, when I 'fell in love' with a man who was married also. I faked with him too but he saw through it and told me that he was very unhappy that he could not make me happy physically and give me an orgasm and that it bothered him so much he feared it would destroy our relationship. I decided to level with him and tell him what really turned me on . . . spankings were what my fantasies were about and I thought I would enjoy his acting it out. It turned him on too, although he had never thought of it before. We tried it (he spanked me) and later I was able to have an orgasm with him through manual clitoral stimulation. I can't describe the full meaning this had for me—that I could have orgasm with another person! I have not since found another partner who digs this kind of thing but it lost its importance and I have always been able to climax since.

"I enjoy having orgasms a great deal. I didn't have them until about two years after we were married, and went through a period of becoming aware that such an experience existed and feeling very frustrated that I didn't have orgasms. Especially as I knew that when I was younger I had had something that I figured was an orgasm (it turns out that it was really more just a feeling of being very turned on). As a teenager I used to put the covers between my legs in bed at night and would get sensations of mild arousal from that which I liked, but I never knew that had anything to do with orgasm. As I recall, my mother explained orgasm to me as something you had when you were married and had sex with a man, so I assumed that was the only time you ever had one, and of course had a very foggy idea of what it was. I learned to have orgasms by experimenting, and got a vibrator which I used to help learn how to have them. I am not ever bored by them. I don't believe I would enjoy sex as much without having them, as otherwise I would probably rather just cuddle than have intercourse. I have just lately, since reading your book, *Sexual Honesty,* decided that I have a right to have an orgasm during love-making when I want one; previously I often didn't do anything about asking my husband to help me have one because I felt guilty about how long it takes me unless we use a vibrator, and uncertain about using that and possibly making him feel unneeded. However, he doesn't mind that at all; those are really my feelings of uncertainty and guilt about asking for something just for myself, and I am finally getting over that. It has improved our sex life already."

"I faked orgasms continuously throughout my marriage, but I didn't do that as a conscious malicious deception. I simply didn't know what an orgasm was—I thought it was when you felt really terrific and in love and surrendering and what not—like a 'climax' of feeling. Also, I was totally into the business of not being a frigid woman. I didn't have an orgasm until six months after we separated. It was then I realized I had never even been fully aroused. And even now I'll fake an orgasm just to get the whole thing over with, but I'm trying not to do that at all any more."

"I am thirty-eight, married and have two children. I had intercourse for the first time with my husband when I was twenty-seven years old, three years before we were married. He was and is the only person I've slept with. About three months ago I had my first orgasm, except for a few in the past two years during my sexy dreams. I really wanted that first orgasm, worked at it, and rejoiced when it happened—during masturbation. Now I have orgasms all the time and I love it; they get better and better. I masturbate at least two times a day, usually more, and always have orgasms. It took longer to learn to have them during intercourse, which happens with us every two or three days, but now I always do. When I was an adolescent and young woman I had very intense feelings about other women only, and my sexual experience was nil. My sexual fantasies didn't get beyond tender caressing and I didn't even imagine myself having an orgasm. I didn't even masturbate. Only about two or three years ago, after years of psychoanalysis and the sexual revolution and the women's movement gradually changed my image of myself, could I begin to open up. Now I can't imagine sex happening without orgasm."

Some women were able to orgasm only with a vibrator. (This is not sad!)

"I have tried dozens of times, maybe hundreds of times, to stimulate myself to orgasm by clitoral stimulation and have found it impossible except with a vibrator."

"The vibrator is a tremendous aid, especially if you've never had an orgasm. You must develop a technique which is just right for you, and this may take some time. I've found the direct contact of the vibrator is too much, causing pain/pleasure. By turning over and muffling the vibrator with a pillow, or using the vibrations in your fingers caused by holding the vibrator, you can muffle the intensity of the vibrations. Some people say women get addicted to a vibrator, but if it gives you pleasure when you thought your genital area was deadened to pleasure, why not use it?!"

"I get the most feeling so far with a vibrator and believe I've come close to orgasm. I like to touch it to the side (usually right side) or top of the clitoris—the top feels 'sweeter' when stimulated with a vibrator—that is, the 'pangs' of pleasure shooting through the whole area (vulva) are sharper, rather than deeper, and earthier, which I feel when I move the vibrator from beneath the clitoris slowly upwards, which I also like to do. I have to put a towel or hanky between me and the vibrator and so far have felt the vibrations to be too intense as my muscle contractions cause my body to jerk forward and I lose my place."

One woman suggested sex workshops for women: "A sex workshop would probably help, with an atmosphere of openness and understanding, erotic films and literature, *no pressure,* a workshop just for women."* Another felt that she would be able to learn from intimacy with another woman: "I would like to make love with a woman I felt really close to. I think another woman would want to teach me about my own sexuality—be both sympathetic and empathetic and truly tender and a turn on for me—I wouldn't feel the need to put on an act with a woman and I would want to be honest."

If you can't orgasm, you could also read books on sex therapy, feminist literature, and try to talk to friends about how they have orgasms.† You could also try a local women's self-help group, perhaps a sex therapist, or a lover who was sensitive enough to help. *Don't give up.* Many women *have* learned to orgasm after years of not knowing how, and it is never too late to discover what works for *you.* I hope that reading many of the things other women have said in this book will help.

---

*Such workshops are listed in *The Catalogue of Sexual Consciousness,* published by Grove Press, and *The New Woman's Survival Sourcebook,* published by Alfred Knopf.
†Good books in this area are *Liberating Masturbation* by Betty Dodson, and *For Yourself* by Lonnie Garfield Barbach.

3 Intercourse

Do most women orgasm from intercourse?

Do women in the twenty-first century feel as worried as women did in 1975 about whether or not they have orgasm during "the act"—vaginal intercourse? Hollywood films and Internet pornography still imply "real women orgasm with coitus/fucking."

Listen to women's descriptions of their inner struggles on this issue:

"This is one of the last questions I've answered—I'm afraid to admit it—but I'm not really sure yes or no—although I've had many orgasms through masturbation, I'm not sure what orgasm from vaginal intercourse is like—I've had very high feelings, but I guess since it wasn't like a masturbatory orgasm I didn't think it was an orgasm."

"I really don't know if I've had an orgasm with a man, unless it's just that I don't really know what to be aware of because if it's supposed to be like when I'm masturbating then I think not. I would like to know if that makes me abnormal."

"I don't think I've ever really experienced an orgasm the way I've read about them. My husband's clitoral stimulation usually leads to a climax for me but never during vaginal stimulation. I keep hoping and working at it. Sometimes I tend to think maybe I'm not supposed to experience a vaginal climax. Sometimes it bothers my husband more than it does me. He really feels badly that I don't experience the same type of pleasure he does. Sometimes I think we work at it too hard and sometimes we think we're getting closer to it, but I never experience anything physically ecstatic."

"I grew up with that wretched word 'frigid'—and I

think that a lot of my desire to have orgasms during intercourse comes from this shame and feeling of inadequacy. I think the only thing that will contribute to my having them is when I change the feelings I have mentioned before—when I stop pressuring myself and hating myself because I don't have orgasm—hell, I don't know—I've been in therapy for two years and it has helped me personally a lot, but I'm still no closer to having them during intercourse. I think it will take some radical change in my perception and attitude towards myself."

"I went along for thirty-four years carrying the burden of not having vaginal orgasms, never telling anyone because I felt something was wrong with me—I thought I was frigid."

"I read *Sex Without Fear* some years ago and was diminished when I read that clitoral orgasms are the sole property of immature sexuality and only vaginal orgasms represent a mature woman. I bought that for a few years but after a time I said, 'So what, I'm immature but enjoying myself just the same!'"

"I would like to have orgasms during intercourse *without* having to play with my clitoris at the same time! If I didn't do that I would almost never come."

"I don't feel that I'm in any way abnormal because I don't have orgasms during intercourse, but I do feel much emotional frustration. It's going to take some time, and I believe eventually a woman will have to tell me how to have an orgasm during sex. Right now I don't know who to ask because I wouldn't want someone to think I was abnormal."

"I feel like a sickie! At thirty, and having screwed for over fifteen years, and still not able to come! I'm fed up."

"Sex in the best of all possible worlds? My clitoris would be in my vagina, for Christ's sake, so I could come when I fuck!"

"I feel that some men's egos are wounded when I don't come with them during intercourse, but I don't feel that I'm abnormal. Mostly, the fact that it's difficult for me irritates me. I'd love to be one of those females who can come at the drop of a hat, but since I'm not I'll just keep trying to relax more and experiment with new ways. At times I've considered the theory that the position of my clitoris is responsible, as it just doesn't seem to be stimulated by anything in my vagina. Perhaps I should try masturbating by penetration, but when I'm actually feeling horny I want to come as quickly and easily as possible."

"I've never had an orgasm during intercourse. Until I was around twelve I felt guilty about masturbation, then when the guilt stopped, I read all these things saying, 'You *must* have an orgasm, and you have to have it *this* way.' That gave me a new worry and blocked my really letting go when I later began having sex."

"I feel a constant need to know I'm 'normal' sexually. All the new information and discussion of sex has made me too conscious of performance. I feel inadequate or immature that I require manual stimulation to reach orgasm."

"I'm especially shy when I have sex with new partners because I'm ashamed I don't have orgasms during intercourse."

"From other women's descriptions I wonder if I could have better ones and I wonder if vaginal orgasms are different and if they exist and how to have one."

"My husband is the best lover I have ever had, and I hope we have sex till we're a hundred and ten years old! I have orgasms from masturbation and clitoral stimulation *only*. I feel very little, and rarely, from penis penetration, and I've *never* had an orgasm from penis stimulation. We've worked that out, so that he knows what I need, provides it, and I almost invariably (99 per cent or more) have an orgasm when we have sex."

"I would like to have orgasms during intercourse *without* having to play with my clitoris at the same time. If I didn't do that I would almost never have orgasms. I would like to be able to have them with just intercourse. Maybe when I develop a long-standing trust with someone, and more confidence in myself, this kind of orgasm will come to me. They say it is a question of letting go, and of trusting enough to let go."

Both of us were disappointed because of no vaginal orgasm and he considered cunnilingus orgasm second best. I used to pout and beg him to finish me after intercourse and he was reluctant, thinking we could achieve vaginal orgasm if I just got horny enough. It took about five years for us to be convinced cunnilingus orgasms were just fine and he decided he really liked cunnilingus."

"I love my boyfriend and had sex with him when I was twelve. I got pregnant when I was thirteen, my parents flipped and tried to break us up, but our love grew. My parents and seven sisters tried to push me to give up my baby. But I had a baby boy and I kept him. My boyfriend has supported me since my parents first discovered I was pregnant. He lives with me now without my parents knowing. We love each other very much. I'm on the pill now and we have sex often. But when we have intercourse I can never feel anything. He feels bad because he can't make me happy and because of that he doesn't want to fill his needs. He kisses me and talks to me but no matter what he won't let his self enjoy me, because of my disadvantage. What could I do about this? Please write me back."

"All the sex manuals I've read tell me that vaginal orgasm went out with the Stone Age, there is no such thing, stop dreaming. Or that there is a g-point inside the vagina and that if I find it and press it, this will cause orgasm (inside the vagina?). I've tried and maybe I can't find it, or whatever. I can't really ask a man to take his penis and poke it against a certain spot, if I don't even know what spot it could be, now can I? I've tried myself, but maybe my fingers aren't long enough or too pointy or in the wrong position. Once when a really sexy guy I know put his fingers inside my vagina and made fucking motions, it felt fabulous . . . maybe that was it, even though I didn't come (maybe if he'd kept it going longer?). I'll keep trying, and meanwhile carry on with my masturbation orgasms. I'll marry the one who makes me really come (Yeah, I know, Prince Charming is a ridiculous idea.)"

Findings of this study

Did most of the women in this study orgasm regularly during intercourse (the penis thrusting in the vagina), without additional clitoral stimulation? No. *It was found that only approximately 30 per cent of the women in this study could orgasm regularly from intercourse*—that is, could have an orgasm during intercourse without more direct manual clitoral stimulation being provided at the time of orgasm.

In other words, the majority of women do not experience orgasm regularly as a result of intercourse.

For most women, orgasming during intercourse as a result of intercourse alone is the exceptional experience, not the usual one. Although a small minority of women *could* orgasm more or less regularly from intercourse itself, since almost *all* women orgasm from clitoral stimulation (during manual stimulation with a partner or masturbation), henceforth we will refer to the stimulation necessary for female orgasm as *clitoral.*

As the figures in the chart on page 214 show, it is clear that intercourse by itself did not regularly lead to orgasm for most women. In fact, for over 70 per cent of the women, intercourse—the penis thrusting in the vagina—did not regularly lead to orgasm. What was thought to be an individual problem is neither unusual nor a problem. In other words, *not* to have orgasm from intercourse is the experience of the majority of women.

We shall see later on in this chapter that, often, the ways in which women do orgasm during intercourse have nothing much to do with intercourse itself. In fact, these methods could probably be adopted by other women who wish to orgasm during intercourse—if this is felt to be a desirable goal.

But do these findings reflect women in general? Or do they only reflect the women in this particular study? Let's compare these findings with those of other researchers.

Seymour Fisher, *The Female Orgasm* (Basic Books, 1972); *Understanding the Female Orgasm* (Bantam Books, 1973).

Dr Fisher conducted a five-year study of some 300 women, all relatively young, married, and of middle economic standing. Of these women, about 39 per cent reported to him that they orgasmed always or nearly always during intercourse. However, "during intercourse," in Fisher's study, could include clitoral stimulation by hand. *Only 20 per cent of these women said they never required a final push to orgasm from manual stimulation.*

In addition, Fisher says that when the women in one of his samples were asked to answer the question: "If you had the choice of receiving only clitoral or only vaginal stimulation, which would you select?" 64 per cent stated they would choose clitoral stimulation, while 36 per cent chose vaginal.

These results are well within the ranges of the figures obtained in this study. That is, only 30 per cent could orgasm regularly from the stimulation of intercourse itself.

Alfred Kinsey, et al., *Sexual Behaviour in the Human Female* (W. B. Saunders, 1953) (Pocket Book edition, 1965).

Kinsey and his associates conducted the famous research that led to the "Kinsey Report" so talked about in the 1950s. In many ways, this is still one standard that sex researchers refer to when trying to establish the validity of their findings for the US population as a whole, since Kinsey made every effort to ensure that his research did include women

Do most women orgasm from intercourse?

Total population	Never has orgasm	Never had intercourse	Has orgasm regularly from intercourse	Has orgasm rarely from intercourse	Has orgasm during intercourse with the addition of simultaneous clitoral stimulation by hand	Does not orgasm from intercourse
Q.I : 100% =	12%	2.6%	29%	16%	15%	25.4%
Q.II : 100% =	11%	3%	25%	19%	15%	27%
Q.III : 100% =	13%	3%	23%	22%	18%	21%
100% =	12%	3%	26%	19%	16%	24%

Total population who does orgasm and has had intercourse	Has orgasm regularly from intercourse*	Has orgasm rarely from intercourse	Has orgasm during intercourse with the addition of simultaneous clitoral stimulation by hand	Does not orgasm from intercourse
Q.I : 100% =	34%	17%	17%	32%
Q.II : 100% =	29%	22%	17%	32%
Q.III : 100% =	28%	26%	22%	24%
	30%	22%	19%	29%

*How many women orgasmed regularly from intercourse? These figures are based only on women who have had intercourse and who do have orgasms at any time, and who answered "yes," "usually," or "always" to the question: How often do you orgasm during intercourse? Figures do not include those who used simultaneous clitoral stimulation by hand, or defined a different type of orgasm during intercourse. See Appendices 3 and 4 for complete breakdown of findings.

representative of all parts of the population. However, a large-scale random sample has never been done to this day in sex research, since so many of the people who might be chosen at random would refuse to answer.

Kinsey and his associates affirmed—albeit obliquely—the importance of the clitoris in female sexuality, although here (as in Fisher's work) there is a blurring of meaning of "orgasm during intercourse" that makes it difficult for us to discern useful figures from his findings. Kinsey's report refers to orgasm during intercourse after marriage, orgasm during petting, and orgasm during masturbation. But what does orgasm during intercourse include? Wardell Pomeroy, one of Kinsey's associates, has stated that Kinsey meant an orgasm attained by *any* means during intercourse. With this criterion, Kinsey found that most women, especially after they had been married a few years, did have orgasm during "intercourse." But the fact that Kinsey frequently brought up the problem of inadequate stimulation for women during intercourse, and the ease with which women could orgasm during masturbation, tells us that clitoral stimulation by hand must have played a large part in how these women orgasmed during intercourse. As Kinsey shyly put it, "The techniques of masturbation and of petting are more specifically calculated to effect orgasm than the techniques of coitus itself."

Kinsey went on to explain that the basic problem for women was *not* an inability to orgasm, but only that "a substantial minority" did not orgasm during "coitus." Furthermore, most of the women he studied who achieved orgasm only sometimes during "coitus" orgasmed promptly and regularly during masturbation. As Edward Brecher summarizes it, "Note that Kinsey did not say that masturbation is more enjoyable than coitus, or that it is preferable in any other way. What Kinsey did report was a very simple fact that tens of millions of women know from their own experience: regardless of the joys of coitus, and regardless of its emotional rewards, it is less likely than masturbation to terminate in orgasm—and for some women it always or almost always terminates without orgasm."[1] Nevertheless, Kinsey never drew the conclusion that clitorally-stimulated orgasms should become a "normal" part of sex. The implication was that women would be lucky to have them during coitus.

Helen Kaplan, *The New Sex Therapy* (Brunner/ Mazel—Quadrangle, 1974).
Dr Kaplan, a sex therapist and psychoanalyst of high repute with extensive clinical experience, stated, "It is difficult to believe that the millions of otherwise responsive women who do not have coital orgasms are all 'sick.'"
As she says:

> *Our own impression, which is based solely on our clinical experience, is that in our society 8 to 10 percent of the female population has never experienced an orgasm, while approximately 90 percent of all women seem to be able to achieve orgasm by some means. However, it is also our impression that only about one-half or even fewer of these orgastic women regularly reach a climax during coitus without additional clitoral stimulation. These impressions are in sharp contrast to the view held by many experts, and shared by the general public, that coital orgasm is the only normal form of female sexual expression and that orgasm attained primarily by direct clitoral stimulation is somehow pathological.[2]*

In other words, Kaplan estimates that perhaps one half or fewer of those 90 per cent who can orgasm do so during intercourse without additional clitoral stimulation. "Half or fewer" of 90 per cent remains within the general area of this book's findings, although the figure, which is an estimate, is slightly higher. It is difficult to imagine today how controversial such a statement was at the time.

William Masters and Virginia Johnson, *Human Sexual Response* (Little, Brown and Company, 1966); *Human*

Sexual Inadequacy (**Little, Brown and Company, 1970**).
Masters and Johnson have given no specific figures with
regard to the prevalence of orgasm from intercourse; indeed,
their research was not undertaken with this question in
mind. Their aim was to study and understand orgasm itself.
The crucial finding of their work, with regard to female sexuality, is that there is only one kind of orgasm, not two; that
orgasms during intercourse are caused by indirect clitoral
stimulation, not vaginal stimulation.

With regard to the question being asked in this chapter,
what does their work have to tell us? First of all, Masters
and Johnson chose their basic study population only from
women who did have orgasm from intercourse; all others
were eliminated. Then in their findings, they labelled not
having orgasm from intercourse "coital orgasmic inadequacy." However, Masters and Johnson obviously recognized
that women orgasm more easily from masturbation and clitoral stimulation and they reported the strongest and most
frequent orgasms occurring in women at this time, even
going so far as to say with regard to intercourse/coitus:

> *Sociocultural influence more often than not places woman*
> *in a position in which she must adapt, sublimate, inhibit,*
> *or even distort her natural capacity to function sexually in*
> *order to fulfil her genetically assigned role (i.e., breeding).*
> Herein lies a major source of woman's sexual
> dysfunction.[3]

Still, one of their major goals seems to have been to "treat"
women so that they would be able to orgasm during intercourse. There is nothing wrong with this, except that it still
leaves women with the impression that not having an orgasm
during intercourse is "sick" and "abnormal"—a dysfunction.
This is especially true since Masters and Johnson's statement
that the clitoris is indirectly stimulated during thrusting has
received so much publicity. We will have more to say about
their theories in the section of this chapter dealing with the
ways in which women orgasm during intercourse.

In summary, the overall consensus of these studies is that most women do not automatically have orgasms from intercourse—in the sense of simple thrusting without additional stimulation. Not only is "failure" to orgasm during coitus (intercourse) the most common female sexual complaint found in sex therapy clinics, but the fact that women very frequently do not orgasm during intercourse has been general popular knowledge for a very long time. For a woman to have orgasm during intercourse, from intercourse, is simply not the majority experience.

Why is this? Even the question being asked is wrong. The question should not be: Why aren't women having orgasms from intercourse? but, rather: *Why have we insisted women* should *orgasm from intercourse?* And why have women found it necessary to try everything in the book, from exercises to extensive analysis to sex therapy, to *make* it happen?

A theory propounded in the 1980s—based around what was popularly known as the "g-spot"—asserted that there is a special spot inside the vagina that, when tickled or pressed, creates orgasm. Yet, if such a spot existed, why hasn't it been causing female orgasm during coitus for centuries? Why do women masturbate clitorally and not vaginally?

The glorification of intercourse

Why have we thought women should orgasm from intercourse?

There are three basic reasons for this insistence, which will be developed in the following pages:

A. The explanation of sexual pleasure as the means of ensuring reproduction.

B. The crucial role of monogamous intercourse in patrilineal inheritance.

C. The widespread influence of the Freudian model of female psychology.

A. Sexual pleasure and the reproductive model

First the idea that since nature gave us a "sex drive" and the capacity for sexual pleasure in order to ensure reproduction, therefore coitus is "the real thing," and all other forms of sexual gratification are substitutions for, or perversions of, this "natural" activity.

It is important to scrutinize this assumption. Intercourse *is* necessary for reproduction, and sexual pleasure and orgasm *are* involved with reproduction. But exactly how? Looking closer, one sees that only *male* orgasm during intercourse is necessary for reproduction. It would make sense, from the point of view of the necessity to deposit semen inside the vagina, that intercourse should provide almost automatic, perfect stimulation for male orgasm, and, of course, it does: men orgasm as regularly during intercourse as women (and men) do during masturbation.

However, since female orgasm is not necessary during intercourse for reproduction to occur, why should nature provide stimulation for female orgasm during intercourse? (As a matter of fact, what is the reason for the existence of female orgasm at all?) There are several possibilities:

1. Some researchers claim that female orgasm helps "suck" the sperm up into the uterus. However, Masters and Johnson believe that this is doubtful, since the contractions of the uterus progress downwards, and so are "more likely to have an expulsive action than a sucking action." To check this, they placed a fluid resembling semen but opaque to X-rays in a cap covering the cervix, so that if there were any sucking, the fluid would be taken into the cervix. However, X-ray films showed no significant gaping of the cervical opening at all. Several respondents in this study mentioned that their contractions move downwards, or outwards. One woman described her orgasm this way: "A clitoral orgasm is a sharp, shuddering, breath-taking pleasure/pain gripping of the muscles in my rectum and vagina. Whatever is in me—

a finger, or penis, or dildo—is gripped and pushed outwards."

2. Dr Mary Jane Sherfey says: "In general, the orgasm in the male is admirably designed to deposit semen where it will do the most good, and in the female, to remove the largest amount of venous congestion in the most effective manner."[4] But orgasm does this for men too, and Sherfey herself has made a point of emphasizing that after one orgasm, women do not completely decongest but remain in a state of partial arousal, and sometimes after one orgasm arousal can become *stronger*. Can this be, then, the only function of female orgasm?

Dr Sherfey has also given a reason why, from the point of view of reproduction, women should *not* have orgasms during intercourse: "In a woman with a lax perineal body who has borne children, semen easily escapes with premature withdrawal, whereas if the woman does *not* have an orgasm, the still-swollen lower third acts as a stopper to semen outflow . . ."[5] Masters and Johnson have also mentioned that there is a greater chance for impregnation for some women if they do not orgasm, for the same reason.

3. Another possibility is that perhaps our orgasmic contractions are for the purpose of further ensuring male orgasm, gripping the penis and pulling slightly downwards rhythmically. In this model of intercourse, thrusting would not be considered as necessary as it now is, and perhaps intercourse in another culture would be less gymnastic and male-dominated—more a mutual lying together in pleasure, penis-in-vagina, or vagina-covering-penis, with female orgasm providing much of the stimulation necessary for male orgasm.

4. On the other hand, perhaps the function of female orgasm is to provide arousal and "receptivity," or interest in the woman in initiating intercourse. Most female primates have a period of oestrus, a specific period of time during which arousal is more or less constant, which guarantees that fertility and intercourse will coincide. Women do not have oestrus; they are theoretically capable of becoming

aroused at any time. We become aroused in many ways—
by kissing, hugging, and even talking. During all these
activities, if we find them arousing, a warm, tickling
sensation—the desire for clitoral stimulation, perhaps—
becomes stronger and stronger. If clitoral stimulation follows, it often leads to a kind of vaginal tickle ("vaginal
ache") that feels to many women like a desire to "be penetrated." While continued stimulation brings orgasm, and,
for many women, a return to arousal, intercourse seems to
quiet this feeling. Perhaps one of the functions of our
orgasm is continuing arousal—and "receptivity."

It is unclear whether the "vaginal ache" part of the out-
line just presented holds true for most women, or even for
very many women, since most women generally don't use
any kind of vaginal entry during masturbation. However,
the general idea of our orgasms perhaps serving the function
of continuing our arousal and keeping it at just manageable
levels for the body is an interesting possibility.

In the same way, it could be argued that since women
do not have oestrus, it is necessary for our clitoris to be
located on the outside of our bodies rather than closer to
the vagina, so that stimulation might happen in the normal
course of things. In other words, since we are not periodically receptive like other mammals, there must be some
mechanism provided for arousal that can be activated at will
and that will not leave us constantly in a state of arousal.

However, none of these theories may be right. For example,
if the purpose of arousal and sexuality in general is really
connected only with reproduction, why can we have just as
much if not stronger arousal and orgasm(s) at times when
we are not capable of conception—i.e., during pregnancy,
after menopause, during menstruation, and at other times
of the month when conception is not possible, and during
childhood?

Perhaps orgasm is basically a release mechanism for the
body, as are other spastic body reactions, such as laughing,
crying, or bodily convulsions. Maybe one function of

orgasm is the discharge of *all* kinds of tensions through this release. Or could it be possible that there is no "reason" for the existence of female orgasm other than pleasure? In any case, whether or not continuing arousal is the function of female orgasm, or the release of all kinds of bodily tensions, it is definitely clear that there is no logical reason for insisting that we have our orgasms during intercourse.

B. Patriarchy and monogamous intercourse

A second reason for insisting women (and men) should find their greatest sexual pleasure in intercourse, and for seeing intercourse as *the* basic sexual act, the basic form of sex—is that our form of society demands it. With a very few isolated exceptions, for the last three or four thousand years all societies have been patrilineal or patriarchal. Family name and inheritance have passed through men, and religious and civil laws have given men authority to determine the course of society. In a non-patriarchal society, where there is either no question of property right or where lineage goes through the mother, there is no need for institutionalizing intercourse as the basic form of sexual pleasure. In the earliest societies we know about, families were mostly extended groups of clans, with aunts and brothers sharing equally in the upbringing of the child; the mother did not particularly "own" the child, and there was no concept of "father" at all. In fact, the male role in reproduction was not understood for quite a long time, and intercourse and male orgasm were not connected with pregnancy which of course only became apparent many months later.

But with the changeover to a patrilineal or partriarchal society,* it becomes necessary for the man to control the sexuality of the woman. Nancy Marval, in a paper printed by The Feminists, explains this further:

*Books related to this subject include *The First Sex*, by Elizabeth Gould Davis; *The Mothers*, by Robert Briffault; *The White Goddess*, by Robert Graves; *The Cult of the Mother Goddess*, by E. O. James; *Woman's Evolution*, by Evelyn Reed; and *Prehistory and the Beginning of Civilization*, by Jacquetta Hawkes and Sir Leonard Woolley.

In a patriarchal culture like the one we were all brought up in, sexuality is a crucial issue. Beyond all the symbolic aspects of the sexual act (symbolizing the male's dominance, manipulation, and control over the female), it assumes an overwhelming practical importance. This is that men have no direct access to reproduction and the survival of the species. As individuals, their claim to any particular child can never be as clear as that of the mother who demonstrably gave birth to that child. Under normal circumstances it is agreed that a man is needed to provide sperm to the conception of the baby, but it is practically impossible to determine which man. The only way a man can be absolutely sure that he is the one to have contributed that sperm is to control the sexuality of the woman.[6]

To do this, he had to insist she be a virgin at marriage, and monogamous thereafter. As Kinsey put it:

Sexual activities for the female before marriage were proscribed in ancient codes primarily because they threatened the male's property rights in the female whom he was taking as a wife. The demand that the female be virgin at the time of her marriage was comparable to the demand that cattle or other goods that he bought should be perfect, according to the standards of the culture in which he lived.[7]

With regard to keeping her monogamous, Marval comments that a man could do this in several ways:

He may keep her separate from any other man as in a harem, he may threaten her with violence if she strays, he may devise a mechanical method of preventing intercourse like a chastity belt, he may remove her clitoris to decrease her erotic impulses, or he may convince her that sex is the same thing as love and if she has sexual relations with anyone else, she is violating the sacred ethics of love. This last method is the one used most commonly in the United States today.[8]

In addition to these practical reasons for controlling sexuality (to maintain the form of social organization we know), in the early period of the changeover to patriarchy there were political reasons as well, in that other forms of sexuality represented rival forms of social organization. For example, it is generally accepted by Bible scholars that the earliest Jewish tribes mentioned in the Old Testament accepted cunnilingus and homosexuality as a valid part physical relations, as did the societies around them—which were not, for the most part, totally patriarchal. In fact, prior to the seventh century BC,* homosexual and other sexual activities were associated with Jewish religious rites, just as in the surrounding cultures. But as the small Jewish tribes sought to consolidate their strength, and their patriarchal social order, and to bind loyalty to the one male god, Yahweh, all forms of sexuality except the one necessary for reproduction were banned by religious code. The Holiness Code, established at the time of their return from the Babylonian exile, sought to fence out the surrounding cultures and set up rules for separating the chosen People of God. It was then that non-heterosexual, non-reproductive sexual acts were condemned as the way of the Canaanite, the way of the pagan. But these activities were proscribed as an indication of allegiance to another culture, an adjunct to idolatry—and *not* as "immoral" or as sexual crimes, as we consider them. They were political crimes.

These codes have continued in our religious and civil law up to this day. Judaeo-Christian codes still specifically condemn all sexual activity that does not have reproduction as its ultimate aim. Our civil law is largely derived from these codes, and the laws of most states condemn non-coital forms of sexuality (in and out of marriage) as punishable misdemeanours or crimes. Thus, intercourse has been *institutionalized* in our culture as the only permissible form of sexual activity.

*Although, according to the *Jews: Biography of a People* by Judd Teller, it was the sixth century BC.

Forms of sexuality other than intercourse are now also considered *psychologically* abnormal and unhealthy, as we shall see later in this chapter. However, the full spectrum of physical contact is enjoyed by the other mammals, and their mental health has not been questioned. Furthermore, intercourse is not the main focus of their sexual relations either, but only one activity out of many. They spend more time on mutual grooming than they do on specifically sexual contact, as Jane Goodall and many other primate researchers have described in great detail. They also masturbate and have homosexual relations quite commonly. Among the animals for whom these activities have been recorded are the rat, chinchilla, rabbit, porcupine, squirrel, ferret, horse, cow, elephant, dog, baboon, monkey, chimpanzee, and many others. Although our culture seems to assume that since sexual feelings are provided by nature to ensure reproduction, and therefore intercourse is or should be the basic form of our sexuality—even though women's sexual feelings are often strongest when women are *not* fertile—it is patently obvious that other forms of sexuality are just as natural and basic as intercourse, and perhaps masturbation is more basic, since chimpanzees brought up in isolation have no idea of how to have intercourse, but do masturbate almost from birth.

To try to limit physical relations between humans to intercourse is artificial. But perhaps it was also necessary to channel all forms of physical contact into heterosexual intercourse to increase the rate of population growth. A high rate of reproduction is the key to power and wealth for a small group, and in the early Jewish tribes, barrenness was a curse. In fact, children have been the basic form of wealth in almost every society up to the present. From the point of view of the larger society, increase in numbers provides the ability to consolidate more territory and to defeat other tribes. On a personal level, children could inherit one's property and also consolidate the family's holdings, and they could till the fields, hunt, gather food, or tend flocks (and later, work in factories) for their parents.

The desire for maximum population growth was institutionalized in our culture, and out of this grew the definition of women as basically serving this ideal. The glorification of marriage, motherhood, and intercourse is part of a very strong pro-natalist bias in our culture, which is discussed in detail in the book *Pronatalism: The Myth of Mom and Apple Pie,* edited by Ellen Peck and Judy Senderowitz.

In summary, since intercourse has been defined as the basic form of sexuality, and the only natural, healthy, and moral form of physical contact, it has automatically been assumed that this is when women should orgasm. Heterosexual intercourse has been *the* definition of sexual expression ever since the beginning of patriarchy, and is the only form of sexual pleasure really condoned in our society. The corollary of this institutionalization of heterosexual intercourse is the villainization and suppression of all other forms of sexuality and pleasurable intimate contact—which explains the historic horror of our culture for masturbation and lesbianism/homosexuality, or even kissing and intimate physical contact or caressing between friends.

C. The Freudian model of female sexuality

The third and final basic reason why women have been expected to orgasm during intercourse is the general acceptance of the Freudian model of female sexuality, the model of female psychology based on it, and in general the acceptance of the concept of "mental health."

Freud was the founding father of vaginal orgasm. He theorized that the clitoral orgasm (orgasm caused by clitoral stimulation) was adolescent and that, upon puberty, when women began having intercourse with men, women should transfer the centre of orgasm to the vagina. The vagina, it was assumed, was able to produce a parallel, but more mature, orgasm than the clitoris. Presumably this vaginally produced orgasm would occur, however, only when the woman had mastered important major conflicts and achieved a "well-integrated," "feminine" identity. The woman who could reach orgasm only through clitoral stimulation was said to be "immature" and not to have resolved fundamental "conflicts" about sexual impulses. Of course, once he had laid down this definition of our sexuality, Freud not so strangely discovered a tremendous "problem" of "frigidity" in women.

These theories of Freud's were based on faulty biology. Freud himself did mention that perhaps his biological knowledge was inaccurate and would turn out, on further study, to be incorrect—and indeed it has been discredited, for some thirty years now. Undoubtedly, Freud would have accepted this research by now, but the profession he originated has been unwilling or slow to do so. All too many psychoanalysts and various "authorities" writing in popular women's magazines continue to insist that we should orgasm through intercourse, via thrusting, with no hands, and still see "vaginal primacy" as a crucial criterion of "normal" functioning in women. They continue to regard orgasm produced by intercourse as the only "authentic" female sexual response, and climax caused by any other form of stimulation (like "clitorism," as they call it) as a symptom of neurotic conflict.

Freud's theory of female sexuality has also been refuted on psychological grounds. Not only, in Freudian psychology, must a woman orgasm by the movement of the penis in the vagina, but if she doesn't, she is "immature" and psychologically flawed. Her difficulty is supposedly a reflection of her over-all maladaptive character structure. She is seen as being significantly disturbed and lacking in "ego integration." It is said that she is struggling with unconscious conflicts that make her anxious and unstable; and her lack of orgasm is only one facet of this general unhappiness.

No major studies in the field of psychology have detected these correlations between personality structure and ability to orgasm during intercourse. If anything, as the most recent large-scale study has shown (Seymour Fisher, *The Female Orgasm*), there is almost an opposite correlation:

*There seems to be good reason for concluding that the more
a woman prefers vaginal stimulation, the greater is her level
of anxiety. The strongly vaginally oriented woman is tense
and has a low threshold for feeling disturbed. This was
demonstrated not only in her overt behaviour but also her
fantasies.*[9]

However, Fisher cautions:

*. . . although the vaginally oriented have been described as
more anxious than the clitorally oriented, this in no way
implies that they are less "healthy" or that they are seriously
maladjusted. There is no intent to replace the equation
between vaginal response and maturity which has so long
been common in the psychoanalytic literature with a reverse
equation. The women who were studied were without
major psychiatric symptoms and generally functioned at
what would be considered a "normal" level. The fact that
the vaginally oriented woman is more anxious or has
experienced more psychological distress than the clitoral
oriented does not mean that she is less mature or that she is
somehow psychologically inferior . . .*[10]

In addition, Fisher reported that:

*Numerous dimensions of the woman's body images were
evaluated. One, called Depersonalization, turned out to be
of special importance with respect to vaginal-clitoral
preference. It concerns the extent to which an individual
perceives her body as alien or foreign, lacking sensory
vividness . . . It was found that the more a woman describes
her body as "depersonalized," the more she prefers vaginal
rather than clitoral stimulation. This finding impressed me
as having an intriguing congruence with the fact that the
woman with high-vaginal preference was inclined to
describe her orgasm as lacking "ecstatic" quality. Just as the
high-vaginal woman apparently experiences the body state
called orgasm in a nonecstatic fashion, she also refers to her*

*body as lacking experiential intensity in a more general
characteristic fashion . . .*[11]

Fisher goes on to speculate that the vaginally oriented
woman might:

> *. . . believe that an intense body experience like sexual
> arousal should occur only when someone else, a male
> partner, becomes so closely involved with her body that he is
> sharing in the responsibility for it. When her body is fused
> sexually with his, she can think of her sexual arousal as a
> joint event. She can perceive the experience as not primarily
> for her own satisfaction but also for another. At the other
> extreme, the clitorally oriented woman would, from this
> viewpoint, have the opposing need to experience her body
> autonomously and to be reassured that an event like intense
> sexual excitement belongs clearly and personally to her. She
> would respond negatively to conditions which seriously
> challenged her sense of body autonomy.*[12]

Despite all these demonstrations of the fallacies of Freudian
theory about women, "treatment" of women along Freudian
lines is still widely performed, the large majority of psychiatrists having been influenced in various ways by his ideas.
Even with all the advances in biological knowledge that
make Freud's interpretation obsolete, and even with the
findings of Masters and Johnson, Fisher, and many others,
psychoanalytic theory has changed very little! As Sherfey,
herself a psychiatrist, asks, "The question must be put and
answered within the profession . . . Could many of the sexual neuroses which seem to be almost endemic to women
today be, in part, induced by doctors attempting to treat
them?"[13]

**"If you don't have orgasms during intercourse, you're
hung up."**
The influence of these psychiatric theories on women has
been strong and pervasive. Whether or not a woman has

been in analysis, she may have heard these unfounded and anti-woman theories endlessly repeated—from women's magazines, popular psychologists, and men during sex. *Everyone*—of all classes, backgrounds, and ages—*knows* a woman should orgasm during intercourse, or at least Hollywood does. If she doesn't, she knows she has only herself and her own hang-ups to blame.

"I see my failure to have orgasms during intercourse as *my* failure largely, i.e., I've had plenty of men who were 1) adept, 2) lasted a long time, 3) were eager for my orgasm to occur, and 4) etc. but none of them were successful. I guess I have a fear of childbearing, a fear of responsibility—I don't know."

"I am interested in having orgasms during intercourse because I see it as a normal natural release which I cannot achieve. My obvious underlying mistrust of men and disgust for their sexuality keeps me from totally letting go and disallows my sexual freedom."

"I could have them if I freed myself of anxiety and felt totally vulnerable."

"I think my mental attitude is wrong, that I have a mental block. But with a mutual atmosphere of trust and faith and love, I am sure I could let go of control and have orgasms."

"I can have an orgasm with clitoral stimulation but I have never had one with intercourse. This is purely a fear thing, as before I thought something was wrong with me, but a while ago I realized I didn't want to come with a man inside me, because basically I never respected any of the men I went to bed with—although I was not conscious at the time of this. My therapist helped me see it."

"I've never come with a man inside me, only by hand or mouth. Personally I think it's because I don't want to. I have very mixed feelings about men—anger vs. love, and I've never been with a man who I totally accept and respect as an equal to me."

"Orgasms, probably multiple, will come with penetration when I relax my vagina and give up the rigid control over what's happening to me, i.e., to not be afraid, to let myself be as vulnerable as I really am."

"I think I don't have them because I don't want to truly 'open up,' to me it's a submission, and the final conquering of me as a woman and person."

"To have orgasms during intercourse I need to cultivate a more sincere loving of self—my whole self, body and soul and mind; and a continuance of a relationship in order to get into and share many experiences harmoniously with each other."

"I wish I knew the answer. I take my lack of orgasms during intercourse very personally and very hard. Trying so hard as I do doesn't seem to be the answer. I seem to need the situation in which the sex act takes place to be perfect emotionally and physically."

"I can never forget that I want to come. Men have said that if I'd just forget about it and relax, I probably would come. I try very hard to come and to forget it too."

"I must let go, relax and trust, unlearn my taboos and defences against violation, resistance to my feelings . . ."

"I have orgasms but I'm not satisfied with them entirely because I still can't give myself completely to a man yet."

"I am one of the few females I know that really doesn't have some sort of psychological hang-up about screwing. No matter how slight, they all do."

"During eighteen years of marriage, we did everything but stand on our heads, but there were few orgasms for me—due to the deeper mental attitudes, probably. Masturbation has always worked."

"I will learn by vacuuming the fear out of my mind and learning to relax."

"Unless you work out your rage and fear about penetration, some energy will be taken by these emotions rather than letting yourself be completely taken over by the emotions and orgasm."

Fisher has something to say about this idea in particular:

> *Another factor often mentioned in the psychoanalytic*
> *literature as inhibiting a woman's orgasm potential is fear*
> *of being penetrated. It is said that anxiety about the*
> *consequences of the penis entering her body not infrequently*
> *prevents a woman from becoming sexually aroused during*
> *intercourse. Presumably the penetrating penis stirs up*
> *fantasies about internal injury, potential body damage*
> *consequent to becoming pregnant, and so forth. Relatedly, it*
> *has often been said in the analytic literature that most*
> *women envy the penis; and this envy may evoke competitive*
> *fantasies which, when intensified by sexual interactions,*
> *interfere with loving and being loved, and thus prevent*
> *orgasmic levels of excitement. No support has been found in*
> *the empirical data for either of these two formulations.*[14]

"It's very difficult for me. I can't forget past hurts. I know I must hold back as a punishment. In therapy I hope to learn to forget, and to relax and not be uptight, to be open and free with someone else."

"My problem is refusal to lose control with someone else, to let my feelings, physical responses take over for a few seconds of vulnerability. I need to truly love and trust the one I am with."

"With my husband, I don't trust him with my innermost being. He would probably consider my having orgasms *his* accomplishment anyway."

"There is some mental block I don't know about."

"In order to have orgasms, I have to deal with my own hang-ups. I don't think it has to do with any failure on my lover's part."

"I do feel I'm not sexually normal because I've never had an orgasm during intercourse, and I've lived with this guy for *years*. I know it's because of my guilt feelings towards sex and it's not him because he's a good lover. It's my own inhibitions."

"Although I do have clitoral orgasms, I do not have

spontaneous vaginal orgasms. I have been in several relationships where there was warmth and tenderness but not the kind of love, I guess (or trust, or commitment, etc.), necessary to get me over the hump. I hover so close to vaginally coming but panic at the last minute—block out my intense feelings. I guess I have a fear of being overwhelmed. Of letting a man have complete control over me. If I only come clitorally, if the relationship ends, no great loss."

The idea that if we would "just relax and let go" during intercourse we would automatically have an orgasm is, of course, based on the fallacious idea that orgasm comes to us automatically by the thrusting penis, and all we have to do is to give ourselves over to what our bodies will naturally and automatically do—that is, orgasm. As one woman put it, "It's our fault that we can't be as natural as they are."

I wish we could have back all the time and energy we have spent blaming ourselves and searching our souls about why we didn't have orgasms during intercourse. And all the money we spent "flocking to the psychiatrists" looking for the hidden and terrible repression that kept us from our "vaginal destiny."

Another reason frequently given for not having orgasms during intercourse was that the "Right Man" (Mr Right) was lacking.

"In order to have orgasms with a man, I would have to have a deep trust in him. He should be a really sensuous and intensely sexual man with a lot of patience and very perceptive, but easygoing. I think once I *knew* someone could satisfy me, I'd be able to come."

"If I could find a sex partner with whom I felt *completely* at ease sexually, I would probably have an orgasm during intercourse or at least other than during masturbation."

"I would very much enjoy having more orgasms with a partner. I guess I'm a bit of a perfectionist now in my expectations regarding sex, and becoming more realistic would contribute to my having more orgasms with a partner. I demand a fairly total understanding of myself by a partner, and expect the same of myself towards him—and this is rarely possible. I've had a few orgasms—(um) I can count only one or two *total* in all my life with approximately fifteen lovers to date. Good grief. That's no average—that's a total! Two orgasms with a partner in my whole life!!!"

"I must seem to have a low threshold of sexual need, to anyone reading this. You see, I've never known what sex is like with a dear, dear *friend* (in my experience marriage and friendship are *not* synonymous). I'm sure an orgasm during intercourse would be possible in a real *friendship*, a *companion* relationship."

"Maybe having sex with someone I knew well and deeply cared about would help."

"I don't know what would help but I think I have to know beyond a doubt that I'm the only piece of pussy he's interested in at the moment, the past ones were sub-standard, and that he'll be damned lucky to find another like me if he lives to be a hundred. I am in counselling now and hope this helps. Doctors have said I'm built alright and shouldn't have any problems."

"I don't know what would give me orgasms during intercourse. I suppose thinking it was worth doing. If you have to work so hard for it, if it doesn't come naturally or easily, then it seems pretty artificial, or wrong to force it. If my body wanted me to have orgasms, I'm sure it would see I did. I'm healthy, normal, well-balanced, and all that, so if I don't have orgasms, there must be something wrong with the act—or the man. I've tried lots and lots of them, from one-nighters to long, long affairs, almost always with men who must meet a very high standard, but none of them made me have an orgasm from intercourse, so I guess they just weren't good enough (meaning I guess I just didn't like them well enough) or else the whole act of intercourse is a concoction of the imagination. You can think yourself into almost any kind of fantasy, especially with a little psychology to help it along: like you aren't fulfilled unless you have orgasm. I think most of those men I was with were jerks (though I tried to pretend at the time they were giants of some kind) and that's why I couldn't get excited enough to have an orgasm. A stream of water is a lot more accommodating, it doesn't try to dominate you, insult you, use you, etc., etc."

"If I could feel my lover was more involved emotionally, if he made me feel secure, then I could come."

"I need to feel absolutely sure of my partner in every way to enable me to feel absolutely free to let go."

"I am only interested in trying with someone I care for and who cares for me, someone I really trust and believe in, and who feels the same about me."

Waiting for the Right Man to make us orgasm is like waiting for the prince to come. However, a partner who is more sensitive and understanding of the realities of female sexuality *can* make a difference in what the experience involves, and so there is some truth to the idea.

But the point still must be: don't wait for the right man to be dependent on, but create your own good situation—which can include yourself as being the Princess Charming, who knows pleasurable things to do and who finds another person to do them with.

Of course, the 30 per cent of women who said they *could* orgasm regularly during intercourse often bragged about it:

"Yes, I always orgasm during intercourse. I do not require a lot of play."

"I have a natural desire for sex, I do not need to be clitorally stimulated."

"Most men don't know the difference until they meet a *woman* who can show them what they have missed with the passive pussycats who hop into bed and fake it."

Like the competition among women fifty years ago as to who made the best pies, attitudes like this sound like we're still competing for male approval and haven't yet come into our own.

We are quite frankly desperate, all too often, to have orgasms during intercourse, no matter what:

"When a woman says, 'I have clitoral orgasms from manual manipulation or cunnilingus, but I never have orgasms from stimulation by my husband's penis, and we're unhappy about it,' and she is told, 'There is only one kind of orgasm, the vaginal orgasm is a myth, so since you're having orgasms, you don't really have a problem, *you only think you do,*' I don't see how the woman's problem has been solved."

"I would like to experience a vaginal orgasm to know what it's like, it must be great! But I don't know why I don't. Neither does my gynaecologist."

"I would like manual clitoral stimulation during intercourse, but feel shy about asking for it since I have a fear of making the man feel shut down about the effectiveness of his penis. Equally or more important, I have felt I ought to be able to do without it."

"I would love to hear from someone who is able to have a super orgasm during intercourse without any direct clitoral manipulation. I suppose it's possible. I wonder if I could 'learn how' the way I've 'learned how' the other way."

Attempts to orgasm by contacting the g-spot inside the vagina typically had responses such as this:

"There is an area on the roof of my vagina that actually provides a greater amount/level of arousal and stimulation than does my clitoris. This area can be stimulated by a finger but is best stimulated when I am on my stomach with my ass slightly raised and my male partner is lying on top of me, thrusting in and out in long hard strokes with his penis. This brings me right to the peak of orgasm in a much more intense way than clitoral stimulation *ever* can but will not actually cause the orgasm. For me to orgasm, either I or my partner reaches underneath my belly and stimulates my clitoris, and I'll come almost immediately. This stimulation is definitely preferable to clitoral stimulation by either one of us, but I do need the clitoral stimulation to have an orgasm. If I had to choose, though, at this point I'd choose clitoral stimulation because I don't want my sex to be purely orgasmless arousal. But I think since I took two years just to have an orgasm the first time when a guy stimulated my clitoris, I could definitely reach a point where this intense vaginal stimulation could bring me to an intense orgasm."

"Do you ever fake orgasms?"

The pressure on women to orgasm during intercourse is so great that an enormous number of women fake orgasms—some infrequently, most "sometimes," but some women say they do it every single time.

Do you fake orgasms?

Yes	567
No	775
Used to	318
"It's no use, it's not convincing"	4
Total	1664

"I used to fake orgasms all the time, and always with vaginal penetration. I came from the school of it's not right—you'll emasculate the man—if you don't let him think he's satisfied you. With the onset of the women's movement, and its personal effect on me, I've stopped faking them. My husband used to ask, 'Did you come?'—and when the answer was 'yes'—even if I was faking it—that was cool for him. Then when I started saying 'no' a couple of times, he quit asking. Now, if I complain I didn't come, he's either asleep, or says he's sorry and turns over and goes to sleep."

"I never fake orgasm. I am angry with other women who do, because then men can tell me that I am incapable sexually, because I do not have vaginal climaxes, and other women they have slept with do. Since I have never had a vaginal climax, I question their existence, or at least their general prevalence, and wonder if another woman's faking an orgasm has made it harder for me when I am honest."

"I fake it during clitoral stimulation and during intercourse when I'm not in the mood. It's easier and faster than saying 'no' and then worrying about my husband's ego and feelings for me, etc. He, like most other men, gets really frightened and hurt when I say no and I hear about it in passing a week later."

"I'm sure it's ridiculous to let him believe I am having an orgasm when he does, it's just turned the twenty-first century and all, but I guess I'm a coward or behind the times. I just can't bear to ruin the moment by blurting out 'how about me?' or something pathetic. I've tried touching myself a little while he's plunging away, but can't really get into it—and it makes him uneasy, I think. He wants me to come with him."

"I have, and occasionally still do fake orgasms during intercourse, but not often. When I do it now it's because I know I'm not going to have an orgasm but my man is really working hard for me and really wants to give me one and would be very disappointed to know it's no use. As we live together longer it becomes less necessary because our sex is better and we know each other better. In the past I would do it to protect the man's ego and occasionally (with one man) because he would be mad if I didn't have one. I hate faking it, though, and I really hated it with that one man, but he was a typical dominant egocentric chauvinistic horse's ass."

"During my marriage I was excellent at faking orgasms and so for maybe four years I never really had any satisfying sexual experiences. Unfortunately, I was totally faithful to my husband so I was pretty miserable physically. I masturbated a whole lot! After my separation I explored sex with a variety of partners and had a sexual awakening, so to speak."

"Yes, I used to, more to give a positive reinforcement for something I liked even though I didn't orgasm."

"I used to, when my husband had a complex about sex and a marriage counsellor told me I should build up his ego."

"No, but I may act more excited than I really am."

"I used to, because my partner was comparing me to another woman he was sleeping with. He made me feel terrible with descriptions of how she went into a screaming orgasm before he even entered her."

"Yes, when I haven't had one for quite a while, I do it so my partner won't think he isn't pleasing me. I don't feel orgasms are all that important (he seems to) and I don't feel it's his fault if I don't come but . . . sometimes it is his fault, though, I guess."

"I was afraid to appear 'less of a woman' and emasculate my partner. So I did it, but he found me out."

"Sometimes it builds a man's ego to let him think he's successful. Therefore if I really like a man and want him to think I enjoyed sex more than I did, I do it."

"Only to get me or him 'off the hook.' "

"He thinks if I don't have an orgasm, he has failed me, even though I've explained that it isn't that way at all. Anyway, sometimes it just seems easier to do it. I used to sometimes when I thought he was anxious to have an orgasm, or getting bored, or impatient, or disappointed."

"I fake orgasms to save his pride and prevent arguments."

"Never. I consider it a denial of all that shared experience means."

"Sometimes I fake them, if he keeps pestering me with 'did you come yet?' "

"I used to, because men would enjoy watching me pant."

"Yes, a couple of times with a partner who thought he was fantastic in bed. He would have to penetrate me almost immediately to prove his prowess, and there was no way he would get off again unless he thought I'd had an orgasm."

"I used to, to avoid having men make a big fuss or act critical or pitying."

"I used to fake them in order not to leave the other person out on a lonely psychological limb."

"Yes, I always fake orgasms. It just seems polite. Why be rude?"

"I have promised myself—no more. I used to because my man expected me to have an orgasm; I thought I was unable to, and I thought faking it was the only way he would continue to want me."

"I used to, to please men and get their approval, and make them believe I was a sexy chick, etc., etc. I remember faking them on acid trips and even on my wedding night, etc. It was grisly and at the time I was sure I was the *only* woman who did this."

"I used to fake orgasms until I started having them at age thirty. I faked them to avoid confrontation with a man, to avoid explaining why I was like I was, to avoid their trite responses of lesbianism, frigidity, etc."

"I did until we were married, because I thought getting married would do the trick. Ha!"

"I used to, but not since I learned the submissive implications of it and the fact that I had a real right to genuine pleasure."

"I fake them often. He and I have had such an abysmal

sex relationship that I don't want to burden him with the knowledge that I don't come during intercourse."

"I *always* did. (I'm sixty-two now.) I was told to do it by male doctors to keep my husband happy (bless me). I was thinking there was something missing in my make-up for about thirty-five years—and that's a long time to imagine you had to fake it!"

"Yes, and especially I fake passion—sometimes to excite myself and sometimes to get the guy off my back and save myself."

"Yes, I used to think the male ego was more important than me."

"I have been faking orgasms for thirty years, because I need approval—I lack self-esteem—I'm ashamed as though I had a club foot or one eye—and because I don't want to hurt my husband, who is also insecure."

"I used to fake them to keep my husband from straying."

"Yes, to please men. It makes me feel a bit empty to do so."

"I used to fake orgasms because I felt it was my duty, and my own inability to orgasm during intercourse."

"Only with my first lover for the first few months—I knew how to pretend great passion and he thought he trained me. I just conformed to his male demands to gain other non-sex privileges of dates to good places. I was a free whore."

"I used to fake them all the time until we discovered my clitoris. I had always thought intercourse was the only right way and that it was my inadequacy—but once I found masturbation I was all set."

"No, I told him that I don't orgasm during intercourse."

"When I've felt insecure and negative about myself: Goddamn, any *normal* woman would have had an orgasm ten minutes ago. He must think I'm weird. This kind of feeling comes from the miserable social pressure for women to be what they're not—if you have brown hair, you *ought* to be blonde. If you have small breasts . . ."

"By omission. I don't say I didn't, and they assume I did."

"I used to, sometimes. When he wouldn't stop until I came, but I wanted him out—or I felt sorry for him—shit!"

"I used to fake orgasms on a regular basis because I was too shy and ashamed to tell the man what I wanted him to do and that it didn't turn me on just to be screwed."

"Fifty per cent of the time—when you just aren't getting there, you know it, and you just want that blood ritual over."

"Several times I faked orgasms when I couldn't stand a heavy, hairy, rough body crushing me. Men outweigh women. Men are stronger. Men use penises as guns and straddle you as they please."

"I always fake them during intercourse. I know it would hurt the guy I live with if he knew otherwise, so I always tell him that it was great."

"Yes, usually I orgasm during foreplay and then fake it during intercourse. He would be concerned if he felt I wasn't orgasming during intercourse."

"I wouldn't know how."

"Rarely—only with an inexperienced guy who's going to lose a lot of self-esteem and is too mortified to talk about what's happening."

"Yes, it's easier and faster than struggling."

"For many years, I thought faking was a part of the game! Then I discovered how much healthier we both were with no fakery, much conversation, description, and exploration together."

"No, I don't owe anyone an orgasm but myself!"

"I used to when my husband's patience was running out."

"Four or five times a month—if we have built up to a certain point. I feel there's something wrong with me, so I fake it out of pride. It does make me feel strange, that after all the stimulation I still can't reach an orgasm. I have often thought that I'm trying too hard. I don't feel like less of a woman, but I do feel embarrassed that I have some kind of a mental block. I fake because I can't make him feel inadequate when it's *me* who's having a psychological problem."

"I don't know if my partner always knows when I have an orgasm. I always enjoy sex so it may be difficult for him to tell."

"I have never consciously faked an orgasm. Sometimes, though, I start the moaning and other signals that indicate the onset of orgasm, and then my partner finishes too quickly for me to come, only he doesn't realize this—in this situation I will allow my partner to keep his assumption that I've come because it makes him feel better and wouldn't do me any good to straighten him out. If he comes right out and says, 'Did you come?' then I refuse to lie; I'll say something like 'almost.' "

"I never have. I'm a very honest person. If my partner mistakenly thinks I did, I may not correct him, though."

"Frequently, yes. To get the social obligation over with for the night."

"Rarely. Only when I come close, then he orgasms and 'freezes up' right when I needed just a bit more."

"Most men either take it for granted that you had one, or they don't care. So sometimes I do it to get it over with."

"No. But I never insisted on stopping in the middle when I wanted to, which was often."

"Like asking if the sky is blue. Yes, during intercourse."

"Yes, often, during intercourse, when I felt my partner would be crushed otherwise. I also used to have the idea that I should be a hot tamale and always come."

"Not usually. Sometimes I kind of 'share his orgasm'

even though I'm not having one myself and kind of grunt and groan along with him while he is having his."

"Yes, I just go along with his orgasm and try for some vicarious emotional climax."

"If suddenly, in the middle of everything I realize I've made a mistake and I didn't even like him, I'll just squeeze hard around four or five times and moan like I'm coming, and that makes him come, and then it's over."

"Definitely—some men want to fuck me till I come or drop dead."

"Yes, if I particularly like a person but I feel they are vulnerable and will blame themselves if I don't come. After that I don't sleep with them again."

"Yes, with one man whom I loved, but who was a lousy lover in bed, I had to do it every time we made love! Can you believe that?"

"Always, unless I'm angry with my partner."

"Yes, when I cannot come and the poor fellow is exhausted and doing his best."

"Rarely. If the person would be made to feel very inadequate and hurt, I will fake an orgasm."

"I fake orgasms when I'm scared of disapproval."

"I faked them to hide my hurt because the other person had an orgasm."

"I felt I couldn't have my partner believe he was inadequate as he had suffered from impotence early in our relationship."

"Yes; as I said, I don't need sex as often as my husband but he gets upset if I don't have an orgasm, so to keep him happy I fake one. I tried playing it straight with him, once, but he got into a terrible thing trying to have it only when I wanted an orgasm, so I fake it. It's really the most satisfactory way. I do not feel put upon or abused—it's part of the TLC."

"I also realize now that many males who seem so concerned with whether you were satisfied or not are only interested in inflating their egos by hearing a 'yes' reply. I'm sure if I said 'no' they'd just be angry and wouldn't think of trying to do something about it."

"I should think it would be lousy to have a wife that came with a touch but never by your penis. I feel badly about this."

"I have faked orgasms until recently, even though I feel it is wrong to do so. I have faked orgasms many, many times. They just didn't have any idea of what to do with the clitoris and I hate to give an anatomy lecture in the middle of love-making."

"No, this is a big mistake, as the man will never learn."

"I have faked it without exception, because I felt men, without exception, need to feel that they are good in bed, usually to feel that *they* are the best in bed."

"For fifteen years I was the world's best faker. Honestly—they should have a phallic trophy—mounted on a pedestal (like in the art history books) for all *women*—I think they all fake it with men."

Conclusion

Insisting that women should have orgasms during intercourse, from intercourse, is to force women to adapt their bodies to inadequate stimulation, and the difficulty of doing this and the frequent failure that is built into the attempt breeds recurring feelings of insecurity and anger. As Ann Koedt* put it, in *The Myth of the Vaginal Orgasm:*

> *Perhaps one of the most infuriating and damaging results of this whole charade has been that women who were perfectly healthy sexually were taught that they were not. So in addition to being sexually deprived, these women were told to blame themselves when they deserved no blame. Looking*

*Ti-Grace Atkinson has also written about this in *Amazon Odyssey* (Links Books), 1974.

for a cure to a problem that has none can lead a woman on
an endless path of self-hatred and insecurity. For she is told
by her analyst that not even in her one role allowed in a
male society—the role of a woman—is she successful. She is
put on the defensive, with phony data as evidence that she
better try to be even more feminine, think more feminine,
and reject her envy of men. That is: Shuffle even harder,
baby.[15]

The old myth that women take longer to orgasm than men, because women are more "psychologically delicate" than men, and our orgasm is more dependent on feelings, is false. In fact, *women* do not *take longer to orgasm than men.* The majority of the women in Kinsey's study masturbated to orgasm within four minutes, similar to the women in this study. It is, obviously, only during inadequate or secondary, insufficient stimulation like intercourse that we take "longer" and need prolonged "foreplay." But this misconception has led to a kind of mystique about female orgasm:

"I believe that a woman needs much more than a man—it's a more complex totality of physical and emotional stimulation for her to have an orgasm."

"Women have orgasm when the spirit moves them. They don't just have or seek functional orgasms that you can always predict."

"All most men need is the up and down friction on the penis. I believe that a woman needs much more. It is a much more subtle combination of physical and emotional feelings."

But female orgasm is *not* particularly mysterious. There is no great mystery about why a woman has an orgasm. It happens with the right stimulation, quickly, pleasurably, and reliably. As we saw in the first chapter, women don't need "foreplay" in masturbation to orgasm. The whole key is adequate stimulation. In the next section, we shall see how some women get this in intercourse.

How do women orgasm during intercourse?

"Penetration is one of the nicest feelings I know, mentally and physically. It practically always leads to an orgasm and takes from twenty to forty minutes. My lover is capable of two and sometimes three orgasms so we are not really slow but we do luxuriate in our love-making. I like to feel him inside of me and to hear him moan and sigh and feel him pulsating. Mentally I enjoy the secure feeling I have when he is in me and I like for him to stay inside as long as possible. Sometimes we go to sleep this way."

Another woman wrote, after reading *Sexual Honesty*, to ask if she was "weird" because she *did* have orgasms rather easily during intercourse. There is certainly no reason for this reverse stereotyping. Some women do orgasm during intercourse, but the causes aren't mysterious; it results from very concrete kind of physical stimulation, which we shall try to describe here.

Masters and Johnson: A Rube Goldberg model?

Before we describe the methods women in this study used to orgasm during intercourse, it remains to mention how Masters and Johnson have explained the way in which orgasm during intercourse occurs.

Stressing that all women's orgasms are caused by stimulation of the clitoris, whether direct or indirect, they have explained that orgasm during intercourse comes from the indirect clitoral stimulation caused by thrusting: as the penis moves back and forth, it pulls the labia minora, which are attached to the skin covering the clitoris (the hood), back and forth with it, so indirectly moving the skin around over the clitoral glands. In Masters and Johnson's own (brief) words:

> *A mechanical traction develops on both sides of the clitoral hood of the minor labia subsequent to penile distension of the vaginal outlet. With active penile thrusting, the clitoral body is pulled downward toward the pudendum by traction exerted on the wings of the clitoral hood . . .*
>
> *When the penile shaft is in the withdrawal phase of active coital stroking, traction on the clitoral hood is somewhat relieved and the body and glans return to the normal pudendal-overhang positioning . . . the rhythmic movement of the clitoral body in conjunction with active penile stroking produces significant indirect or secondary clitoral stimulation.*
>
> *It should be emphasized that this same type of secondary clitoral stimulation occurs in every coital position when there is a full penetration of the vaginal barrel by the erect penis.*[16]

In other words, the clitoris is surrounded by skin known as the "clitoral hood" that is connected, in turn, to the labia minora. Supposedly, during intercourse the thrusting penis (notice the assumption of female passivity) exerts rhythmic mechanical traction on the swollen labia minora, and so provides stimulation for the clitoris via movements of the clitoral hood. Sherfey has termed this the "preputial-glandar mechanism" wherein "the thrusting movement of the penis in the vagina pulls on the labia minora which, via their extension around the clitoris (the clitoral hood or prepuce) is then pulled back and forth over the erect clitoris."[17] That is, the final stimulation is provided to the clitoris by friction against its own hood.

The development of this theory was a great advance in

that it no longer said friction against the walls of the vagina had anything to do with stimulating female orgasm. However, the existence of this model, and its publicity, has left women with the impression that orgasm during intercourse is still to be expected as part of the automatic "normal" course of things.

Masters and Johnson developed this model of how women's sexuality works by observing the women they had selected for study, all of whom were chosen only if they were able to have orgasms during intercourse. It would seem that to analyse what is probably an unusual group of women, and then to generalize from these women, is a mistake. Indeed, it is only possible if you assume that to orgasm during intercourse is somehow "normal," and not "dysfunctional." (Masters and Johnson have labelled the "inability" to orgasm during intercourse "coital orgasmic inadequacy"; "primary sexual dysfunction" is never having an orgasm in any way.)

Besides the fallacy of generalizing from a special population about just that very thing which makes them special, there is a second problem with this model. That is, there can only be traction between the penis and vagina when the woman is already at a certain stage of arousal, because only then do the labia swell up enough to cause traction (the stage Masters and Johnson call late plateau arousal). In other words, the penis can only pull the labia back and forth with it if the woman is at the last stage of arousal before orgasm so that there is sufficient engorgement of the area to cause a tight fit between penis and vaginal opening. (You can check how well this mechanism works for you, by the way, by placing a dildo or similarly sized inanimate object in your vagina when you reach this state of arousal, and then moving it in and out and seeing what you feel.)

Masters and Johnson have not explained how they arrived at the conclusion that this mechanism is the means of orgasm during intercourse of the women they studied. It does seem clear that this mechanism is indeed the means by which most women orgasm during clitoral stimulation or masturbation, in that during masturbation the skin of the clitoral area, or the upper lips, are pulled around or moved around slightly, thus causing the skin to move back and forth over the clitoral glans. As Sherfey puts it, "Mons area friction will have exactly the same effect on the prepuce-glans action as the penile thrusting motion: the *prepuce is rhythmically pulled back and forth over the glans.*"[18]

It seems that the thrusting activates this mechanism for very few women, however. Most researchers and sex therapists agree that thrusting is less efficient in causing female orgasm than clitoral area stimulation. Pulling your ear slightly back and forth can also pull the skin on your cheek. Just so, it is possible for thrusting to pull the skin near your clitoris in just the right way to stimulate you to orgasm, and it may happen regularly for a small percentage of women—but not for most women most of the time.

This brings to mind the fact that Masters and Johnson have insisted on treating women, but not men, with their *usual* sexual partners, whom they must bring with them. (Men were allowed surrogates.) This is usually understood to imply adherence to a moral double standard, but the reason for this rule may in fact have been that, for a woman to orgasm during intercourse, she must adapt her body to inadequate stimulation, and so it is essential that she work out this procedure with a regular partner.

More recently, in lectures and private therapy, Masters and Johnson have emphasized the specific techniques women can use to orgasm during intercourse, such as being on top of the man, doing most of the moving, etc. Perhaps they have too found that the "preputial-glandar mechanism" does not work for most women. However, if this is indeed the case, the message has not reached the general public. The woman-in-the-street (most of us) still has the impression that it is "normal" to orgasm from male thrusting.

There is nothing wrong with saying that the movement of the clitoral hood over the clitoris is what is responsible for orgasm; this is true. What *is* wrong is to say that thrusting in itself will activate this mechanism in most women. As

Alex Shulman has pointedly remarked:

> *Masters and Johnson observe that the clitoris is automatically "stimulated" in intercourse since the hood covering the clitoris is pulled over the clitoris with each thrust of the penis in the vagina—much, I suppose, as a penis is automatically "stimulated" by a man's underwear whenever he takes a step.*[19]

But let's apply this same logic to men with more scientific precision: As Dr Sanford Copley put it, when interviewed on the television show *Woman*, this indirect stimulation of women could be compared to the stimulation that would be produced in a man by the rubbing of the scrotal skin (balls), perhaps pulling it back and forth, and so causing the skin of the upper tip of the penis to move, or quiver, and in this way achieving "stimulation." Would it work? Admittedly, this form of stimulation would probably require a good deal more foreplay for the man to have an orgasm! You would have to be patient and "understand" if it did not lead to orgasm "every time."

Masters and Johnson's theory that the thrusting penis pulls the woman's labia, which in turn pull the clitoral hood, which thereby causes friction of the clitoral glans and thereby causes orgasm sounds more like a Rube Goldberg scheme than a reliable way to orgasm, an analogy first drawn by Pauline Bart.

It is not that the mechanism doesn't work. It does: if you pull any skin around the area it can stimulate the clitoris. But the question is, does thrusting do this effectively? The answer would seem to be that, for most women, without some special effort or some special set of circumstances, it does not.

Perhaps, finally, it is important to point out that, if this mechanism works so well, why hasn't it been working all along, for centuries? Why is "coital frigidity" the well-known "problem" that it is? And why don't women masturbate this way sometimes? No, having an orgasm during intercourse is an adaptation of our bodies. Intercourse was never meant to stimulate women to orgasm.

Women who orgasm during intercourse: How they do it

Orgasms during intercourse in this study usually seemed to result from a conscious attempt by the woman to centre some kind of clitoral area contact for herself during intercourse, usually involving contact with the man's pubic area. This clitoral stimulation during intercourse could be thought of, then, as basically stimulating yourself while intercourse is in progress. Of course the other person must cooperate. This is essentially the way men get stimulation during intercourse: they rub their penises against our vaginal walls so that the same area they stimulate during masturbation is being stimulated during intercourse. In other words, *you* have to get the stimulation centred where it feels good.

Answers seemed to define six basic ways of having orgasm during intercourse, descriptions of which follow.

1. The position of woman on top

There isn't anything that *automatically* makes this position work—it is the freedom of movement it gives the woman to seek her own satisfaction, which in large part explains why it is so effective for so many women, and especially women of masturbation type III (thrusting into a pillow). Also it can allow you to have your legs together, or to adjust the amount of penetration to hit your pubic area against his pubic bone in a good way for you. And this position is the one seen in the earliest Stone Age drawings, as well as on the wall murals at Pompeii.

"A very exciting feeling is for me to rub myself up and down while sitting on the man's pelvis, with his penis inside. Then I have the right stimulation for me physically, plus the psychological stimulation of his excitement."

"How I orgasm involves being on top and moving back and forth so my clitoris rubs against the base of the penis without the penis moving in and out of the vagina."

"I have an orgasm during intercourse when I assume the 'dominant' position, and rub my clitoris against his belly and pubic area."

"He sits or half reclines, I above him, with his penis in my vagina at just the right angle and to get pressure on my clitoris from his pubic bone. At the same time he plays with my nipples while I move my pelvis whatever way feels good."

"My ideal position would be in the female above position with a slow but complete penetration in a rather rhythmic rocking motion, with my legs together, and breasts being fondled. But with prolonged 'straight' (missionary position) intercourse, my interest lags."

"I like to be on top, because I can better control the amount of friction in the right places. My legs are usually apart and there has to be a lot of the 'right kind' of movement."

"I prefer lying down, stomach to stomach, with me on top. This gives me more freedom in setting the pace, and much more clitoral stimulation from our intercourse."

"When I am 'on top' my chances of orgasm are improved because I can look for my orgasm and my partner waits till I make mine before he makes his."

"On top I prefer the man not to move at all but they simply don't pay attention and move anyhow."

"I do it by sitting on top of him after he comes and rubbing up and down. Sometimes he comes again when I do this."

"I had my most satisfying orgasm on top of a man

who was lying exhausted and still, after *his* orgasm. I rubbed myself (my clitoris) against him and had a very easy total orgasm."

"On top, I could have orgasms during intercourse, but I've always felt that essentially I'd be masturbating—i.e., being on top, rubbing my clitoris against the man's pubic hair or something. This prevents penis-vaginal movement (thrusting in and out) and thus has always hung me up—made me feel selfish or infantile (thanks to Freud, I guess) or something. So I don't *seek* orgasms during intercourse. The vaginal trip feels good in itself."

"We have intercourse with me on top. I create my own rhythm through up and down, back and forth movements until I achieve orgasm or until I know the capacity has passed."

"In heterosexual intercourse, after being generally aroused, I reach a climax by getting on top, in the female superior position, and moving my pelvic area around in a sometimes up and down, sometimes circular, motion. It usually takes less than a minute if I'm really turned on."

The woman on her stomach.
A position that can work for many women, especially those who masturbate by type III, is lying face down on the bed, with the man entering from the rear, since this enables the woman to rub against the bed or sheets in her accustomed manner, with the added pleasure, perhaps, of the other person's body on top of her.

2. Grinding pubic/mons areas together

Very similar to the position of woman on top is the grinding friction method, although it can be done in any position. Grinding involves complete penetration, with little or no thrusting, one person moving around and around so that the two genital areas are rubbing together and massaging each other, especially the female lips and vulva, or the mons area.

"My orgasms during intercourse are usually triggered by a thick penis buried deep for me to grind slowly on."

"We lie side by side with legs entwined, so that one of his legs is between my two legs, which makes one of my legs between his legs, with the penis inserted, which causes my clitoris to be riding on his front muscle or pubic bone. Then wriggling around."

"Very close body contact. I enjoy it when the penis is completely inserted and when we sort of rub together more than making bouncing motions."

"I prefer the top position and/or grinding together, face to face. The problem here is that both positions he finds uncomfortable and appears to accommodate me resentfully and passively. Naturally this affects my state of mind negatively so I rarely insist upon these two positions."

"I lie on the bottom with my legs around him, then grind my pelvis and pubic area against his."

"I can orgasm by pressing and rubbing my pubic area, which is spongy and very sensitive, against him, with the penis inside but not going in and out."

"I press my clitoris rather hard against my man and move my pelvis back and forth or in circles. Sometimes he keeps moving when I do this, and sometimes he stops. I can either lie on my back with my legs up on his shoulders, or with them around his hips. Sometimes I sit on top and he lies underneath, or sometimes we both sit up and face each other. Sometimes I tighten my vaginal muscles and hip muscles to speed up the orgasm."

"We use the missionary position with the man's body (the part directly above his genital area) pressed against my clitoral area. Until the orgasm is reached, it is necessary for him to remain in contact with my clitoral area, rubbing and pressing, and he should not prop himself up on his elbows until after I come."

"Most men move too much for me. I like him to penetrate deeply, press to the front and then remain still for a while but few men seem able or willing to do this. At orgasm, I want the man to be very hard, in very deep and remaining still. It always diminishes the intensity of my orgasm if the man is moving fast as I orgasm. And most men, sensing I am coming, immediately rush their own orgasm and this often spoils mine."

"There is a particular rhythm I find most helpful. It is that when the man pushes in, he stays pressed against me for a few seconds, instead of backing up right away. Also that he does not back away as soon as I press against him, which some men have a tendency to do."

3. Touching of pubic bones together during intercourse

Getting clitoral stimulation by the man's pubic bone hitting against the woman's with each thrust was another method used by some women. In most of the examples, the man was doing the moving. Positions included the man on top, or one or both sitting up; the women's leg positions included everything from together to apart to up or bent up and back. The thrusting makes it hard to keep the stimulation on just the right spot, so it is important to have freedom of movement for yourself.

"I prefer having the man on top, but I move a lot because I am finicky about the timing and thrusting that's going on. It requires a lot of squirming around to get certain places that are pleasurable. Also, if I keep my legs together, my grasp regulates the pressure as I like it."

"Usually I receive clitoral stimulation by pressing my mons area against the pubic area of my partner in a rhythmic fashion. It is difficult for me to come in a standing or rear entry position, because the vital pubic bone to pubic bone pressure is missing. When he is on the top, I usually grab my partner's buttocks with my hands and guide him in his movements, if he isn't already doing what I want."

"We have intercourse with him on top, bodies arched slightly so that my clitoral area is exposed and receiving stimulation by the natural thrusts of our bodies together."

"During intercourse, I am on the bottom. I am scooted down so that the penis is more at a right angle to his body. The energy required to resist his weight, and to move my hips seems to concentrate in the clitoral area of my pelvis. At this point, I lift my feet to concentrate the energy even more."

"There is one position with me underneath with my legs up over my partner's shoulders that I can come in with no arousal. It blows my mind."

"I like not too deep penetration, long and smooth strokes, my legs straight out or close together, and pubic areas rubbing together."

"I use slow and gentle movements trying to touch my clitoral area to his pubic area, then faster."

"To have orgasms during intercourse, I had to learn to make use of my vaginal-perineal muscles, and I had to learn to position myself and move my body in such a way as to maximize the pressure I received on the mons area. I also learned to give my partners the feedback they needed to know what I needed; usually this communication is non-verbal but occasionally verbal when I have difficulty getting the point across. I had to adjust to a lesser intensity of stimulation to obtain orgasm during intercourse. I had masturbated for several years before I fucked, and was used to intense, direct stimulation right on and around the clitoris. Of course, the movements of the penis in the vagina do not provide this intensity. I had to learn how to focus on the vaginal sensations, the more subtle 'pressure' sensations on the clitoris, and the deeper sensations."

"We have intercourse with me on the bottom. My husband inserts his penis and moves his pelvis, and I move my pelvis so my clitoris moves against his pelvic bone."

"During intercourse, if he is very active and regular,

not altering the rhythm or pressure, and if I actively pursue the feeling, sometimes I have orgasms. It also depends on the partner and his particular body aligning with my particular body."

"I think that this is a matter of anatomy as well as psychology—i.e., with one man in particular our bodies fit together in such a way that the in and out motions of his penis did stimulate my clitoris to orgasm. But usually this doesn't happen."

"I think the positioning of a couple's genitals (due to their respective sizes) has a lot to do with stimulation. One of my partners fit me perfectly."

"I need the rhythmic movements of two bodies together, which doesn't have to be interrupted due to the man's 'almost' ejaculating every minute or so. If I can feel the penis at a steady timing going in and out of the vagina, I can get the feeling centred for myself, and begin my own steady climb to orgasm."

"My most recent steady boyfriend is the best lover I've ever had (i.e., I respond best), and I think it is because he fucks me rhythmically and continuously for long periods (e.g., half an hour to an hour). This steady rhythmical uninterrupted thrusting by him is overall very soothing, and enables that degree of relaxation necessary for the delicate quivering response of the vaginal walls to begin."

"His penetrations/thrusts are very smooth and continuous and unhurried for a long time, *then* whenever I begin to react a little, he quickens his thrusts, penetrates more strongly and excitingly and thereby heightens the response from what it started as. The excitement builds like this, then he returns to steady quiet soothing movements, then again I begin to respond delicately, etc., etc., etc. It is the first time I really enjoyed sex *enormously* and it's all vaginal."

However, not everyone can orgasm in these ways, so don't expect too much of yourself: position, whether you are on top, or grinding your pubic bones together, or whatever, does not work for many, many (most?) women. It is always an individual adaptation for each woman. If it doesn't work for you, don't be surprised; as one woman commented, "I haven't found a position yet that works. And I've tried everything."

Position is a very tricky way of having orgasm, as are the other indirect ways yet to be discussed. They require your partner's full cooperation or, at least, some cooperation. And even then you may find that the same way doesn't always work regularly, or with a new partner—because his body is shaped differently, or his sense of rhythm may be different,* and this type of touch-and-go indirect stimulation requires that everything be perfectly meshed. That is why many women said that the best sex came after practice with one individual. As one woman put it, "With each new partner, I have to relearn to have orgasms with them."

Perhaps it is important to mention here that the emphasis on the mechanical and technical aspects of intercourse in this section is not meant to minimize the importance of the individual feelings and emotions experienced during intercourse. Actually, as will become apparent in other chapters, the emotional context is the primary value of intercourse for most women. However, the point here is to dissect and analyse the various parts of our *physical* sexual experience, disassembled from the whole, so that we can become not only "emotional experts" but also knowledgeable "physical experts."

Preferred type of movement during "pubic bones together" stimulation, when the man is doing most of the moving.

"Slow, tender, sensitive, firm."

"Not a battering ram, not rammed to the floor."

"Soft then harder. (Most men do 'harder' too hard. If

---

*"For the past twenty years or so, I have not had orgasms during intercourse, although I once did, over a period of nearly five years, with my first husband. I have literally racked my brain for the intervening twenty years to try to figure out why with that one man, during intercourse, and never since (and never before), I was able to have orgasms."

a man could use his penis like his hand, it might be more fun.)"

"A definite rhythm I can count on for some time."

"Hard, slow shoves, with a grind when penetration is complete."

"Gentle entry, then slow, full-length strokes of the penis in and out, getting faster. I've found that when the movement is generally rhythmical, I can relax and have an orgasm easier because I don't have to concentrate on what is coming next."

"I dislike being roughly ridden and prefer a more slithery approach."

"Slow, prolonged gentle love-making and not a demonstration of semen-power and muscle thrusts."

"Tender and passionate."

"Gentle. I do not like being raped, if you know what I mean."

The only persons who liked rough treatment were generally those who didn't have orgasms during intercourse. One woman wrote, "I like rough treatment. Why? I often think of it as massive frustration—like, I don't care what you do to me, just do it and do it soon, because I want to come in the most desperate way, and what you're doing now just isn't going to get me there."

Preferred type of movement during "grinding" stimulation.

"Soft but deep—almost no thrusting, sort of just lying together in a *deep* penetration."

"Deep 'hugging positions.'"

It should also be kept in mind that women require continuous stimulation to orgasm, as opposed to the discontinuous stimulation adequate for men. This is one of the few *basic* differences in female and male sexual physiology. As Sherfey explains it:

A universal feature of the response cycle in women is the necessity for continuous stimulation. If stimulation is

stopped even in the middle of the orgasm, the orgasm stops.
This is true with clitoral area and vaginally induced
orgasms.[20]

To depend on thrusting to bring your pubic bones together
is risky since a *very* steady, dependable rhythm must be
maintained, at the very least. Since this rhythm is more
important to the woman than the man, because she needs
continuous stimulation, perhaps she should be the one in
control of the thrusting.

Leg position/body position.
Remember, too, that the kind of intercourse that may work
for you may very well depend on the leg position you
require and the general orgasm type (masturbation type) you
are. If you have to have your legs together, or knees bent, or
if you have to be on your stomach, this will influence the
positions you find most appealing during intercourse. In
general it is important to have enough freedom of movement so that whatever body movement and especially leg
movement you may need to orgasm is not blocked.

4. Partial holding of the penis in the vagina, without moving in and out

This is a kind of positioning wherein the head of the penis
is just inside the vaginal lips, with the base of the penis
pulled up toward the clitoris, sort of draped around the
vulva, as it were. This can be a hard position to maintain.

"The only partner with whom I had orgasm during
intercourse was Mickey and it was because his pubic
bone was constructed so it pressed down on me during
intercourse. I felt exactly like I was masturbating. Also,
with Mickey, my legs were together. This way, his penis
couldn't enter me very deeply and so it was sort of
draped up over/bent around from my vagina to my
clitoris—i.e., the base of his penis wound up being

against my upper vulva. It was great. I was younger then, and I got off on the idea that I was finally coming through intercourse! (Like a grown-up.) It kept us together for the longest time, even after we really had nothing much more in common."

"During intercourse, I actually position the male so his penis touches my clitoris. This is probably the reason I prefer the missionary position and avoid overweight males. Slender males are best for this. Besides, you can really move under them if you need to."

"I like to have my clitoris against the base of his penis, then I want my partner to move in concert with me, gently, slightly, but in the same rhythm. When the partner breaks through my rhythm, it disrupts my progress toward orgasm. The only exception is when we have not been together for a period of time. The first intercourse following separation for a long time is a joyous spontaneous explosive experience."

"Best is him going in and out, slowly rubbing the base of his penis over my clitoris. I know it sounds like it's impossible, but the penis ends up hitting the opposite wall of the vagina towards the back."

However, the irony is that what feels good for the woman often doesn't for the man:

"No man I've met will agree to partial penetration."

"Unfortunately sex for me is like a fight. I put the penis where I want it; I say 'it feels good *there*.' He shoves it deep inside and says, 'No, *that's* where it feels good.' This may sound far-fetched, but it's true; God, I wish it weren't. I usually lose the fight."

5. Frequent re-entry of the penis into the vagina

There is also a type of intercourse with even *less* penetration than partial. It involves just basically moving the penis around the outer lips, or coming completely out with every stroke, so that the entranceway or lips are constantly being pulled and stimulated.

"I appreciate fairly slow, deep rhythmic thrusts, nearly leaving the vagina as he prepares for the next thrust. Too many men give short thrusts mostly inside their own skins, which result in too little friction on the vaginal opening. I also like the poking of the vaginal entry with the penis head for a bit before intercourse starts."

"What feels good is any pulling or stretching at the vaginal opening. Coming all the way in, then out again, etc."

"With one lover, an older experienced man who was not able to get an erection, I found the soft penis at the mouth of my vagina very exciting. I was able to have 'vaginal' orgasm with him. My only one."

"I need a rotating, building process around the lips with some clitoral stimulation and a final, deep penetration."

"I like my hips elevated, with considerable withdrawal and re-entry of the penis—actually requiring more time that most men can allow for."

"I orgasm when I feel the head of his penis enter and move slowly in and out, but not entering more than just the head itself, moving around the vaginal lips."

"Well, it takes a lot of kissing and hugging, possibly some oral stimulation, then me on top with only very limited penetration, and much withdrawing, bumping, and nuzzling, then when I'm coming, deeper penetration but still not too far in—until I'm coming. Also sometimes he puts his hands around my buttocks and his fingers between my labia minora and majora, which is nice."

Orgasm on entry of the penis.
In this way of having orgasm during intercourse, the orgasm is actually in progress as entry occurs, and therefore

it is not listed in the statistical tables. Since it depends on the woman being already in the throes of orgasm when entry takes place, usually the woman must tell the man when the time is right. Once again, as in many of these methods, orgasm during intercourse is more of a victory by virtue of a "technicality" than by anything having purely to do with the presence of the penis in the vagina. However, if this provides a feeling of satisfaction, there is no reason not to do it.

> "I usually have an orgasm when I have been stimulated prior to penetration . . . and then the nature of the penetration is the critical finishing touch."

> "I have orgasms by kissing, sucking on my breasts, then his fingers stimulating my clitoris, the penetration of fingers into my vagina, the penis touching my clitoris, and then one hard thrust and the penis kept there."

> "Sometimes, if my clitoris is stimulated enough, and his penis is inserted very fast and hard at the right time, and kept still, it is easy for me to have an orgasm."

> "I like vaginal penetration only when I'm ready for it but I usually get it when I'm not ready so it usually doesn't lead to orgasm. A really important thing is letting him know I'm definitely *not* ready for intercourse, even if he is."

Trying to penetrate just at the moment of orgasm can actually ruin or make orgasm impossible for many other women. In the first place, if the focus of sensation is suddenly drastically changed, just at the most critical moment, it can stop the orgasm. And second, as we have seen in the chapter on orgasm, many women do not feel the pleasure of orgasm as well during penetration:

> "Last night, for example, he was giving me manual clitoral stimulation, and then just before I orgasmed, he penetrated and it just ruined the whole thing. All of a sudden, he took his hand away—I mean, you should have seen the look on my face, I was shocked, and then he dived in. I was to the point where I was rigid and

shaking a little with the orgasm but when he put it in, it just stopped it and the more he just kept on going in and out, in and out, the more it just started fading away."

"I mean, I can have orgasm on penetration after a lot of clitoral stimulation, but I have to really press against the guy and even then it is really hard and usually one of those orgasms that never really makes it and just kind of fades away."

6. Extended "be-foreplay": Clitoral stimulation or other stimulation to pre-orgasm, then followed by entry or joining

Another method, very similar to the preceding one, is extended "foreplay," which is recommended by many sex therapists, and seems to be very traditional if one remembers all the clichés about women needing longer "foreplay" than men.

The difference between #5 as a type and this one is that here orgasm does not occur at the moment of joining, but rather usually shortly thereafter, and orgasm is considered to continue to be "worked up to" during actual intercourse via one of the means mentioned earlier.

The term "foreplay" is a very strange one. *What is "foreplay"?* "For me to have an orgasm, intercourse must be preceded by foreplay. But I don't like that word because it makes it sound more subordinate than it is." Well, it is common knowledge that "foreplay" is all of the body stimulation prior to, "before," intercourse. There is no "be-foreplay" to speak of in masturbation for most women. Why is "foreplay" necessary before intercourse*? Obviously because

*Of course this is not to imply that people would not enjoy caressing each other simply for its own sake.

there is so little real stimulation for women involved in intercourse. The term "be-fore" has been retained here because its meaning is so clear, but in general it is important to emphasize that there is no reason why "be-foreplay" must come "be-fore" anything.

The question of what else these activities could be called is interesting. The lack of an appropriate word for them in our language reflects the way our culture has rigidly defined the ways in which we touch each other: only activities surrounding intercourse have been considered legitimate. Thus "clitoral stimulation" and general touching is referred to only as "foreplay," which everyone "knows" precedes intercourse, and which everyone also "knows" will end in male ejaculation. In short, all our terms are geared to a linear progression: "foreplay" is to be followed by "penetration" of the penis into the vagina, and then intercourse (thrusting in and out), followed by male orgasm, and then "rest." If one does not accept this pattern as being what "sex" is, one is left with almost no vocabulary to describe what *could* be alternatives. Of course the *possibility* does exist for many different patterns of sexuality, and many different kinds of physical contact between people that are sensual/sexual, and that do not necessarily have orgasm (or anything else) as their goal, as we will discuss in the chapter on older women.

In any case, some women did have orgasm during intercourse through the use of extensive "be-foreplay":

"My best sex has always been when foreplay and sexual stimulation (without actual penis insertion) was carried out and engaged in for long periods of time before actual intercourse. Having my partner tease me and cause me to have orgasms time and time again during the afternoon and evening and finally leading up to intercourse late in the evening. Excitement runs so high that when you finally do have intercourse it is a terrific experience. This is so much better than getting all prepared for it and then it is over so quickly with little anticipation."

"I like: a romantic mood, being undressed, stroking my entire body, putting pressure to my pelvic area with hands and fingers, his nude body held tightly to mine, talking to me about our bodies and feelings while I watch in the mirror, then oral stimulation, soft, wet kisses, rectal stimulation while having my vagina stimulated with fingers, biting all over, blowing in my ear, then finally penis penetration and intercourse with close contact of our pelvic areas."

"I think the feeling that allows me the most pleasure is of unhurried, unpressured, undisturbed time for love-making. I like my whole body to be stimulated with another's whole body—our bodies touching at as many points as possible. I like to be caressed with hands and arms and fingers and held tight. Then I like to have my vulva stimulated, first with fingers, then with a tongue lapping my clitoris and labia. If I'm having intercourse with a man (I've never made love with a woman), I like him to insert his penis in my vagina. I need a lot of freedom to rock and sway and move my pelvis for pressure stimulation, and eventually without rushing, go on to orgasm."

Orgasm during intercourse after having the first orgasm, or several orgasms, by more direct stimulation.
Actually, the longer one is aroused (whether by extended be-foreplay or successive orgasms), the deeper into the outer vulva and lips the arousal may reach. Therefore some women found they could have orgasms during intercourse after their second or third orgasm. As one woman described it:

"First I can have a clitoral touch orgasm, then lower for the next orgasm, then lower again, then finally my outer vaginal area can be stimulated to orgasm. But when not at the height of intensity, intercourse can turn off my responses altogether and even stop me from coming."

Clitoral stimulation
by hand during intercourse

Of course, the women in this group were not counted as part of the 30 per cent of women who did orgasm from intercourse. However, it is perhaps the best way for most women to orgasm during intercourse, and therefore there are many quotes offered here of women telling how they adapted this stimulation to their needs during intercourse.

This way is very popular because you can be sure the stimulation is right "on target." Although stimulation by hand during intercourse has been recommended by marriage manuals for a long time, it is unfortunate that now it is often considered to be "second best" or "cheating." All too many women explaining their use of this method had some special rationale concerning why they did so, or worried about why they needed to.

"I was not *ever* having any orgasms all through four years of college and I was *mortified* and thought something was terribly wrong with me. I could masturbate to orgasm *very* easily but couldn't feel a damned thing during intercourse. Well, I was with my long-standing boyfriend one day and we were making love and I got really pissed at my not having orgasms so, with him in me and moving, I just reached down, rubbed around my clitoris and decided that, by God, I was going to get off, and 1 to 2 minutes later, I sure did—I had a fantastic orgasm, and have been successful ever since, *every* time, by using this method!"

"I believe that the current emphasis on pleasure coming from the clitoris has given me the courage to go after that—which has improved my sex life enormously. I always found it very frustrating to get my clitoris stimulated just enough by trying to rub it against my partner—who was moving around in ways that were intended to achieve his orgasm and didn't necessarily correspond to what I needed. That is really catch as catch can, and my clitoris never seemed to be fitting right anyway so that it could really be rubbed. I have decided that it's much better to do it with a hand."

"During intercourse, sideways, I place my hand around that part of the penis not in the vagina, massage it, and at the same time create clitoral stimulation and orgasms occur!"

"My partner is lying on his back, I am on top of him with his penis inside my vagina. I am kneeling with my upper body raised up away from his chest so that my breasts are hanging down in such a way that he is able to lift his head and suck on my nipples. One of his hands is down between us, and his fingers are directly stimulating my clitoris and the area around it. With his other hand he is feeling other areas of my body, especially my bottom. Meanwhile, I am free to move in whatever way gives me the most pleasure."

"I can't squeeze my legs together during regular intercourse. That is still necessary for me to make myself come. And I never have the same sort of violently physical orgasm with vaginal penetration with the penis that I do with direct clitoral stimulation. I'm not even sure if I come. I get a great sensation of pleasure, but it never peaks like it does the other way. I wish it did. I'd love to come right when he does without any extra attention. The only way we've been able to achieve this is if he lies on his back, and I on mine, with my rear on his pelvis. In this manner, his penis can be inside me, but my clitoris is free to be stroked by him and my stomach and leg muscles are unrestricted so they can react freely in the often violent spasmodic way they do when I'm coming. I would love to hear from someone who is able to have a super orgasm during intercourse without any direct clitoral manipulation. I suppose it's possible. I wonder if I could 'learn how' the way I've 'learned' how the other way."

"I have orgasms during intercourse only by masturbating simultaneously. While I'm doing this I don't like my partner to move around too much because it's distracting."

"I have often had the desire to have an orgasm with penetration and have tried to have my partner penetrate me, lying on my side across him, and stimulate my clitoris at the same time, but this doesn't work too well, because sometimes he can't hold his erection and also I have the problem of having to keep my legs tightly together in order to climax."

"Positions and movements are better or worse for all sorts of things, both physical and psychological, but they have never yet led to direct enough clitoral stimulation to lead to orgasm for me without a helping hand."

"Intercourse is okay providing some form of clitoral stimulation is continued during intercourse. If we are in such a position that penis/clitoris contact is impossible or at least impractical, then my mate would need only to use a free hand to manipulate my clitoris."

"My most beautiful sexual experience ever was one afternoon I spent with my lover. He sat with his penis in my vagina while I was lying down, and he vibrated me from one orgasm to another while pushing himself in and out. There was so much love coming out of him, I'll never forget it."

"I am on top, sitting up, during intercourse. He touches my clitoris lightly with his finger, hand, or both hands, in a way that I can move against it as I want to."

"I have not found a lasting position that will give me maximum clitoral stimulation during intercourse. Direct stimulation with a hand is necessary to orgasm."

"I enjoy entry from behind, so I can stimulate my own clitoris at the same time."

"We have intercourse with slow, writhing movements on both of our parts, pressing my labia around his penis while my hands caress his stroking penis, or while I masturbate and/or close my legs tightly together."

"If I am feeling especially 'horny' and feel the need to be penetrated, then intercourse itself is good. But physically, it is satisfying only if accompanied by clitoral stimulation. I don't feel overly excited by vaginal penetration. Psychologically, it can be exciting by just the thought of what the man is doing to you and at times I'll experience a physical excitement which is a feeling that is not as intense or high-pitched as clitoral stimulation, but definitely a sexual feeling in the vagina during penetration. Intercourse *without* clitoral stimulation has *never* led to orgasm (so far for me, anyway)."

"So far, I have only had one partner who *really knows* what I like, and provides it without my actually directing him. Usually, I try to let it be known what kind of stimulation I want, but if my partner does not catch on, I think nothing of stimulating myself in front of him. It doesn't embarrass me to do this. I have no qualms about manually stimulating myself during intercourse. To hell with what the guy thinks of me; I deserve satisfaction as much as he does!"

"None of the positions of intercourse bring the penis into a position where it offers direct or frictional contact to my clitoris. I have been embarrassed to touch myself during partner sex. I'd like to do it but it would feel inappropriate."

"It is hard to get a hand at the clitoris during intercourse, but it can be done in almost any position with a little effort."

"He is on top. I reach down—pretending to just rest my hand on my stomach—and touch my clitoris. I've only done this a few times. Those times I came very close to orgasm, but I think my inhibitions kept me from coming."

"We do male on side, woman on back with one leg over both of his, penis inserted, I or he masturbates me. And the woman controls the body movements."

"I like to lie on my belly, over a pillow, so I can be

clitorally stimulated by my partner's hand at the same time as he penetrates me."

"I sit on him with his penis inside my vagina. Then I lean back until I am on my back and he stimulates my clitoris with his fingers."

"Best for me is doggie position (on my stomach with penetration from behind) plus manual stimulation with his hand on top of mine."

"If I like him, and am not angry with him at the time, and he is not clumsy, he can make slow movements in my vagina, holding me with one hand, and stroking my clitoris with the other, saying sweet things. We can lie on our sides with his stomach to my back, and he is a tender and loving partner—he starts with kissing and fondling of my breasts, ears, arms and legs, almost all over until he begins to concentrate in the genital areas—then he touches the clitoris, then orally, until I want to feel his penis inside me. He lies on his back, and I kneel over him with my knees around his chest and I sit on his penis. His left hand is free to stimulate my clitoris. And we very gradually and very gently begin the long climb to orgasm until I want more and faster and harder pressure, and I come."

"Some men say they ought to be able to make me come by themselves, without my helping. But it just won't work that way. And I *do* try. If a man understands this, and we can talk about it, then the sex works out. For the few minutes that I play, there are many compensations for him in the overall scene, and usually, his stimulation is combined with mine. However, if he can't work this out after we've talked, then I won't let him make me feel guilty again. I'll change partners."

"The way we work it is, my man keeps his dick inside me sort of poised for action while I manually stimulate myself just to the point of orgasm then actually come by pushing against him. The clitoris hits the root of his dick or his pubic bone or something— anyway, it works. I used to be concerned because it still isn't the famous 'no-hands' orgasm till I realized how stupid it is to take such a competitive or comparative point of view. Maybe eventually I will be able to come from intercourse alone but it doesn't hang me up. He's happy and I'm happy, so what the fuck?"

"You know it's weird that in porno films people who are fucking always seem to go faster toward the end—we do the opposite. When it starts to get into the 'build-up' stage we slow down to almost no movement at all. My man has incredible control of his responses, he can stay right on the edge of orgasm for a long time (and keep me there too) with tiny, subtle, intricate little riffs. If sex is an art form, he is the Picasso of it. The only thing is I just can't come unless I can get a finger in there—this has to be purely a mental problem. After a long period of 'build-up' I feel a slackening off in my response, and that's when I bring myself to the verge and push against him."

"All different kinds of movements are nice at different times. In one session of love-making my present lover uses the whole spectrum of choices—soft, hard, back, front, partial, complete, etc. If a particular way of doing it is good for him, I usually 'catch' his excitement and he keeps it up until he starts to lose the maximum effect, then tries something else. If the method is good for me, he catches my excitement and keeps it up until I lose it, then goes on to something else. When a particular method doesn't do it for either of us, it's abandoned and another one is used. If I am being the active one and moving either underneath while he holds still or sitting on him, I do the same thing, experimenting with this way and that till somebody strikes pay dirt."

"We use three different positions. If I'm going to come first, he lies sort of on his back but kind of on his side, I lie on my back at a ninety-degree angle with his dick inside me from the rear. He can reach my tits and I can reach my clitoris. If we are aiming for more or less simultaneous orgasm, we go in the missionary position.

He fucks me for a while, getting aroused to a certain point, then sort of leans sideways so I can play with my clitoris while he's still inside. When I get to a certain point, he takes over the action again. We take turns till somebody gets tired or can't take it any more. If I come first, intercourse is not painful as I have read in some alleged sex manuals, but is extremely pleasant. I am super-sensitive inside and can feel the surges or waves of his orgasm. If he comes first, he stays on me and in me till the last sensations have subsided, then lies beside me lending encouragement while I bring myself off. I'm glad we discovered that idea of taking turns to gradually build, each using our own peculiar rhythms. I get off on being both active and passive in this; each feels wonderful in its own way. He may give me clitoral stimulation in any one of these positions, and sometimes he does it better than I do!"

Length of intercourse.
Many people believe *long* intercourse is the key to having orgasm during intercourse; that is, "premature ejaculation" in men is what prevents orgasm during intercourse in women. But it seems that unless there is some specific form of good contact, of one of the kinds referred to in the preceding section, long intercourse is not helpful to most women. In fact, there were several complaints about intercourse going on too long:

"If intercourse lasts more than ten–fifteen minutes, it begins to irritate me and then the next time I urinate I get a burning feeling."

"If the man is grinding away in a boring fashion, then I get bored. If he'll let me be active (get on top, for example), I can keep interested for any length of time."

"After too long my lubrication decreases."

"The moment of penetration is usually the most exciting and then it's usually downhill."

"Sometimes I get 'numb' if the activity is too heavy, and I feel unhappy. Sometimes I am too lubricated to feel anything. Then I feel too much like a receptacle instead of a participant."

"I usually find intercourse with men a struggle; it doesn't usually flow, so usually the longer it goes on, the less interested I become. I get too physically tired."

"After thirty minutes, I ask to stop."

"It becomes no more stimulating than someone shoving a hand on my arm."

"I have a terrific emotional reaction to penetration right at the beginning. After that it fades."

"I love the first few penetrations, then I just go downhill after that."

"Yes, I like intercourse, if I am aroused. Excitement leads to a desire for deep vaginal penetration. I don't like too much of it though (pumping). It just makes me sore or I get a urinary infection."

"Although the initial penetration is exciting and satisfying, penetration in general (intercourse) is disappointing and without any specific attempt to get simultaneous clitoral stimulation by position or manually—just jiggling."

Variations in anatomy.
Some researchers feel that a possible cause of "coital frigidity" may be variations in the sexual anatomies of individual women. This idea seems to have caught the fancy of many women who—for good reason—would like to find a non-psychological reason for the fact that they don't have orgasms during intercourse:

"My clitoris is hooded, therefore I do not come during intercourse."

"I think my clitoris is placed too high to have an orgasm during intercourse—or maybe it's psychological; I don't trust me."

"I guess I could have an orgasm during intercourse if my clitoris could be in the right place, getting the right kind of pressure—which never ever happens when I'm with a dude."

"I went to a doctor and he said my clitoris is hooded and is very small so therefore it would take more to get me to come. He did not want to operate because he said it is a dangerous operation. I felt he would not have said that if it were a man who was having that problem. Anyway I have orgasms through masturbation with a vibrator and if I am sitting on top of the man and moving forward and backward so my clitoris is rubbing on his bone."

"I have a very small clitoris so maybe that is why it is hard to stimulate it through 'normal' intercourse. I do not feel my clitoris being stimulated at all when his penis is inside me."

"Although I have not read Masters and Johnson, so maybe it is covered there, it seems to me my clitoris is *too far away* from my vagina to be stimulated by normal intercourse, unless it is already stimulated. Is it possible that breaking a hymen early tends to allow the clitoris and vagina to grow apart?"

"I wonder if I'm like other people. I don't feel abnormal, but perhaps the position of my clitoris is responsible. It just doesn't seem to be stimulated by anything in my vagina."

"I really believe my clitoris may not be physically positioned quite right because I almost never can find a position for stimulating it while his penis is in my vagina."

The truth is that clitoral and labial anatomy are highly variable, in size, shape, placement, texture, and other factors. However, that does not mean that our anatomy is *wrong*, deformed. It is the cultural pressure on women to orgasm during intercourse that is wrong, and the stereotyped way in which we define sex.

It is doubtful whether anatomy is an important factor in whether or not we orgasm during intercourse. Masters and Johnson found no evidence to support the belief that differences in clitoral anatomy can influence sexual response.

However, Barbara Seaman, who wrote *Free and Female,* cautions that "this must be viewed as a highly tentative finding since they were unable to observe any clitorises during orgasm." Sherfey also feels that more research should be done in this area. Masters and Johnson have said that they think certain *vaginal* conditions can operate to prevent the thrusting penis from exercising traction on the labia and clitoral hood. But it's all animal crackers in the end. The real thing to keep in mind is that it is more unusual than not to orgasm from intercourse, especially without making some kind of special effort to do so by getting additional clitoral stimulation at the same time.

It is sometimes possible to learn to orgasm during intercourse.

"I didn't orgasm for the first seven years of sexual intercourse with my husband; I thought pleasing him was enough, and also I took pleasure in the act itself. But eventually I became frustrated and went to a lot of trouble to learn how to please myself too."

"I almost never had orgasms with my husband during the ten years I was married. I thought I was frigid, but when I was taught by a man who seduced me two years after my divorce, I was shocked to learn how unfrigid I am. In a sense I had to learn—that is, what positions, etc. were best and most likely to produce my orgasm. I wish I had learned earlier."

"Orgasm during intercourse is definitely a learned response; if I were illiterate and had never heard anybody talk about how to do it, I'd probably still be lying on my back, looking at the ceiling and wondering if that's all there is to love. But thanks to the *Little Yellow Book* by Berg and Street, I learned how to have orgasm pretty regularly during intercourse, me on top so I can control the pressure. Although the regular male thrust is stimulating and fun, what brings me to climax is my own lateral or circular writhing on the pole. Rarely do I have a non-orgasmic encounter."

"As I just turned forty-nine (ancient, can you believe it?), I decided it was time I pulled myself together and decided to work on my techniques. Enough of just lying back and thinking of England . . . and bloody well enjoying it! It was easier and more pleasurable for me to do this with my husband than to work at something else. However, I always judged myself as somewhat immature for doing this. What am I, wimp or woman? My husband knows how I masturbate, and we regularly do that together during sex, but now it's 1999 and all that, I told him . . . So (to get graphic, sorry about that) I got on top of him and tried pressing my mons against his body with him inside of me, and told him if he dared to come, I'd chop it off (sorry) . . . so he grinned and lay there, letting me move around and try this thing and that thing. The first time, it didn't work, but after a few tries (and deciding to fantasize like I do when I'm alone masturbating) I forgot about him and really didn't care about pushing too hard or something or if or when he came, etc. etc., and voila! We don't do it every time, though, lots of work for me, more than when I do it without intercourse at the same time. Neither of us is sure it's worth it, but now I'm a Full Woman—an adult!"

Finally, in this study there was no apparent correlation between ability to orgasm during intercourse and age, number of children, or amount of experience.

Other women felt that, although they could orgasm during intercourse, they would rather just enjoy it for its own sake than concentrate on working toward their own orgasm.

"Orgasm requires almost no effort at all, as long as there is direct stimulation of my clitoris. However, the effort required to orgasm during intercourse is prodigious. So I usually don't bother. Now I just relax and enjoy the closeness and his orgasm."

"Thrusting in and out and moving while the penis is in me, so that I can control the amount of clitoral stimulation, are the most exciting. I guess I have given up, though, on trying for an orgasm during penetration. In the traditional way, I focus more on my partner's satisfaction. I find it's more enjoyable in the long run, and then I can relax and enjoy mine after, with manual stimulation, with all the attention on myself."

Conclusion: Do it yourself

To have an orgasm during intercourse, there are two ways a woman can increase her chances, always remembering that she is adapting her body to less than adequate stimulation. First and most important, she must consciously try to apply her masturbation techniques to intercourse, or experiment to find out what else may work for her to get clitoral stimulation; or, she can work out a sexual relationship with a particular man who can meet her individual needs.

Do it yourself
The women who had orgasm during intercourse were usually those who, in a sense, did it themselves. They did not expect to "receive" orgasm automatically from the thrusting of the partner:

"The main thing I suppose is that a woman is more involved in the intercourse and love-making bit than I had thought originally."

"It's important for women to be able to stimulate themselves. If they just accept what a man does, it's no wonder they don't experience orgasm."

"For a long time I didn't have orgasms because I was so concerned about responding correctly to my partner and breathing hard when he came—to fake it. I think it's all part of the Catch That Man game. I didn't have them until I really started looking for them."

"In sex, the more I involved myself in going after my

own pleasure, in following my own genital feelings (by thrusting and placing my body) the closer I got to orgasm. I used to worry that such seriousness, working for your pleasure, was unfeminine."

"I once experienced definite clitoral sensation while balling. I was on my back, but we were turned slightly to one side. Perhaps I should be more aggressive but men I've known seem to lose momentum while I try pressing against them, or make verbal suggestions."

The cardinal rule is you must make it happen yourself, not just wait for it to "happen," or for him to happen to hit the right spot out of luck:

"When I can freely rotate my pelvis, I can determine where I want the pressure, and in what pattern."

"During intercourse I am quite active and talk to him, saying what I like better than other things, etc."

"I have orgasms during intercourse by very subtle fucking—attention to nuances of feeling and sensation—great slowness and also I am very careful to stay 'on' where it feels good."

The most successful women have adapted their masturbatory techniques unabashedly and unashamedly to relations with others.

"You have to care about yourself and *want* to please yourself, and you have to feel it is your *right*. Do it, whatever it is—or ask for it, clearly and specifically."

The connection between orgasm during intercourse and masturbation

There is an old myth that masturbation causes "clitoral fixation" and "frigidity":

"Perhaps if you masturbate, you can get a fixation on

your clitoris and are thus unable to come during intercourse."

"The fact that I've been masturbating since I was ten has made it more difficult for me to orgasm vaginally."

"Having been used to masturbating for years as a teenager and repressing my desire for actual intercourse with boys, I feel I developed a conditioned reflex that did not allow me to have a vaginal orgasm with my husband even though I enjoyed the act itself."

The truth, however, is just the opposite: masturbation increases your ability to orgasm in general, and also your ability to orgasm during intercourse. Why not? It's the same stimulation. Only 19 per cent of the women in this study who did not masturbate orgasmed regularly from intercourse—quite a drop from the 30 per cent in the overall population. Of course, masturbating to orgasm does not automatically enable you to orgasm during intercourse. There is no mystical connection between the two—just the practical experience with orgasm—how it feels and how to get it.

"Are your techniques in masturbation similar to your techniques for orgasming during intercourse?

Was there any correlation between type of masturbation and method used for having orgasm during intercourse? Are some types of masturbation easier to adapt to intercourse than others?

Some women felt their methods were similar during masturbation and intercourse.

"Masturbation for me involves the circular rubbing of my clitoris and the edge of my vagina, and intercourse is basically the same."

"They are the same when his penis is rubbing directly against my clitoris, or his body is pressing against the area of my clitoris. Otherwise, when I masturbate, my stimulation of the areas that are most sensitive for me is much more direct and intense."

"Yes, it's the same during intercourse as during masturbation. It's the difference between rubbing my clitoris around on the base of a penis as opposed to rubbing my clitoris around on a clump of bedsheets."

However, most women who answered this question (and especially almost all the women who did not orgasm during intercourse) felt that stimulation during masturbation and intercourse were not the same at all.

"I attempt to use the same technique, but intercourse often makes this difficult, as my clitoris becomes less sensitive, and sometimes seems to be sort of submerged."

"No, for one thing, I can't squeeze my legs together. That is still necessary for *me,* to make myself come. I never have the same sort of violently physical orgasm with vaginal penetration with the penis as I do with direct clitoral stimulation. I'm not even sure if I come."

"I don't think I will ever have many orgasms during intercourse because masturbation has accustomed me to close my legs hard and this doesn't work too well with a man."

"No. During intercourse there is more pushing pressure; in masturbation it's more back and forth with one finger against my clitoris."

"No. In masturbation, I mainly play with the clitoris—just inserting my finger in my vagina to satisfy the need that was created by my orgasm causing my vagina to throb for something in it."

"In masturbation it is important that the muscles are massaged so as to provide a kind of stretching and release of the clitoral area. The same stretching and release has not been accomplished by any up and down or in and out movement on my partner's part."

"No, the different position and the closeness of the partner prevent a successful masturbating technique."

"Supposedly you should be able to have a climax with a man if you masturbate by rubbing the outside of your vagina, sometimes penetrating the inside. I have a climax fairly easily by myself. I have since I was a little child. It seems like it shouldn't be too hard to have one with a man but so far I have been unsuccessful. Is there a way to have a climax with a man's penis in your vagina if one masturbates in the way I described?"

Actually, most of the answers to this question were unintelligible or very confused; most women did not seem sure what the question even meant, so compartmentalized has our thinking been. In this sense, perhaps the preceding quotes are not representative. What really emerged from the answers was the fact that most women had never even thought about a possible connection.

Finally, was there a correlation between type of masturbation and "ability" to orgasm during intercourse? Were some orgasm types more likely to orgasm during intercourse than others? My impression was that these figures are imprecise because too many women were disqualified from being counted; they included those who did not specify how they had orgasmed during intercourse, those who masturbated in more than one way, and the "questionable-orgasm-definition" group. This left a very small number from which to make correlations.

However, despite all these problems, two definable trends did appear. Most likely to orgasm during intercourse were those who masturbated on their stomachs, especially those who did not use their hands (type II). Least likely were those who held their legs together or crossed.

Other than this there were no really clear-cut correlations, and many women whose type suggested they might be able to were still not able to orgasm during intercourse. A lot seemed to depend on how interested the individual was in applying her own knowledge of her body to intercourse and actively directing the stimulation unabashedly to herself.

Of course it remains an unanswered question whether these body types are made or born. That is, once you learn to orgasm a certain way, does that become a basically fixed pattern for you? For example, if you learned with your legs together, could you later learn with them apart? Or, are some types of bodies only able to orgasm in certain positions?

This question is, however, important only academically. Women who masturbate with their legs together, for example, can just as well adapt this position to intercourse as other masturbation types. No one body type is "better" than another. While a woman who needs to have her legs together to orgasm may have slightly more trouble teaching new lovers ways to have intercourse in which she can orgasm, it is also true that women who hold their legs together are more likely to be able to have many sequential orgasms than other women, since they do not stimulate their clitorises so directly (the bunched-up skin forms a protective cushion). Whatever body type a woman has, she can have fully as much pleasure as every other woman. All she has to do is be active and explore.

What is the difference between "to orgasm" and "to have an orgasm"?

This idea that we really make our own orgasms, even during intercourse, is in direct contradiction to what we have been taught. Therefore I suggest that we use "to orgasm" as a verb rather than a noun "to have orgasm." The latter is more passive while saying "I orgasm" is made active. Most of us were taught that "you should relax and enjoy it"—or at most help him out with the thrusting—because *he* would "give" you the orgasm:

"If you try too hard, you will never have an orgasm; it should come naturally as a result of the loving."

"You don't have to make it happen, it's a response. You should just naturally be grasped in the flow."

"Orgasms are as natural to women as ejaculations are to men. If a woman is in touch with herself physically and emotionally, I think orgasms will be very natural for her."

"In a normal woman orgasm is a natural part of sex."

"No effort should be necessary . . . it just happens when the time is right, two people caring for each other. Learn to accept and love your body and yourself, and you will have orgasm."

"I feel you shouldn't have to concentrate so much on having an orgasm, but on the glory of what's happening at that moment when your two bodies are one. The beauty of that time will make you come."

It should be mentioned that many of the women who answered in this way were also not having orgasms regularly in sex. As we saw in the preceding section, orgasm is most likely to come when the woman takes over responsibility for and control of her own stimulation. You always, in essence, create your own orgasm.

"I create my own orgasm. Sometimes no amount of stimulation will turn me on, because I don't want it. I really resent men who boast of 'giving' a woman a good come. I always feel I have created it myself, even if he was doing the stimulating."

"My orgasm is my own. I control it, produce it, and dig it."

"Although I think mutual pleasure is wonderful, the orgasm is in the end one's own. You have to put in the concentration and physical effort yourself."

We do give ourselves orgasm, even, in a sense, when someone else is providing us with stimulation, since we must make sure it is on target, by moving or offering suggestions, and by tensing our bodies and getting into whatever position(s) we need—and then there is a final step necessary in most cases: we need to focus on the sensation and concentrate, actively desire and work toward the orgasm.

"Is having an orgasm a concentrated effort?"

"Yes, you can't just lie there and wait for an orgasm. You sense that one is approaching, and so of course you concentrate on helping it."

"Yes, I wilfully strain the muscles of my upper thighs, rectum, and vagina. It has taken a long time to learn to concentrate on my body and what's happening during sex rather than only on what he's thinking or is he ready."

"Yes, each person probably has to learn her own body's way to reach it, how to tense it, maybe even what thoughts or words help it happen. For many years I was unable to have orgasms with another person; then finally I taught myself to tense my body so much that I'd push myself over the brink."

"I forcibly contract my vaginal muscles during clitoral stimulation, and it helps a lot to cause my orgasms."

"Sometimes I really have to make an effort—tense my muscles, tremble, sort of force myself. A man I dated suggested I force myself to as he did from time to time, and it worked."

"Yes, I concentrate all of my energies. Every muscle and every nerve."

"When I feel an orgasm approaching, I often make a concentrated effort to make sure that I reach it. That means moving on my own and/or telling my partner what to do."

'They *can* happen, and do, without great effort, but unless you take control and make them happen the way you want them and when you want them, they are probably going to be inadequate and infrequent."

"Just before orgasm, my mind and senses focus down to controlling one area rather than the coordinated system."

"I try to position my pelvis to my best satisfaction by rhythmic movements and then concentrate my body energies to this great explosion."

It would almost seem as if there is a definite break between sensuality (diffuse, non-focused physical feeling), and sexuality (drive towards orgasm), and that in order to have an orgasm, at least most of the time, it is necessary to think and work and concentrate towards one.

"At a certain point you have to stop relaxing and having fun and build yourself up to this earth-moving experience, orgasm, and sometimes it seems like too much trouble."

"Occasionally when I am feeling passive and very attuned to being touched all over my body, 1 will sort of 'forget' to get super-genitally stimulated and not come unless I roll over and work at it."

"I could not have an orgasm if in the last few moments before the orgasm I didn't give it complete concentration. If this isn't the case with other women, I envy them."

"The more involved I am with active interaction with my partner, the more aroused I am. But if I become too involved with someone else's stimulation, I don't stay in touch with my own."

"During orgasm, I concentrate on my body, not on him."

"It is a totally personal experience and during orgasm especially there is *no* way to share that with your partner. But I like that he is there."

"I have always wanted to keep my eyes open during an orgasm but I have never succeeded. I thought it would make me feel closer to my partner, but during an orgasm the only thing I am conscious of is my own pleasure—and in the back of my mind, how my partner is moving so I can coordinate my movements."

This process of concentrating or focusing on physical sensations as you make the effort to have an orgasm is probably the same thing Masters and Johnson have called "sensate focus."

"Full concentration like hypnosis is needed to attain orgasm—your whole mind and body is focusing on it."

"Yes, I definitely have to concentrate to orgasm. If I think about anything other than the sensation, or any unsexual thoughts, I immediately lose the excitement."

"You have to focus your attention in your genitals."

You can bring on an orgasm, not exactly by fantasizing (that is, thinking of a story or situation, which is often used more for arousal), but by a kind of self-hypnotism, sort of "picturing" the feeling and the "organs" involved:

"The specific act sort of fantasies are almost always used to bring on an orgasm faster while masturbating, and never have a story. Sometimes, in fact, they don't even have a real character, simply a fantasy that 'someone' is sucking my clitoris, or that a cock is in my cunt. These fantasy people are sometimes identified at least as far as being 'a man' but are other times so vague as to be only 'a long tongue' with no person attached."

"I do not fantasize during sex with someone. I only have a mental picture of the penis moving and penetrating in my vagina."

"I am *thinking* of the friction of the man's penis."

"The concentration of your mind must *be* focused with all your might between your legs—*on the vagina.*"

"I have to concentrate really hard on my clitoris or my thoughts wander and I don't feel sexual at all. It took me a while to learn to concentrate like this and that's how I learned to come."

"Yes, I have to *want* to come and think about only that. Forget everything except what I am doing and what is being done to me. I close my eyes and picture it in my mind."

"At the beginning, I just think of what I'm doing,

and then I feel like waves on a beach are coming in and out, and I think, 'do it—do it—do it—.'"

"I concentrate very hard on the inward outward movement of the penis. And what it looks like as it's going in and out."

"I concentrate on body-'wanting' sensations."

"I like pornography which leads to anticipation—for example, I think of someone bent over and waiting to be entered."

"I concentrate on mentally thinking of what he is doing to me."

"I have fantasies of Swiss or US woodlands, generally with a directional left or right pathway, very pictorial and recallable visually. They serve to keep me closed up in myself and free from distraction in the last five minutes leading to orgasm and they are wholly mental. They are my 'movies' and I invariably have them."

"To have an orgasm for sure if I'm nervous or in a hurry, I say to myself: he cannot get up, he must keep doing what he is doing, I cannot make him stop, I have no choice but to be here, and to have an orgasm. Then I concentrate real hard on my vagina. It always works."

Get active in a new way!

"One has to develop freedom."

"You have to learn to not be afraid of your partner's response."

"Not learn, but perhaps on a larger level learn how to handle the whole thing."

"Maybe in the beginning it's accidental, but then you learn what stimulates you the most, or not to stop something when it's working or encourage something that started to work."

"You have to learn to move your body to get maximum stimulation for an orgasm. The thrust of the penis or finger or tongue or whatever may not be in the right spot or be firm enough or last long enough, so that I have to thrust my vagina or clitoris against the penis, etc., in a way that feels most intense at the time that I feel ready to explode."

"In my experience I never had to learn anything but to be forward enough to demand clitoral stimulation."

"Yes, a woman often has to learn how to achieve orgasms in *spite of* her partner, not *because* of him."

"Yes, and the devil of it is that each woman will probably have to learn how for herself."

4 Clitoral stimulation

Does "sex" for most women include clitoral area stimulation *to orgasm*? Is heterosexual "sex" focused on coitus?

"How do most men have sex with you?"

The following answers represent the overwhelming majority of answers received to this question: that sex—whether enjoyable or exploitative—generally follows the reproductive pattern described in the chapter on intercourse: "foreplay" followed by "penetration" and "intercourse" (thrusting) followed by orgasm (especially male orgasm), which is then defined as the "end" of sex. Answers not falling into this category, not including the lesbian replies, composed less than 5 per cent of those in the study.

"In bed with the man above me, in the dark."

"I've only had sex with my husband. (We were just married for a few months.) He always initiates it. We kiss and he plays with my breasts. He puts one hand down and sticks his finger into my vagina and moves it back and forth like a penis would go. When he's doing this, I lie on my back, and he lies on his side so his body is pressed against my side. He moves his hips back and forth so that his penis rubs against the side of my leg. When he's ready, he has me get on my hands and knees, and he gets in back of me. He sticks his penis into me and moves it back and forth until he finishes."

"Most of the men I've slept with have had absolutely no idea of what I want or need and no interest in finding out. There have been several men who seemed to care whether I was happy, but they wanted to make me happy according to *their* conception of what ought to do it (fucking harder or longer or whatever) and acted as if it was damned impertinent of me to suggest that my responses weren't programmed exactly like those of mythical women in the classics of porn. All I can say is, after years of sexual experience that ranged from brutal to trivial to misguided, etc., it's a wonder I didn't just blow off the whole thing a long time ago. I'm glad I stuck with it until I found a partner whose eroticism complements mine so beautifully."

"I find that a lot of men care nothing about sex foreplay and are only interested in 'getting it off.' These are the kind that really burn me up. Usually, they are the type that have never had or never wanted to really love someone for the sake of love and the pleasure it brings; they are only interested in themselves. I find that most men like you to perform orally on them."

"There has always been some kind of preliminaries, only the length has differed. The preliminaries consisted mostly of vaginal stimulation and necking. Not as much breast fondling and sucking as I would have liked."

"It's usually a short period of foreplay then male on top, female on back, with legs drawn apart, standard slam-bam-thank you ma'am."

"Most men do it on top of the girl and would probably continue to do so if I didn't suggest different positions."

"We undress separately, start making out, he does foreplay not very long then he goes in and we're rhythmic. Generally I get to the verge but he comes first. It's very tense for me and that's the usual."

"Very perfunctory. A little kiss, a little feel, a finger for arousal, a touch of breast and he's on top, wham it's over."

"A lot of it used to be get it up, get it in, and get it out."

"There was from a minimum to a maximum of kissing and touching. Usually once our clothes were altogether off, the screwing began. All the sex I have had with men, they were on top, bouncing up and down. I always wished a little bit of kissing or even tight holding would go on during it, but the men seemed to be off in their own world."

"Most men, if left to their own devices, will engage in a little (ten to fifteen minutes) foreplay of a not very imaginative kind, paying little attention to my clitoris. They then go immediately to penetration in the 'missionary position,' have a whale of a good time, and go to sleep immediately afterwards. This is an extreme picture, but is too well defined to ignore."

"They undress me and try to penetrate at once. It's horrible."

"Whenever I have had sex with a man they always are trying to get there, of course. That seems standard."

"A little foreplay, to one end."

"Unfortunately most men just get into you."

"In general, they tended to minimize foreplay and to concentrate just on intercourse. I can't generalize about technique other than usually foreplay and just good old hugging and kissing. Gets less and less once we get to know each other."

"Foreplay with constant pressure to have intercourse."

"They try to arouse me, then as soon as possible, start intercourse. Some *few* do not hurry and wait for *me* to advance to the next step."

"Nothing really standard except the bed, the penetration, the ejaculation, and orgasms (real or faked)."

"In and out."

"Caressing my body, breasts, vagina . . . asking me to caress their penis . . . then bang bang . . ."

"Kiss, pet, go down on me, then lie me on the bottom and unless I've really wanted this person for a long time this isn't satisfactory."

"Men are very uninformed about women's sexual desires. Most men will engage in a little manual stimulation but expect a woman to reach orgasm during intercourse. They cannot understand that some women prefer clitoral stimulation."

"They jumped on and rode."

"It used to be pretty standard until we saw that fucking mechanically was damaging to us. Now usually we are tender, sometimes intense and passionate, sometimes just affectionate and close without 'real sex.' Our sexual times are very varied."

"With some recent and beautiful exceptions, the encounters have been too short, not affectionate enough and too impersonal."

"Small amount of foreplay, then intercourse till he comes, The End."

"Preliminaries—kissing, foreplay, clitoral massaging— then he jumps on top and all of a sudden I don't matter any more. Sometimes, I'm not even there to him."

"Most didn't seem to be aware that what brought them to climax was not what brought me to climax. That about sums it up."

"They climbed on top, after what they thought was enough foreplay, and pumped away. A few knew about the clitoris but generally they overlooked it completely."

"Most often: one or two kisses, if any, maybe some (very little) breast stimulation or vaginal stimulation, then jump right in till he's finished."

"Some men just kiss, feel, finger, and fuck. Then come and light a cigarette."

"Most men have fucked me with a minimum of foreplay, have been reluctant to touch me (not from repulsion just lack of interest), and have shown more interest in demonstrating their longevity and great prowess in various gymnastics, etc., than in real mutual pleasure."

"First comes kissing, then the taking off clothes ritual, then breast and body kissing, sucking, nuzzling, then cunnilingus, cocksucking, direct clitoral stimulation (order of last three items can change), and intercourse."

"Foreplay, *always* too short, then penetration."

"Begins with kissing, which gets deeper and more

passionate, proceeds to body caresses, undressing, usually he leads me to the couch or bed, we lie down, kiss and pet some more, then he gets on top of me, inserts his penis and comes. If I know him well enough, he knows that I need to have my clitoris stimulated and places his hand between my thighs for me to rub myself on."

"Men can be put into two groups: straight intercourse men and foreplay men. Straight intercourse men I have had are usually less experienced, they just screw. Others indulge in a great deal of foreplay including oral-genital contact, which they often want to bring me to climax in."

"Most men just kiss and stick it in. These are the creeps. The few good men who I've had and stuck with ask my desires and then proceed very slowly and tantalizingly."

"Most were speed demons."

"They move too quickly to enter and move to their climax too fast for me to keep up. I often do, but at the expense of my feelings. It becomes a 'job' to come."

"Most of them start kissing, petting, really get off on the breasts—then the fingers in the vagina bit, some love talk, when we're ready, cunnilingus and fellatio simultaneously, then I get on top, then he does. This is fairly standard with a lot of guys."

"Most of them are the same—take what you can get and don't give any. Before my husband, that is, who is the most erotic, imaginative man I ever met."

"The usual pattern is love-making, then oral sex upon each other, and then whatever position he wants."

"American men come within ten minutes; Europeans take time and give *beautiful* head!"

"Most climb on top of me. We don't even have a chance to get acquainted and love and kiss first. They are too anxious."

"I find *most* men are willing to experiment with several positions of intercourse, and a significant number do not like oral sex, and all but two or three wouldn't even have sex if I was having my period."

"A little foreplay by them and wanting a lot of foreplay by me, then they just sort of start getting on and getting it over with as soon as possible. Sometimes one of them will really take his time and give me a real good time."

"Before my present lover, they would *expect* me to jump into the hay whenever they got horny, go through a perfunctory foreplay, enter me, thrust rapidly for fifteen to thirty seconds, shoot their wad, graciously condescend to 'finish me' with their finger, roll away and let me sleep on the wet spot. It was monotonous, drill-like, and boring."

"When you think about it like *that*, it's a wonder it isn't boring: Most men seem to go in for minimal foreplay, and prefer the man on top, woman on bottom, face to face position."

"Lately, I've detected a very specific pattern. He comes over, we sit around on the living room floor, drinking wine and listening to music, move on to kissing, stroking, and at this point, he whispers, 'Let's go into the bedroom,' whereupon we disrobe, get in bed, embrace, indulge in further foreplay, and then intercourse. I'm beginning to think there must be something like a sexual 'Robert's Rules of Order' which every guy follows."

"My sexual encounters have followed very traditional (or so they seem to me) patterns. Kisses and general caresses moved to caressing of my clitoris and vagina, then usually to oral stimulation of my clitoris. Often then either oral or manual stimulation of my partner's penis and then fucking. Written here, this sounds rather cold and 1, 2, 3 but embroidered with all the details that really *are* sexual contact, it takes on a warmth that isn't part of these words."

"All the men I have had sex with have been alike, except for *one* who took time to sufficiently arouse me before intercourse."

"There is a pattern but it's too boring to tell about."

"Men differ, but most do not seem to understand a woman's body. They seem to think that vaginal penetration is the only important thing and that all else should be done only to 'get you ready.' They think that once you are lubricated you are immediately ready and want to be penetrated then."

"With the first man I slept with, sex was tender, innocent and beautiful—it was basically kissing and light petting as foreplay to coitus. But then my appetite began to decline and I was afraid to say so. So it became very forced. I was submissive and resentful. It became more of a chore than anything else. With the second, sex was tender, exciting and fulfilling in a way it had never been with the first man. Foreplay included kissing and heavy petting. Coitus takes place in the male dominant and female dominant position. I feel he makes love more emotionally than the other did and shows more genuine concern for me."

"I feel guilty when the man appears disinterested. A sensuous man (one in a million) enjoys a woman's body—touching it and giving her pleasure seem to turn him on. Most men, though, seem to consider it a waste of energy and just want to get on with the intercourse part."

"The only pattern I can discern is one of brevity. Men arrive and depart as if they had a round-trip ticket. It has reached the point that I almost know it is no use starting any more."

"Usually the man has been on top and had the most pleasure—I like sex, but I know it hasn't been as good as it should be and could be for me. The men have assumed that they should make the first move, and all that bull. They've been pretty sensitive, gentle, they've tried, but obviously not enough."

"I hate the usual pattern—kiss—feel—eat—fuck, simply because it's usual. I like when people talk to me and moan a lot. I like when people are expressive and creative with me."

"I find that many men expect fellatio but don't want to perform cunnilingus, after I've washed and they haven't."

"Many men are far more hung up about sex than I am. They are not as curious, as explorative, as into just touching. They are squeamish about my vagina. They aren't as talkative or as open nor do they feel as much of a desire to rid themselves of all inhibitions as I do."

"I have very limited experience so I'm not sure—but there may be one: they ask what you like, find out it's hard for you to have orgasms, try very hard to make you orgasm *one* night, then thereafter, pretty much please themselves thinking you won't orgasm anyway or just being caught up with their own sensations."

"Most men I have been with have been conventional lovers—missionary position and came too soon. Men don't seem to have much imagination about sex. They don't readily accept new ideas or suggestions."

"Most men—brief foreplay (which gets briefer every time) then missionary position, unless I climb on top first. Most men don't continue kissing during climax. It's a breath problem, I guess, but I would like it."

"I have found most men to be very unimaginative and prosaic in their approach to sex. Most go about it in the so-called 'missionary' manner."

"Slam-bam-thank you ma'am. No, that's a simplification. He tries to make it last long, so I'll come, but he just isn't able or willing to indulge in the foreplay I want and need."

"It's hard to remember any patterns since I've been happily married for thirty-five years—but I do remember that most of the men seemed totally unaware of what I was really feeling; they thought their penises were fantastic instruments that drove a woman insane with desire and satisfaction just by being in the room with her! Only two of the many I slept with made a real effort to stimulate and satisfy me. And I was too young, embarrassed, and unaware myself to do much but keep quiet and/or pretend orgasm or excitement."

"With the exception of my husband, most of the men I have had sex with have just satisfied themselves and that's all. They seemed concerned that I reach climax but did nothing to make it happen. And most men seemed more sexually hung up than I was. For the most part, the encounters were more of an ego booster for me than physically satisfying."

"There is no particular pattern except that I have always done as was expected, put on whatever sexual performance, or done whatever act was demanded of me. The majority of men I have had sex with wanted the ordinary man on top position, or fellatio. Most have believed the rough, tough approach was best."

"Most of them have been basically dominant—though consistently 'gentle.' Some have had a partial aversion to female genitalia (oral stimulation or actually looking at what it looks like, etc.) None have ever seemed concerned enough about my satisfaction to continue manual stimulation after they have 'come.' "

"Mostly with an excess of activity. It's too much too fast and I don't even have a chance to begin to feel involved before he is all finished. Perhaps that is why I have been monogamous for the last few years. I feel something *deeper* should develop each time."

"When I'm first going out with a man, there is usually much kissing on the mouth, ears, and neck, then graduated play to fondling of breasts, on to my genitals, touching, hopefully oral stimulation, then intercourse, usually in the old Missionaire. Then, after having sex once or twice, most men like to get a little experimental with positions; me on my back, me on top. Then, unfortunately, sex begins to deteriorate for me. First, it's the kissing of my mouth that goes. Sex is just preceded by a few short kisses, and then on to the rest with increasing brevity. Stimulation of my breasts is sometimes cut out entirely, or else reduced to five seconds of attention to each one. Making love becomes strictly (and restrictingly) genital. Most men get to the point where sixty seconds of head is it, then the old in-out for five minutes and it's over. It seems that they must feel that they have to seduce a woman to get her to 'give in' to their lust at first, and then, once she's fallen, she's only to expect intercourse in the narrowest sense. They don't seem to realize that a woman doesn't necessarily have to be convinced to have sex—and the reason why so-called seduction practices work is that she simply is an erotic being in her own right, and with the proper attention and stimulation she'll be at a point where she'd rather have sex than anything! At least that's the way it is for me and my girlfriends. If the only reason a man spends two hours making love to a woman is that he wants a hole around to fuck regularly, let him carve one out of a meat loaf and keep it in bed with him. I want to be with a man who feels the way I do, that making love to the other person is the most important thing—you both get what you want and need that way. As it stands, few women are making it clear that they expect men to make love to them the way that is best for a woman—we've been 'come buckets' for them long enough."

"The first time a man fucks me, he seems to be extremely aroused but wants to put in a good performance. There is usually a long and passionate foreplay, but once intercourse begins he's been dying to fuck for so long that he may come pretty fast. If time permits he may fuck me a second time, and this is longer and better. Some men with a lot of experience and control have run a real enduro with me on the first fuck, but this is the unusual case. The better lays will usually go down on me the first time, and I am very hot to do the same for them, particularly to help them gain a strong second erection. For me, the first fuck with most men may be the most passionate and spectacular, but is not the loosest nor the most orgasmic by a long shot. Sex seems to improve over time, up to the point where boredom, laziness, or apathy sets in. At this point the partner is not so eager to please and the routine is seldom altered. The routine? Quick (if any) foreplay, quick fuck in one of two positions (man or woman on top), an orgasm for each of us, then crash. Unfortunately, if it's been too quick for me to come, it's too bad, because sex is officially over. On these occasions I listen to my lover sleep and wish I had the nerve to masturbate. Masturbation of any kind is seldom a part of sex, particularly with male partners. I've never masturbated in front of a man. I've never seen a man masturbate. I have never masturbated a man to orgasm, and a few times, with one man, I've been masturbated to orgasm. I wish my partners and I could learn to be more relaxed and uninhibited in this respect, because I think we could learn a lot from each other this way. Although there have been quite a few situations in which I did not come or I came but still felt unsatisfied, I have *very rarely* been asked if I would like to be stimulated to orgasm when intercourse is over. Almost invariably, when the man has come and intercourse is concluded, the sexual encounter is over, irregardless of my satisfaction."

"A few other little patterns I can think of: as a sexual relationship continues, a man will either emerge as the type who would rather not eat you out, or the type who would. If he is the former type he will either never give you head, or only occasionally give you head. If he is the latter type, he will usually, but not always eat you, sometimes as foreplay and sometimes more extended, to give you orgasms. Most men are very responsive to fellatio, but a few men are very touchy about it, and it is difficult to give them a full blow job because they seem so uptight and may not be able to come. Men are usually much quicker lovers in the morning than in the evening. Most of my male partners have shown themselves to be distinctly non-adventurous. They have a limited repertoire of love-making techniques which they rely on, never seeming to give much thought to trying something new or a bit different. I myself am guilty of staying stuck in the feminine role of never making suggestions, just hoping my lover will make them. I usually keep on hoping. . . I have had a few lovers whom I would call the erotic adventurers. They will make suggestions that raise my eyebrows and my respiration level. I find myself thinking 'and *what* have you got in mind *now*???' These men seem a lot less inhibited, and exhibit a genuine love for pure eros and sex for sex's sake. Many men dearly love getting their rocks off, but few show this real lust for the erotic."

"How most men have tried to have sex with me can be summed up as Insert A into B. Dulldulldulldull."

"Who decides when it's over?"

"It's over after his orgasm. Isn't that the natural end of sex??"

"Usually it's over when he ejaculates and loses his erection, whether I have had an orgasm or not."

"Ideally it would be both of us who decide but of course it never is. The man decides when it's over for anatomical reasons."

"'Dick power'—the penis decides when it's over."

"Obviously the man! He goes to sleep at once and snores!"

"The one thing I hate is that no matter how you go about it, intercourse ends almost always when he comes and becomes limp, which has many political implications."

"It's over when the male ejaculates, unless the woman is lucky enough to have more than one man in bed."

"Nature decides when it's over."

"If the partner is male, the woman is stuck with the limits of his sexuality."

"He does, as he ejaculates."

"My partner ends it, but he does make sure I'm completely pleased and satisfied, and then he holds me and touches me until I'm asleep."

"I like getting into the sex experience as much as possible and feel terribly frustrated emotionally if I am not allowed to because he has an orgasm and falls asleep. I would like to have continuing love after and not make an orgasm the end!"

"My partner decides when sex is over because when he comes he usually loses interest in sex. He may be tired if it is in the evening or if during the day he may have other things to do. If he stays in a sexual mood long enough to gain a second erection, then the love-making may go on for a long period, but that is the unusual case. I feel it is a great pity that males and females were sexually-biologically built such that males are ready to quit just as females are getting started. I wonder to what extent men realize this? That when he is feeling exhausted and satisfied and sleepy as hell she is feeling hot-wired and dying to come again, and sleep is the last thing on her mind. Of course this is not always the situation, but I know I've played satisfied and exhausted many many times just because I knew my partner was, and I'd damned well better be."

Orgasm from clitoral stimulation by hand

Do most women orgasm regularly from clitoral stimulation by hand?

In the reproductive pattern of sex just described, which is far and away the most prevalent in our culture—if not the *only* definition for most people—were women having orgasms during "foreplay" with clitoral stimulation?

Frequency of orgasm during clitoral stimulation by hand

	Q.I	Q.II	Q.III		Total
"Yes"	279	220	67	=	566
Always	16	36	25	=	77
Usually	9	102	24	=	135
Sometimes	12	40	17	=	69
Rarely	0	14	2	=	16
Total	316	412	135		863
Orgasm regularly	44%	39%	49%	=	44%

Those who orgasm regularly (those who answered "yes," always or usually) during clitoral stimulation by hand during sex with a partner comprise approximately 44 per cent of the total sample.

In other words, although nowhere near the overwhelming majority of women who orgasmed regularly with masturbation, those who orgasmed with the manual clitoral stimulation of their partners comprised a much larger number than those who orgasmed during intercourse (30 per cent). But why don't women orgasm as easily during clitoral stimulation with others as they do with themselves?

First, a note on the derivation of the preceding figures.

There were here, as there were in the chapter on "intercourse," difficulties with coming to a general, overall figure. The main problem here, and with oral sex, is that clitoral stimulation is often offered mainly for purposes of arousal ("foreplay"); because of this, it was not always clear whether the woman's answer meant she had the *ability* to orgasm "usually" or "sometimes," etc., through this kind of stimulation or whether she and her partner "usually," "always," or "sometimes" did engage in this stimulation to orgasm. Women who answered with regard to ability might have caused the figures to be slightly higher than the actual frequency of the practice of clitoral stimulation to orgasm would warrant. However, as in the intercourse figures, every effort was made to crosscheck answers, and in most cases the meaning could be surmised.

Further, in Questionnaires I and II, the question was phrased, "What positions and movements are best for stimulating yourself clitorally with a partner? Do you have orgasms this way usually, sometimes, rarely, or never? Please explain ways you and your partner(s) practise clitoral stimulation." The active voice was used as a way of suggesting that the woman herself could be active about getting clitoral stimulation, but this caused many women to misunderstand the question:

"I don't understand the question—me stimulating myself? Is that what is asked? I rarely do this with a partner."

"I don't stimulate myself clitorally with a partner. He does."

"What is clitoral stimulation? Is that when the partner masturbates you?"

"I don't know what any of this means."

"This question doesn't make sense. Clitoral

stimulation is part of the warm-up exercises."

"I'm not sure what you mean. I've never had a homosexual relationship."

Perhaps to some women even the idea of having an orgasm this way was novel. The ultimate significance of how many women misunderstood or didn't answer this question is that a culture concerning the needs of female sexuality, a way of relating that truly concerns itself with the needs of women's bodies, hardly exists.

When the question was changed to the more usual passive voice in Questionnaire III, it was perfectly understood, which accounts for the higher percentage of positive answers in Questionnaire III.

It should be pointed out that it cannot be assumed that the total percentages of women who orgasm from intercourse (30 per cent) and from manual clitoral stimulation (44 per cent) can be simply added together to represent the total percentage of women having orgasms during sex with their partners. Many of these women are the same women, who can have orgasms in both ways. There were, unfortunately, many women w orgasmed regularly during masturbation but almost never during sex with another person in any way.

The first reason women don't orgasm as frequently from the clitoral stimulation of another person as they do from their own, is that, more often than not, clitoral stimulation is not *intended* to lead to orgasm. The reproductive model of sex has traditionally included just enough clitoral stimulation in "foreplay" for purposes of arousal but not for orgasm—which is perhaps worse than no clitoral stimulation at all, a kind of "cock teasing" in reverse:

"I vividly remember reading in some marriage manual (at an age when I still found the idea of intercourse and genitals disgusting—maybe eight or nine years old) about where the sensitive parts were on a woman, and how the man should stimulate them before attempting intercourse, so the woman would be ready. It sounded so unpleasant and obligatory—and I never wanted a man to do that to *me* in order to get me ready, so that he could get on with what he really wanted to do—fuck. I never got the idea that anyone would want to touch and caress for its own sake. It was always an obligation one did so that he could be proud of his 'technique' as a lover."

"My partners seem to be slow to understand this is what I enjoy most, and therefore I rarely have an orgasm with my partners because they mount me before I've been satisfied."

"When having intercourse, this is used for stimulation only. If I do not attain orgasm during intercourse, then clitoral stimulation *may* be used again, if I'm lucky."

"Men usually do manual stimulation a very short time—they wanna get in there."

"He only does clitoral stimulation before intercourse. If I don't come during intercourse, he figures it's my problem."

"They tell me they want me to come, but they don't do anything about it so I'm suspicious. This 'why don't you come?' talk may be just another way to make me feel badly."

"He doesn't usually give me much foreplay, but I encourage it, sometimes unsuccessfully. If it happens, it's usually before intercourse."

"They have touched me there, but I doubt if they knew what they were doing."

"Most men will finger the genitals, poke a finger inside, etc., without being asked. This is preliminary and doesn't last long. Sometimes some attempt cunnilingus."

"My partners do sometimes stimulate my clitoral area manually. It is usually for purposes of arousal, rather than orgasm. I wish they would *continue* and that I would be able to *let go* enough to *have an orgasm* or to tell them to continue or show them how to do it so that it does lead to orgasm."

And many men did not even stimulate their partners at all:

"We don't practise clitoral stimulation. I could agree with what's in the chapter on the subject in a dozen books, but first hand I have nothing much to say. Basically I dislike the notion of deliberate stimulation— wishing romance would take care of all the lubrication, etc.—just the back and forth of emotional energy. However, it doesn't."

"Sometime in the first year of marriage eight years ago, my husband said he did not particularly enjoy using his hand. I would not consider it after that, and grew to feel disgust when touching him, too. Now I am totally ice cold with him."

"My man is a little hung up about stimulating me so I have to rely on penetration."

"My lovers never have attempted to stimulate my clitoris specifically."

"My partner disapproves of this technique and I can't usually relax and enjoy it for this reason."

"I like it, but I don't think my husband even knows where the clitoris is, and I'm too embarrassed to tell him. He does hit it by accident sometimes."

"I have never been clitorally stimulated to orgasm. Most of my partners have not been really aware of the clitoris's significance."

"My present partner doesn't realize, or doesn't want to realize (he may see it as a threat to his masculinity), that my clitoris is for me what his phallus is for him. He doesn't want to spend the time to stimulate me."

"My partner does not do this too much. He is more interested in penetration."

"Masturbation by men is usually to check if I'm wet."

Feelings about clitoral stimulation

"Do you feel guilty about taking time for yourself in sexual play which may not be specifically stimulating to your partner? Which activities are you including in your answer?"

Many women interpreted this question to mean, did they feel guilty about needing "foreplay"—rather than interpreting "taking time for yourself" to mean to have an orgasm. This only underscores more strongly the picture already presented—that clitoral stimulation is commonly used for purposes of arousal but not orgasm. And nevertheless, many women felt guilty—even *without* orgasm—for "needing" this kind of "extra" stimulation. As one woman put it, "Women are made to feel that *sexy* women don't require it."

"Most men enjoy the girl playing with them usually, more or as much as intercourse, and therefore each partner should have equal rights to this situation, which is not mutually satisfying. But I personally feel ill at ease asking for my share."

"Yes, sometimes I feel guilty, or like I'm intruding, bothering him. I *know* it's ridiculous and masochistic, but I still *do.*"

"My boyfriend stimulates my clitoris usually with his tongue and sometimes his finger. This is satisfying but it seems so computerized and mechanical and lustless—he doesn't mind doing it for me but sometimes I experience *enormous* guilt feelings that he has to. I wish I could come during intercourse. If you know how could you please let me know!"

"I feel afraid more than guilty—of how he'll react and how I'll feel if he's angry."

"Yes. I cannot abide the thought that he is working to make me feel something; he works *too* hard and makes a performance of it, so screw it, I won't ask."

"I don't bother with it. It decreases my pleasure if my partner seems the least put out or obliging."

"Long foreplay makes me uncomfortable because I worry that I'm putting my man through too much work, when I know that he could come so much sooner if he let himself."

"I resent men engaging in some activity because they think it will stimulate me. I doubt that clitoral stimulation is even remotely interesting to men except that it makes them feel powerful in getting a reaction from the woman. I do not cooperate with patronizing nonsense."

"Yes. I feel anxiety, distrust, and resentment at being manoeuvred, even in disguised forms; I don't like feeling I'm being 'worked on' by someone who feels I should have 'orgasms.' "

"To me, sexual satisfaction is selfish. Each person takes the most she or he can from the stimulation being offered. The trick for women is to unabashedly take and not give a fuck."

"Orgasm by clitoral stimulation occurs seldom with my partner because I feel very self-conscious when being acted upon without doing anything to the other person."

"I asked my lovers to stimulate my clitoris, but my husband always says, 'Only whores enjoy clitoral contact and going down on the man,' so I don't ask him."

"I feel embarrassed because men think it means I masturbate."

"Yes, I feel this way about foreplay. I want more of it than my husband does. Sometimes after intercourse (sometimes with orgasm) I want to go on with clitoral stimulation. But I'm slowly getting over this hang up."

"Yes, I definitely feel guilty about taking time for myself in activities such as clitoral stimulation, erotic massage, and cunnilingus simply because these activities are not specifically stimulating to my partner. I feel selfish, I imagine that my partner is either impatient to 'get on with it' or is not enjoying himself very much, or feels uncomfortable because he doesn't quite know what he's doing (which he usually doesn't because he does it so seldom and doesn't ask for any feedback from me, and I'm so reluctant to volunteer it); in other words I can't relax very well when things are being done to me, only, and I don't come very easily as a result."

"Yes, I feel very guilty (or obligated) taking time for myself, because during intercourse my partner is getting at least as much pleasure as I am. This could relate to the fact that I always resented stimulating my partners in the past—especially when I was a teenager—and perhaps I don't want them to resent me the way I resented them. I remember how my hand would get tired, or, with my husband, how my jaw would ache from having him in my mouth too long. I knew I didn't enjoy stimulating them, and I knew it caused me to resent them, and I never want anyone to feel that way about me. Sometimes when my partner plays with my nipples while I masturbate I feel uncomfortable, also because he usually does it after he's come, when he's not excited any more; he's so dispassionate about it."

"I don't feel guilty because I've never taken time for myself or been given the opportunity to do so. I have always rendered a service to the man, even though I didn't realize it when I was very young. It was expected. There has never been a question of *myself* in a sexual relationship. It has never arisen except in my own mind lately."

"Guilty feelings or not, someone who 'doesn't want to play' is a colossal bummer. I just refuse to capitulate to that 'you're making demands on me' garbage.

Especially when it's non-verbal. I get out of bed and read a good book."

"I think in terms of debits and credits—I blew him so he should go down on me, etc."

"I don't make much demand for sexual play. It's the mood that sets the situation, not special physical stimulation. Also I kind of hate to ask my man for things, for fear of being a bother."

"Men think they are really being hip and up front in the vanguard if they do it without your asking. Out of all the information popularized about female sexuality since the 'sexual revolution,' the idea of clitoral stimulation has really made the heaviest impact. But still I feel my partner is doing something that for him is a mere technical obstacle to deal with before going on to the 'real thing,' and I resent feeling uptight about having him do that to me."

"When I ask, and receive, I feel inordinately grateful. Yet I just did what *he* needed to come to climax, and I didn't feel he owed *me* anything."

"I have many problems in this area. I need manual stimulation to orgasm, plus gentle fondling of the breasts, and lots of soft kisses. First of all, I have never stimulated myself when I was with a partner, unless one counts rubbing my clitoral area over his thigh or penis as self-stimulation. Yeah, I guess it is; but I could never use my hand then without feeling really weird, exposed. And I hate giving directions to men almost as much as they hate taking them. Even when they say they want to know what I like, and I tell them, they invariably forget the next time—and I hate like hell giving the schtick again. It's embarrassing and humiliating, like I'm the only weirdo who does things this way."

"Both people participate in a clear unity of purpose with penetration, whereas the manual stimulation is one doing it to the other, so I feel funny about it."

"I used to feel guilty and afraid, but it turns out it's fairly easy to ask. It feels like longed-for honesty."

"I ask, but he stimulates me for three seconds and then just goes ahead and penetrates—he thinks women are just like men. Sex is so much easier and automatic for them. I feel cheated to be a woman as far as sex is concerned."

"When I ask a man to stimulate me manually, they become insulting and suggest I've had lesbian experiences."

"It's rather hard to ask. It's nice if they know on their own, because I feel a little embarrassed saying those words."

"Yes, I feel it's an imposition. That's why I like men who dig it anyway; there's never the implicit question 'is that enough?'"

"I don't feel he enjoys my body as he says he does. He does enjoy my breasts, and it shows from the way he does it."

"I feel he must be thinking, 'This is too much like masturbation.'"

"Yes, I would not ask him. In fact, the last time we had sex he told me he was not going to masturbate me. He feels this is a reflection on his sexual abilities, i.e., his penis should do the job. I couldn't tell him that his penis couldn't possibly do the job as well."

"I still have an uneasy feeling that I am inconveniencing him. I really need more foreplay than what my husband gives me and I have told him so frequently, but he usually doesn't bother. He seems very orgasm oriented—that is, *his* orgasm; that's all that's important to him."

"Yes, it's a matter of dependence on a man's willingness to do an aggressive action for me while I am mostly passive—whereas during intercourse a man orgasms through his aggressiveness. Men also are under the illusion that fucking involves two people in physical enjoyment, whereas clitoral stimulation is only for the woman."

"What I believe contributes to my not having an orgasm sometimes with a partner is my unwillingness to risk letting my partner know he/she is stimulating me in the wrong area or not going fast enough or hard enough or not taking long enough. When I realize I'm not going to climax right away and I think my partner is getting bored, I frustrate myself and stop."

"When he comes, I want to too, but then it always seems like him masturbating me, so I get all worried and say let's go eat some berries and yoghurt."

"Do you feel embarrassed asking for clitoral stimulation? Do you feel your partner is sacrificing to give it to you?"

"I've only managed to talk about it a few times. I talked a long time once to one man and told him what I liked and then I did come with him. I think if I had done that with other men, I could have come with them. But it's less exciting that way, at least at first. If men were more honest and sensual it would be easier too."

"I finally managed to communicate the situation to one man so that he managed to Get It. The others just could never grasp it, evidently, or I was too shy to get the point across clearly."

"He was furious the last time I asked him to stimulate me (as it stopped his readiness to 'dive in'). He's really timid and clumsy and too unsure for me to risk spoiling another evening by coaching. So I accept him this way (it's really okay)."

"I ask for it sometimes even though it's embarrassing—and then it's hard to be very specific on what you like, and you feel like a nut in being so limited in what turns you on."

"I don't think I ever asked for what I wanted. I just thought some guys knew and some didn't, and it was very exciting when they did. I always was intimidated by

the concept of a controlling and/or castrating woman—
it was holy writ to me not to make a guy feel inadequate
(a result of my intellectual male friends and my
psychoanalyst), and to suggest that he do something
more or different would have been to appear to suggest
that he wasn't adequate. Now the women's movement
has helped me to be outspoken. I ask for what I want in
all sorts of situations—church, work, the supermarket,
local government—and in bed."

"It used to be embarrassing, but then my partner and
I learned how to touch each other by oral instructions.
Dialogue goes like this: me: 'What would you like?'
'Touch my penis.' 'How hard?' 'Harder.' 'Like this or
this?' 'The second way.' 'What else?' 'Touch the tip.'
'How?' 'Rub gently.' 'Like this or this?', etc. I really
insisted that he be literal and use all the words. Then we
reversed it. I had a hard time asking him to touch my
breast or clitoris. Now it is easier, but *still* hard to
suggest something new."

"No, I don't ask for it usually. That would be
embarrassing to me and is something I know I must
struggle with. If I can tell them a foot massage feels
wonderful, why not feelings related to sex??? I'm trying
though, and it's getting better. If my friend ever reads
these answers I'm writing to you, it'll be a long night,
but it'll be worth it!"

"Yes! He's *always in the wrong place!* and I'm too
embarrassed to show him *exactly* how. Funny, I'm not
embarrassed to do anything a man likes or that occurs to
us, but I am embarrassed to say, 'a little to the right' or
'higher' or 'stroke my back.'"

"My present lover feels even more affectionate when
I tell him what I want—but I'm only able to do this
because we really love and care about each other and I
am very secure with him. With previous lovers I felt
uptight and insecure about asking and I rarely did. I
don't think I expected very much of them, or, more
importantly, of myself. I was too hung up on

maintaining *their* approval, which ultimately, however, didn't matter very much."

"It did embarrass me to say 'not there—here.' Then I closed my legs and said, 'Let's make it for real.'"

"I used to resent not coming, but I reasoned it would be better to put resentment aside and ask for what I wanted. This state of mind took a lot of effort to achieve and it involved learning to be willing to ask outright for what I wanted if I wasn't getting it already. I think being open and direct about one's desires is the best way of getting them satisfied. Lying there and hoping he will make the right move at the right time is too maddening."

"Though I have been really shy about saying to a man what I have said here, perhaps the next time I am with one of my men friends, I'll try telling them about all this and see where it gets me."

If women couldn't ask for clitoral stimulation to orgasm, or do it themselves, they were unlikely, in many cases, to get it from the man they were with.

"Are your partners well informed? Are they sensitive to the stimulation you want?'

Answers to this question indicated that in general only regular partners came anywhere near being well informed— and that women often felt that their needs for clitoral stimulation were unusual, evidenced by statements like, "Not all women are the same," or "Some women are different," or "I usually have to explain how stimulation works for me, that I don't come during intercourse."

"Men are uninformed. They must all read the same book. Of course, passivity in women contributes to their miseducation."

"My husband is now well informed because I explained exactly what I like to have done to me."

"Most men are not exactly uninformed; they seem to know about all the right places of a woman's body, but too often most of them seem to be just not tuned into Woman."

"There are many myths about what men and women want and enjoy. Great honesty is necessary."

"My male partners seemed to be well *mis*informed about female sexuality."

"Men feel we're rarely capable of orgasm."

"Nice but dumb men are unaware that orgasm in women is not a chance occurrence beyond their control!"

"The only partner I've ever had who was 'sensitive' is my husband and it's taken years for us to be honest about our sexual desires. I'm still embarrassed if I have to verbally say what I want."

"Men have been brainwashed to think they're the sexual experts, and furthermore, that whatever feels good to them is what feels good and 'fulfills' us also. Most men I have first slept with seemed to have the attitude, 'Here, dear, let me show you how.' Of all the presumption!"

"They are uninformed and they don't seem to *want* the information about the clitoris, as people once refused to believe the earth went around the sun. And women are still being dishonest about telling them, usually as a way of holding the man."

"They are uninformed but I teach them! Sometimes this is thrown up in my face as part of being a 'demanding female.'"

"My husband isn't fully informed, but he's eagerly reading these answers, and I shall try to be more explicit at appropriate times from now on."

"Most of my partners never gave a thought to what pleased me and totally ignored anything I said. They invariably knew what was best for me. I tried a few times to ask for what helped me but was ignored or ridiculed."

"I don't like men who fancy themselves as sex

therapists and try to tell you what should feel good. But the male ego is a pretty tricky thing—you have to go to bed with a guy at least three times before you begin to tell *him* how to do it."

"When we first got married, my husband would just stick his penis in and move it in and out—and he had been married before!"

"They are uninformed in any way specific enough to be useful. I feel as though I should have a physiology training course with each new lover. I asked one man if he had ever seen a woman's genitals, and he said, no, it had always been in the dark . . . "

"They've read those awful manuals, and take a very mechanical approach. They also don't understand their own sexuality very well."

"What should one do? Post a manual over one's bed?"

"It was like they were foreigners. Often they cared but were ignorant."

"I've never met a man who knew how to stimulate me very well until after I told or showed him what to do. Are all men this insensitive to what turns women on? I know what turns men on and have known since I was fifteen."

"My lover, who was an obstetrician, was not well informed."

"Staggeringly uninformed. The more confident they are of their sexual prowess and the effectiveness of their techniques, the more ignorant they seem to be of the facts and realities."

"We are all uninformed. We need to discuss sex openly and freely together, privately and in public, and show each other with our bodies how we do things— just as is done in other fields. I, for one, have told very few people what I am telling you here. Not good!"

"Most of the men I've encountered *lately* seem really concerned about bringing me to orgasm and always try to manually stimulate me after they've come. They seem to feel bad if I don't come. I guess today it worries them."

"He seems fascinated by what I tell him about myself, as if amazed that I have preferences, etc."

"Men are especially uninformed about the clitoris but it's getting slightly better. Now they are aware of its importance, but don't know where to find it!"

"Very few have had any idea of the number of sensitive places and variety of on-turning things to do—most seem to be very limited themselves in what they like and where they're sensitive. It's unaccountably hard for me (impossible in the throes of passion) to tell them about it either verbally or any other way—and even harder to get them to abandon their preconceived and usual methods even if they think they want to please."

"Most partners seemed to think that I would be automatically aroused by two minutes of kissing and touching and then would be just as ready for intercourse as they were. I have had to tell them or show them what I wanted. No one has ever asked me, or known already what would turn me on. It hasn't been embarrassing, exactly, but it's hard to strike the right tone; showing lovingly what pleases without suggesting that the man is an ill-informed, selfish animal (unless, of course, he is!!)."

"Men should ask flat out? 'What do you want?'"

"Not one man has consistently performed sexually in a way that would be the best possible and most satisfying for me. It isn't that I don't enjoy intercourse or can't have orgasms in intercourse—it's just a simple fact that in order to enjoy it the most I need more direct clitoral stimulation. And it's not so much work—just three minutes done well is enough to help me fly through half a dozen orgasms in intercourse. It doesn't require suffocating, straining, or sacrificing his pleasure. A gentle hand or sensitive tongue can accomplish miracles. And please, no pressure on the clock. Any man that makes it seem like a favour is going to make the woman feel guilty and pressured, two things that aren't conducive to having orgasms."

"It seems like over the past five years I have met a lot of premature ejaculators, and a lot of inconsiderate, selfish men. They either didn't know about a clitoris and foreplay, or they just wanted to get their rocks off and then roll over. Consequently, I built up a lot of fears and expectations and anxiety and learned (I realize now) not to get too turned on. That way I wouldn't get too disappointed. I put blocks up because I figured the man would come right away anyway, so what's the use? Now my current partner is very considerate and very sensitive to my needs, always asking what feels best, etc. But I have been with men who, when I told them what I liked or how to rub my clit, didn't pay attention. I would repeat myself, but only for so long because it began to sound like nagging. The biggest thing I think I've come up against is men who don't seem to realize the value of foreplay and that some women take longer to be ready. It was not really embarrassing to ask for a certain stimulation, but I hesitate sometimes, because I don't want to hurt their feelings, etc. I have begun to look out for myself more lately, though, and risked."

"No, most of my partners were not well informed about my body and sexual desires—except my husband. It was always difficult for me to ask for something, or correct or instruct. And often, after summoning the courage to instruct, I would notice that my partner would 'forget' the instructions the next time. Few of my partners ever tried to find out what I liked."

"My husband isn't well informed (but right now he's reading *Sexual Honesty!!!*). I am a little embarrassed to tell him what makes me feel good but, strangely enough, I'm not embarrassed with my lover. I suppose that's because my lover and I have a very honest, open relationship which depends a lot on sex. He has only been with four women besides me, but seems surprisingly well informed with what pleases women.

He is a very quick learner, and takes criticism very well. My husband, on the other hand, can't handle criticism at all, which is partly why I never tell him."

"I *did* the Masters and Johnson's bit—two weeks in St Louis. I learned that good sex followed almost effortlessly after good communication. Communication is what they tried to teach my husband and me. I bought it, he didn't. It takes two to talk, tango, or screw."

"The unique men are those who have outgrown the need for techniques, etc., and are comfortable offering themselves. The important thing is just to *listen* to yourself and to the other person."

It is not news that masturbation for women is done clitorally. Why has this—our own silent testimony to what is efficient stimulation for our bodies—been so ignored in favour of the way men think we *should* have orgasms? All too many men still seem to believe, in a rather naive and egocentric way, that what feels good to them is automatically what feels good to women:

"Most men didn't seem to be aware that what brought them to climax wasn't what brought me to climax. That about sums it up."

"Most partners seem to have a minimal knowledge about female desires and anatomy. My women partners have shown an intuitive knowledge of my needs, so I exclude them in this discussion. Most male partners have a general idea about how to please a woman, but each woman is so different that initially a man may not know how to please *me,* as different from any other woman he's fucked. I may have to let him know that the clitoral stimulation he is giving me is *too* direct and too sensitive, or I may have to adjust my body to his so that I get the right stimulation in intercourse that I need. Initially he cannot know how I like to be fucked. If I'm feeling really loose and nervy and horny I may just say, 'Heeey, I really love it this way,' and show him what I mean by fucking him in a certain way, maybe really deep or complete thrusts or real grindy and a lot of pelvic and pubic bone pressure. *Most men do not know that a woman may need clitoral stimulation aside from intercourse to get off.* I can't imagine what women who do not come easily from intercourse, as I do, and who can't bring themselves to communicate their needs, do—they must want to climb walls. It is very easy to communicate my desires in intercourse—men seem to have a bit of intuition about this—but very difficult to communicate needs and desires in clitoral stimulation, cunnilingus, etc. Unless a man volunteers to do these things (which most seldom do), I would never even bring it up. I have begun to wonder why this is. It seems that once a man discovers how 'nicely' I come from intercourse, he decides that this is all I want or need: I *do* love intercourse and I usually moan and yell as I come, so the man knows I've come and assumes my satisfaction, I guess. If I was like some other women who don't often come in intercourse then maybe he'd try to please me in other ways, like clitoral stimulation and cunnilingus, which I really miss. There seems to be a tacit assumption on the part of most men I've fucked that fucking is the best way to come, and if you can come that way there's no use bothering with any of that other stuff. It's an odd assumption, though, when you think of it, cause most men I've been with, even though they loved to fuck, still really dug a good blow job or hand job now and then. In short, what is a man thinking when we are both horny, I stimulate him orally to really get him in a mood, he communicates that he'd like to be blown, I lovingly make him come, and then he assumes that sex is over because he has come? What about me? Doesn't he realize that I expect some kind of reciprocation and sexual release? Apparently not, because this has happened to me so many times. And I'll be damned if I can figure out how to communicate this without making him feel like a real 'dildo' (dumb prick) or making me feel like a demanding bitch."

Often, even when men did clitorally stimulate their partners, they didn't do it well—perhaps because they felt awkward, embarrassed, or resentful.

"Done to suit *me,* clitoral stimulation would be done by somebody who really wanted to do it, instead of just doing it because it was chic this year or because he thought it might finally get me off, and is doing me some big favour, or because if he does it for me I will do it for him. In short, it is the attitude that really counts."

"The men I usually choose I have sensed are not all that into it. I am looking forward someday to somebody being really into stimulating me so I don't have to concentrate on a thing but just that."

"Once I let a man use my vibrator, but he turned it into something of a weapon, jamming it into my vagina, using it roughly, doing what he pleased, playing his own little game, hurting me, and I never tried again."

"Only one partner ever cared about stimulating me clitorally—no that's not right. Some other men did, but I think they were trying to hurt me, they rubbed so hard. The stimulation has to be the same as when I masturbate."

"It seems like he is trying to *erase* my clitoris!"

"They do it sometimes for arousal, and sometimes for orgasm, but it never leads to orgasm for me because they either 'stimulate' too hard, or too directly, or not long enough. I don't explain what I want too well so it's partly my fault, but manual clitoral stimulation is important to me because I do it to them, and I believe turn about is fair play."

"It invariably seems that they're left-handed, and I have a right-handed clitoris."

"Usually we just try to find the damned thing."

"My husband is pretty clumsy in the clitoral stimulation area, and our hang-ups keep me from telling him how I could enjoy sex more. I've been very disappointed in my ability to deal with this whole area of our relationship."

"I try to communicate with my lover as to what does it for me. Usually they don't like me to rub the clitoris myself and they insist on doing it for me—all wrong, too fast, too hard, just irritating the tissues. When I come to the realization that I'm not going to reach orgasm, I fake one, so he'll stop rubbing the life out of my clitoris and get on to the business of coming and it will be over with. In order to teach him how to do it right would take a major education and psychotherapy job which is only worth going through with someone I really dig."

"My partners usually are very clumsy when it comes to clitoral stimulation—either they press too hard, or right in the centre which is agonizing, or they move too jerkily. I use my whole hand and not fingers like they do so that the pressure is evenly distributed and my clitoris doesn't get poked and shocked to death."

"There's just one thing I can't stand—that's when someone rubs my clitoris hard and rough directly on it. It's the most annoying feeling."

"Men always do it too roughly. And they'll change the rhythm at just the wrong time."

"The main problem with having someone else stimulate my clitoris is that he usually doesn't increase the pressure enough or stroke fast enough for me to orgasm."

"I try to show men how I like it, but most of them can't do it right or don't want to, so I seldom have man-made orgasms."

"My partner sometimes tries direct stimulation with his hand rubbing my clitoris, but he never gets it on the right spot, or else he doesn't stay on it when he does hit it."

"If he could just stimulate me with his fingers—but he goes around my clitoris and *misses* it."

"My husband does stimulate my clitoris but his touch is much harder than I like and though I tell him this on occasion, he doesn't seem to be able to remember the light touch for long. I do become stimulated from this touch, but it seldom leads to orgasm. It is used mostly as foreplay."

What kind of clitoral stimulation do women like?

Of course, it is impossible to give any kind of quick answer that will be true for every woman every time, because each person is slightly different; the answers contained thousands of subtle but very important nuances. In general it is always necessary to be sensitive, and to feel what the other person's body is saying. Most women like clitoral stimulation to start out softly and slowly, gradually building up to a little more pressure. It is often safer to use the whole hand, or palm of the hand, rather than one or two fingers.

"Gentle but firm with a rhythm I can count on. But the surprises and unknowns of my partner's fingers make his stimulation of me much more erotic than if I were using my fingers. He strokes gently up and down the groove."

"I like it when his fingers are slightly spread and moving the genital area around slowly and softly, then increasing the pressure."

"I like irregular ('clumsy') rhythmic movements— soft—sometimes a little *too* soft (like teasing), so I must press up against his hand."

"Changing the position of the hand or fingers would make me lose whatever height of excitement I had gained. It should stay in one place all the way up to and through my orgasm."

"Four fingers placed slightly above my vagina moving lightly around is just about right."

"Pressure or harsh rubbing irritates my clitoris; there must be an even sort of gentle movement and pressure with much fluid for lubrication. At the same time I move my body in the rhythm to help."

"I usually like a gentle but insistent pressure on my clitoral area (that is, against that upper bone). Direct stimulation of my clitoris is uncomfortable."

"I like direct stimulation of my clitoris with fingers or tongue, round and round, at first not constantly, but at different speeds and tempos, and then finally all the time real fast."

"Firm, quick, constant movements, increasing in strength (firmness) and speed as orgasm comes close."

"Soft first, then the more times I climax, the harder I like it."

"Soft then hard, the position varying for each orgasm, but not varying *within* an orgasm."

"Best for me is sort of shaking my clitoral area with the palm."

"The vibrator *concept is* helpful when showing my lover how to masturbate me. He should vibrate his hand on my pubic area."

"If they do not do it on their own, I place their finger where I want it, then show them the motion I want and the amount of pressure that I desire. It always leads to orgasm, if they are patient and sensitive enough to follow my instructions."

"They should use a light, teasing, tentative touch, not too regular—I like an attitude of playfulness, exploring, sensing."

"I need a certain quality of touch from soft to medium, otherwise my body gets numb and loses the feelings."

"Diddling is what I like—playing around—medium intensity—a rhythm with syncopation—a little jolt, a little surprise—drives me crazy!"

"A break or change in the rhythm can even stop my coming altogether."

"There is nothing worse than a partner who is not knowledgeable in this technique—i.e., fingers planted firmly and directly on the clitoris."

"I like soft and rhythmic rubbing, accompanied by kissing."

"A gentle massage then gradually firmer. Hard massaging causes pain when it is directly on my clitoris—a common mistake men make. The more vigorous massage has to be around the edges—never directly on the clitoris, but softer movements can be direct. I like direct movements around my clitoris, alternating with up and down movements. The rhythm should be maintained—gives me more confidence, I think."

"I find I always have to say, *Don't stop now!*"

"Soft massage, position constant, rhythm constant. Actually stroking is not involved, but pressing and then moving the hand around is."

"I prefer the use of the hand or a larger object because it's softer than fingers."

"I like the very front of me rubbed, higher than my clitoris."

"The fingers should be well lubricated."

"Direct physical stimulation is physically irritating; I prefer indirect clitoral stimulation where he uses his entire hand, not just fingers."

"Direct clitoral stimulation with a regular rhythm but a variety of methods, sometimes slight interruptions of rhythm plus mouth kissing at the same time; also my partner should appear excited."

"The guy shouldn't act like he's doing seven years of hard labour, he should be creative. It should be gentle, loving, and passionate contact."

"The light touch is better than the gorilla approach."

"Soft and circular movements. I prefer contact over the labia (i.e., fingers push the labia against my clitoris) rather than direct touch on the clitoris."

"Please don't try to push it back into my body, it doesn't do a thing!"

"Stimulate the tips of the labia very close to the front of my body."

"Stimulation of the whole mons area is more important than direct clitoral stimulation for me."

"I like him to draw back the foreskin and rub the clitoris itself."

"Sometimes my husband goes under the hood and touches and lifts, touches and lifts. I once had a lover who seemed to shake it. That was wonderful. As for myself, I just do a simple circular motion."

"Begin slow, and end near a frenzy."

"Soft, rhythmic, clitoral, with 'excursions' to the vagina. Pressure can be increased as I get more aroused, but medium or hard pressure at the beginning will turn me off."

"Towards orgasm he should not slow down—it drives me crazy, I hate it!"

"Mellow and affectionate, yet with spunk."

"The general area but not the clitoris directly. As I become more and more *quiet* this means I am closer and closer to orgasm and until the moment of orgasm when movement begins, it is very important that my partner not interrupt the continuing gentle and rhythmic stroking of the area, by misinterpreting my quietness. The area should be wet and lubricated, not dry, especially when using the hand."

"Rapid side to side massaging of the clitoris, by either tongue or finger, starting gently, increasing in pressure as I become more excited. Corollary stimulation of the nipple of one or both breasts helps immeasurably."

"It's best to vary the position at first to find the one which gives the most stimulation, and then keep it constant."

"I like a slow and soft massage that becomes harder and faster, and then goes back to the beginning again (teasing element)."

"It should be a medium massage with rhythm and empathy."

"Soft massage with rhythm and position constant because in that way it builds up; if it is changed, I have to build up again."

"The position should be stable, because the change of position could turn me off at the wrong moment."

"As arousal gets more acute, I need a more firm, rhythmic and quite constant massaging around my clitoris. But too much manipulation of the very sensitive clitoris would end by hurting and immediately closing up and turning off the feeling. A relaxing of the rhythm, or a break or change in it at the final stage—when all the feeling in the entire body, breasts, torso, head, legs and feet, seem to be gushing up and surging towards an overflow point—would be terrible, an awful letdown of the trust put in the lover who got so careless (uncaring)."

"Medium or soft massage, I like to be 'teased' a bit—once the feeling of excitement starts in my clitoris, the movements should be rhythmic and the position constant."

"The most reliable technique is one finger placed along either the length of the clitoral shaft, or just above it, rubbing rhythmically, beginning light and slow, then harder and faster. Doing this for fifteen to thirty seconds, then stopping, then beginning again, repeated five to six times."

"Sometimes, frustratingly, too constant a pressure numbs me more than anything, and I find it hard to come."

"Barely brushing the skin."

Positions used during manual clitoral stimulation with a partner.
Here again, preferences depend on individual needs, especially with regard to leg position. However, there should always be room for freedom of movement of the legs and lower body.

"I lie on my back or my side, especially with my back arched over my partner's extended leg, while he rubs my clitoris up and down."

"I like him on my left side, me cuddling up with

him, while he rubs me with his left hand. (I would like oral, but he refuses to do it or have it done to him.)"

"I stand in the shower with my partner soaping me clean between the legs."

"She lies beside me, using one hand to stimulate my clitoris—and we're kissing, and I'm holding her."

"I stand in front of my spouse, who is seated. He uses his finger or the vibrator on my clitoris with a slow, moving action, then as I become aroused, he increases the speed of rhythm until orgasm, and then he pushes either his finger or the vibrator up into my vagina."

"My partner rests her hand, palm facing into my pubic area, with one or two fingers on my clitoris with gentle pressure."

"I lie on my back and my partner lies to my right on his side—his left hand under my buttocks with his middle finger inserted in my vagina, stimulating my clitoris with his right hand."

"Usually I'm lying on my back and my husband is on his side kissing me on the lips and neck, while using his middle finger to exert the primary pressure while the other fingers stimulate my vaginal lips."

"I am on my back with my legs apart and his head and hands are between my legs watching what he is doing."

"He lies gently playing with my clitoris, rubbing up and down while teasing and talking dirty."

"I lie on my stomach and he's on my back reaching up under me and makes me come and come and come, and he won't stop and he won't let me up! *Wow!*"

"My thighs are wide apart, but not necessarily my feet. I am on my back. He has a finger on each inner labium, rubbing them against the base of the clitoris."

"I like to be on my side with her beside me on her side, with both of us moving back and forth, with one of her hands on my clitoris, the other on one of my breasts, one of my hands in her hair and the other on her leg or her stomach."

"The man stands behind me with me facing a mirror.

He uses his right hand and with the left massages my left breast—or the man lies in front of my open legs, watching closely as the clitoris gets harder and redder."

"I'd rather have a part of the other person's body stimulate me than a hand or finger, so that leaves open a lot of positions."

"We lie facing each other, with our legs entwined and fondle each other's bodies until one of us comes near to orgasm, then I or she concentrates on that person until orgasm. Then it's the other's turn."

"I like to move myself against a man's body, usually his leg or sometimes his penis (though I'm shy about the latter). Also it can be his hand moving but I need to be already aroused, enough to be lubricated, and it seems to be very difficult for men to learn what the right kind of pressure or motion is."

"He rubs around my genital area and then down into the lips—opens the lips and explores until I signify (non-verbally) excitement. He continues rubbing through an orgasm or two, then might stimulate my clitoris orally by licking or sucking the area—hard actions are more satisfying and during these actions he is wetting his fingers with vaginal secretion and inserting one or two fingers into my vagina. Sometimes he licks deep into my vagina also."

"I like being backed against a wall, with clothes on, feeling his whole hand pushing up against me—great!"

Stimulation of the clitoral area with the man's penis.*
"Before penetration, I hold his penis and use it to fiddle with my clitoris."

"We lie on our sides, face to face, and I move his penis with my hand so the tip stimulates my clitoris. On top, I can balance the tip of his penis in the strategic

---

*This and the following type are not included in the statistics regarding frequency of orgasms by manual stimulation, but can be found separately in Appendix 3.

area and can stimulate myself with a rocking motion."

"We lie on our sides with my back to him and I take his penis through my legs from behind with both hands and give myself direct stimulation. This can be varied by caressing his testicles and inner thighs but at the same time stimulating the clitoris. Orgasms are great this way."

"I can orgasm by getting on top of him while clothed and moving up and down on his penis, or by moving my hips in a circular motion while straddling him and sitting on the head of his penis."

"I lie on my back, one leg hooked over my partner's shoulder with him brushing his penis and balls across my clitoris."

"We pet heavily and I put my hand down his pants so he gets an erection. Then he moves it up and down on me."

"I hold my partner's penis between my thighs and have him simulate intercourse."

"My husband is on top, not penetrating, moving hard."

"Him on top, with me holding his penis and rubbing it against my clitoris."

"Another way is both lying face down, me on top, while I rub my clitoris on his buttocks. Sometimes my hands play with his testicles and penis too."

"One man had the most stimulating habit of pushing his penis inside my vagina then rubbing it up and down on my clitoral area (holding his penis with his hand) then into my vagina again, then rubbing my clitoris, etc.

I don't usually like fingers, because men are too rough and clumsy."

"Lying sideways, he puts his penis between my legs near the clitoral area and then moves back and forth."

"Sitting, facing each other, with the lips of my vulva around his penis and the top part of his penis rubbing my clitoris—marvellously warm."

"Side by side, we place his penis between my lips, and begin stroking."

"After many years of trial and error, my lover and I have finally found a foolproof (almost) way for me to orgasm. His penis is used to stimulate my clitoris after we have had some preliminary intercourse. He pulls out, does not have orgasm and uses his penis to stimulate my clitoris. He or I use a hand to guide his penis to massage my clitoris. I invariably achieve orgasm then, and while I am in the throes of orgasm, he enters, we fuck, then he orgasms."

"Standing (clothed) with his erect penis pressing against my clitoris, breasts against breasts, hands holding bottoms, we press and rub against other."

"For clitoral stimulation, I like to stand between two legs with hands pressing my ass into a stiff cock. In that position, two persons begin to rotate and move and press against each other, and sometimes I have an orgasm this way. It's great on a dance floor."

Tribadism: stimulation by rubbing two clitoral areas together.

"Lying or standing very close to one another, pressing hard with rocking movements against each other's pubic areas."

Tribadism is only mentioned here in passing, as sex between women will be discussed extensively in the following chapter.

Do it yourself.

Is the "answer" to the oppression and neglect of female sexuality, and especially orgasm, that men should learn to give (better) clitoral stimulation? Yes and no. Of course men should learn these things but, even more important, we should find the freedom to take control over whether or not we get this stimulation. One way we can do this is to move in ways that increase our pleasure, for example, during clitoral stimulation. Men certainly have control of their own stimulation to orgasm: during intercourse they move and thrust in ways that are best for them to orgasm. Why should this be wrong for women—even if it interferes, at least temporarily, with what the man is enjoying? Here are some answers from the *few* women who did do this:

"I rub against his buttocks. Or I ride him, doing all of the motion—I have to be kinda careful not to press too hard against his pubic area (causes pain for him). My head is always rested on his left side for some reason."

"I prefer to do the moving so I can set my own rhythm or help my partner to understand it."

"Me on top, sometimes sitting with the penis inside. I just move around a lot. Men have tried oral and manual stimulation but it's never worked with me. Maybe I'm too sensitive."

"I lie on my stomach with my legs spread. I need complete freedom of movement, and move my pelvis in a circular thrusting motion. I lift my buttocks up and down rhythmically to vary the pressure. Meanwhile my partner also strokes and rubs my buttocks."

"I used to accept sex without orgasm, faked orgasms, concentrated only on the man's pleasure, tried to convince myself of non-existent vaginal feelings (like feeling the 'hot' sperm inside me where you can't feel anything), and didn't think I should 'work' or do anything 'unfeminine' in bed. Now I usually do what I want along with what they're doing."

"I rub the top of the fleshy part of my vagina against the man's bone right above his penis."

"I lie on my side facing my lover, with her thigh between mine, and rub my clitoris against her thigh."

"I can sometimes achieve an orgasm by having my partner bring his thigh up between my legs. I then hold it tight by wrapping my legs around it, and by moving my hips I can rub the area of my clitoris against his thigh."

"I hold my legs together tight and even crossed. I squeeze them together hard and relax them over and over again, as I press against him."

And what is wrong with using your own hand, for example, to stimulate yourself—"masturbating" with your partner?

"A partner can't stimulate the clitoris to orgasm. I have to do it myself. He can't feel what the stimulation is doing—I can."

"*I* have to do it. My partners usually can't find it, or are too rough with it. If he is an erotic man, he is fascinated and usually gets turned on."

"I use a vibrator-like motion, moving my clitoris from side to side as rapidly as possible. I do this for myself as no man seems to sustain it for as long as I need."

"If he doesn't exactly know how, I will show him by putting my hand on his hand. The thing is, I don't like being the only one getting turned on. I feel insecure about it—more naked than him."

"He is sensitive but I think it necessary to stimulate myself. I don't like giving orders. It ruins the sensitivity for me. I would rather satisfy myself than give instructions."

"The best thing we've found so far is for me to stimulate myself directly before fucking. This keeps it in the family and lubricates and prepares my vagina for intercourse, which I then enjoy very much. And my husband enjoys watching me do this. So it works."

"I like sucking a man and masturbating at the same time."

"I enjoy mutual face-to-face voyeuristic masturbation!"

"I lie on my back, and he slides my own hand and fingers over my body."

"My body achieves orgasm 'best' by a combined effort of my lover and myself. She uses her mouth and tongue to stimulate my clitoris and then gently blows into my vagina; while she does this I masturbate. This combined effort leads me to a most terrific orgasm."

"I do most of the clitoral massaging while my husband plays with my cunt, runs his hands gently between my legs, plays with and sucks my breasts, and talks to me softly all the time about coming."

These were very unusual answers.

Orgasm from cunnilingus

How many women orgasm regularly from cunnilingus?

The other widely practised form of clitoral stimulation is cunnilingus—oral sex. Do women have orgasms frequently during oral sex? The percentages here are similar to those for clitoral stimulation by hand: whereas 44 per cent of the women orgasmed regularly with clitoral stimulation by hand, 42 per cent orgasmed regularly during oral stimulation.

Frequency of orgasm during cunnilingus

	Total population		Never orgasm in any way	Didn't answer	Never had cunnilingus	No orgasm during cunnilingus	Do orgasm during cunnilingus
Q.I	690	=	82	75	15	121	397
Q.II	919	=	102	115	24	131	547
Q.III	235	=	30	39	7	28	131
Total	1844	=	214	229	46	280	1075

Breakdown of frequency of orgasm during cunnilingus

	Q.I	Q.II	Q.III		Total
"Yes"	350*	50	10	=	410
Always	6	95	16	=	117
Usually	3	201	57	=	261
Sometimes	24	122	34	=	180
Rarely	14	79	14	=	107
Total	397	547	131	=	1075
Percentage of total population who orgasm regularly during cunnilingus	52%*	38%	35%	=	42%

Once again, the problem with counting accurately here was, as with clitoral stimulation by hand, the fact that most oral stimulation was done for arousal and not for orgasm. That is, although most women loved cunnilingus, especially since there was hardly ever any chance for pain as with manual clitoral stimulation, all too often cunnilingus was offered by the partner for very short intervals, and that not continuously on the clitoris, as "foreplay." So here again it was at times unclear whether the woman's answer meant how often she had orgasms during cunnilingus, or how often she would be able to orgasm during cunnilingus, if given the chance.

In addition, Questionnaires I and II used only the term "cunnilingus" and did not provide the definition "oral sex," as did Questionnaire III. Some women did not know what "cunnilingus" was, and even in Questionnaire III, when it was defined as "oral sex," a few women responded regarding fellatio—perhaps never having experienced oral sex

*The wording of the question in this version of the questionnaire was different, and accounts for the irregular per centage: "Do you usually orgasm during cunnilingus?" rather than "Do you orgasm during cunnilingus—usually, sometimes, rarely, or never?"

themselves. But the most common reaction was that oral sex was most often a form of "foreplay," not done long enough for orgasm or with the understanding that it would be "acceptable" for the woman to have an orgasm then:

"I've gotten to dislike cunnilingus because I've gotten so aroused without coming. Men seem to think that once they've done that for a while that's all, they can just climb back on and come, having done their best for the good of the cause. I guess it's this feeling I have that they are doing it in a mechanical way because they read that it's a nice thing to do to women and that all women really like it, and that they are good guys to do it."

"I wish I could be told sometimes in the middle of the day or in bed at night, 'Lie down, relax, enjoy; I'm going to give you head for an *hour*.' Ah-h-h-h . . ."

And often, perhaps more often than not, it was done in conjunction with fellatio—"69"—making it a little difficult to really concentrate on having an orgasm oneself.

However, cunnilingus was still described very frequently as one of the most favourite and exciting activities; women mentioned over and over again how much they loved it:

"A tongue offers gentleness and precision and wetness and is the perfect organ for contact. And, besides, it produces sensational orgasms!"

"Cunnilingus is very sweet, tender, and tense."

"It's sexy! What can I say!"

"It's erotic because it's forbidden—another kind of 'soul kissing.' "

"It arouses me *greatly*, but I get tense and don't have orgasms. I have some feeling that neither I nor my husband should be enjoying it!"

"It really puts me in orbit, and I *always* have an orgasm!"

Feelings about cunnilingus

If women find cunnilingus so enjoyable, why doesn't it lead to orgasm more frequently?

Once again, many women were held back by feelings of embarrassment and self-consciousness. The most common worries about cunnilingus were: Is the other person enjoying it? And, especially, Do I smell bad?

"I haven't gotten away from the feeling I'm 'dirty' 'down there.'"

"I never had orgasm during cunnilingus. I hope to soon but I still feel my cunt is dirty and this preoccupies me if anyone attempts it with me."

"I'm afraid I will 'gross him out' if I orgasm then."

"If I were a man I would *never* do it!"

"I am *always* self-conscious that I might smell or look disgusting."

"It's messy. My husband must brush his teeth and wash his face after."

"It feels like I'm being 'serviced' somehow."

"Men seem to be more squeamish about oral sex than I am."

"I am too concerned about my husband's reaction to tastes and smells to fully enjoy it, but I'll never use sprays and douches."

"I think it's fine if I feel clean and don't have my period."

"Madonna's song says 'I want you to go down there, down where it's warm inside, down where you cannot hide'—beautiful lyrics. People I know say things like 'get down on me' during sex, or 'kiss my crotch.' They don't use the term 'cunnilingus'! It's a mouthful to say, for a start. Nobody would understand each other, for another."

"I'm 18 and at college in Cambridge. I don't know

how many students are having oral sex with women, I know it's really popular for women to suck the guys, you're supposed to want it, crave it. I don't hear so much said about it if a guy goes down on a female student. I've only had it done to me once. I didn't come and it was funny to smell me on his lips later when he kissed me."

"I think perhaps it seems a little gross, or I think it isn't 'ladylike.' I got a big dose of 'ladylike' when I was growing up. Perhaps I think I smell bad."

"I used to always orgasm during it, but now I rarely do because of my current partner's reticence, which sometimes turns into active distaste (pardon the pun) and sometimes he puts on a big martyr act."

"Yes, I like it now, but it took me years to 'allow' it. Why must we feel so unclean??"

"I often wonder if it really does anything for him."

"My man has a mental block here. He thinks the vulva area smells ghastly and gags when he tries. He's tried, but can't get over it."

"The odour bothers me; but sometimes it really turns me on!"

"I go back to what I now understand is my learned repugnance to my genitals. I find it physically pleasing but can't understand why any man would want to put his mouth there."

"I get uptight if I haven't recently showered, because of my discharge."

"As much as I like cunnilingus, I want it to be over fast. I have a conflict about this because I feel it must be unpleasant for him to get his face wet."

"I can't really believe my partner likes it and feel that he is doing it for some other reason he won't admit or tell me."

"I feel that I don't smell or taste right. I feel ashamed."

"I don't like it because I have a feeling he feels obligated to do it, and I don't care for sacrifices."

"I enjoy cunnilingus, although it feels more

comfortable for me to eat a man. Men have never made me feel comfortable and beautiful in that position. I hope someday I can enjoy it."

"I enjoy it, but feel a certain amount of distaste about it. I am a little shy about kissing a partner who has just had his mouth on my vagina. Probably a very early hang-up, having to do with dislike of the 'lower' parts, etc."

"I kind of enjoy having it done to me, although it makes me feel vulnerable emotionally, slightly like it's something dirty, and the other person doesn't like doing it. I have performed it several times on others, but it seems like they weren't comfortable with it and didn't all that much enjoy it."

"I wonder sometimes if my partner is enjoying it, or if he is only doing it to please me, especially when I like to take a long time. The feeling he is not enjoying it lessens my pleasure and I get self-conscious about coming."

"I am afraid I smell. I also feel that I *must* come when so much attention is paid to my doing just that—and that pressures me, and I don't feel free enough to come."

This concern with cleanliness and odour is part of the more general problem of accepting female genitals:

"I am ashamed of my genitals, and don't want anyone to see them."

"I don't believe our society likes vaginas. I think it finds vaginas dirty, smelly, hairy, wet, etc. They want us to spray them with deodorant."

"They think our vaginas are dirty because we menstruate and eject babies and smell bad from urine, blood, discharges, and sex fluids. Women should stop pretending that they have dry genitals."

Even the word "pudendum," which means "the external genitals of the female," comes from the Latin *pudere*, "to be ashamed." Artist Betty Dodson has done many drawings, personal "portraits" of friends and other women, which can be found in her book *Liberating Masturbation*. They show how varied vulval anatomy can be, and how sensuous and elegant. The fact that there is no "iconography" of women's genitals, while penises are glorified, is a further reflection of the way sex mirrors the general cultural inequality between women and men.

"Do you think your vagina and genital area are ugly or beautiful? Do they smell good or bad?"

"You know what turns me on? The smell of my own human mush!"

"I think my vagina is beautiful, rich, fertile—I especially like my black pubic hair. The smell is at times erotic and this turns me on—but I don't believe in not bathing to keep the smell!"

"I used to dislike touching my cunt to wash it—I used to think it smelled bad and I used deodorant. Now I think it's beautiful, thanks to the women's movement."

"They're ugly, like an unhealed wound. The male genitals are beautiful."

'It's small, cute, and attractive like the rest of me. It smells good if clean.'

"Beauty is in the eye of the beholder. If I'm horny, they're beautiful. Artistically, they're ugly. There's no reason it should smell good."

"It's ugly—lots of extra flabby skin, all wrinkled and flapping. My two-year-old daughter's is beautiful, very firm and smooth."

"Ugly. But then I have a long ways to go in making peace with my body generally, although there's a cyclical nature to it all—sometimes I'm much more comfortable in myself than others. I've tried to see some beauty in my genitals, but without much success. But then I remember that it took me three years of not shaving my legs before I could look at them without getting freaked, so surely it will take a long time to undo the damage of my social conditioning in such a heavily loaded area . . ."

"I am just beginning to relate to my vagina as something good, personal, and beautiful. Pre-lesbian, I was very unrelated to my cunt, feared it, was ashamed of it, etc."

"The outside is ugly like a plucked chicken."

"I've gone from feeling they were unknown and unmentionable to feeling they're fine and usually nice."

"Logically they're ugly and smell bad, but a man's genitals aren't better. Emotionally, they're beautiful, but I fear he won't think so."

"Ideally, genitals are beautiful and smell sensuous. But really they are bad-looking and sometimes stink."

"They're beautiful—the secretions are exciting and smell unusual."

"I put my finger into myself and got so sick to my stomach after a second that I never tried it again, not even to put in a Tampax."

"Funny and crooked."

"I used to be embarrassed by my protruding vaginal lips."

"The vaginal smell is one of the most complex and mysterious."

"It's ugly if viewed from directly below, although the pubic hair is attractive frontally."

"My husband is more beautiful and smells better. I look funny and smell bad during my period."

"Beautiful—and smell womanly."

"Not as pretty as the one woman's I slept with (who I thought was beautiful). Both of ours smelled bad."

"One thing makes me *sick* and that is that a picture of a woman with her legs open is called pornographic and dirty. How dare they call the most beautiful part of me dirty!"

"Very non-symmetrical with all that loose skin."

"They're interesting, delicate, and fascinating in design."

"Not beautiful, not good. But in good sex, they become supersensitive and beautiful."

"They're ugly, smell warm, moist, and different from anything else—there is a sensuous smell in sex."

"I used to feel bad about the smell and douched and sprayed and washed every minute because one man said it was bad."

"I think it's good, even when it smells bad!"

"It's just 'there'—what's so beautiful about flaps of hair and slimy skin?"

"The vagina's good and natural but not aesthetic. Appealing but not repelling."

"It smells so good, I smell my fingers after masturbation!"

"The genitalia are ugly, but pubic hair is feminine and mysterious and quite beautiful."

"Vaginal and pubic hair look fine and smell good—but the colour inside of the lips, no. I would probably have designed them to look different if given the chance."

"Healthy and warm and erotic-looking; smell intriguing."

"I used to like them but now after being exposed to men's attitudes, I think they're ugly and bad."

"Beautiful in a strange way."

"Beautiful—fantastic—wonderful."

"I think I smell good and taste all right too. Any lover that wants me to smell like a lilac or rose is discarded very quickly."

"Lovely, fascinating, curious, mysterious, despite self-examination. I like my smell—but will he?"

"The inside of the vagina is gorgeous—outside is weird-looking. When young, and when on the pill, there was only a faint odour, but now I'm on the IUD and it is stronger and not kissable."

"Ugly, but I am trying to accept them. I have never

in my life seen another woman's genital area, only my baby daughter's. They are so pink and clean. I'm kind of purple and red and brown. The modesty of my mother's generation dictated that I should ever be humiliated by my private parts. On top of that, the first man I was with spread my legs and told me I looked like a dried prune."

"When I was little I thought 'that' part of me was ugly—the red colour reminded me of pictures I had seen of intestines and organs which had grossed me out. Also I remember sitting in the bathroom while my father took a shower talking to him. I thought his penis was ugly because of its shape and colour. I was glad to be a girl because I was much prettier and didn't have one of those ugly dark dangling things. (Did you ever notice pornography always shows *erect* penises, not dangling ones?) Now I like to look at my vagina. I don't think of it as beautiful but I like to look at it. To me my vagina is warm, moist and soft, I like to feel it, me."

"I bought a very valid, informative book called *Liberating Masturbation** and I learned a good deal about both myself and other women—especially valuable things such as the fact that my long, uneven labia were not a deformity, but women could look all different ways."

"I think I have a nicely made pretty genital area, but do not belong to the vaginal fascination cult. If not washed, it smells bad but no worse than the penis."

"I don't think it's ugly, but am not sure I'd say it is beautiful, more that it seems strange and exotic to me. I love the way I smell. When I was young, and now, I used to masturbate, and then smell my fingers. The odour really turned (and still does) me on, and my mother caught me quite often, and really freaked out. She tried to get me to stop, but I never did. To her it

*By Betty Dodson. Published and distributed by Betty Dodson, Box 1933, New York, NY 10001.

was and is, perverted, and I guess she'll never change."

"Neither. Some faces are so beautiful it takes my breath away. I've never felt anything like that about genitals, male or female."

"They look ugly, but *feel* beautiful!"

"Neither, but I am shy about people seeing them."

"They were nice before I had a baby, but not now. My pubic hair is too long, so I cut it. I wash two times a day and douche every three days."

"Gorgeous. I put my finger in my cunt and rub it behind my ears!"

"Beautiful and soft and warm."

"The smell and the taste excites me. I have begun to taste myself regularly, and wonder why it tastes bland every once in a while? Usually it tastes good."

"Smells bad to others, but I'm used to it."

"When I was in the hospital, some male doctors said I have too much hair there. Now I feel embarrassed when I get undressed."

"I watched another woman become aroused, and it was fascinating to watch the genital/vaginal changes."

"I wish I could truly believe my cunt is beautiful like my husband says, that it smells and tastes good, but deep down, I'm always afraid."

"Ugly, embarrassing. I refer to 'it' in the third person, as not part of my own body. I'm trying to overcome this feeling."

"I don't think of it as *beautiful* just as I don't think of my face as beautiful. But it's part of my body, part of *me*, and that's nice."

"I guess my generation was not taught that the genital area was beautiful, so I have a few hang-ups."

"Until I met Don, I thought about them as little as possible. After I met him, I felt much better about myself. When we are making love, I see myself and him as *gorgeous!*"

"I worked in a doctor's office once where I saw lots of them and I don't think they are beautiful; I think they are ugly—like a gaping wound with dirty brown edges. On the other hand a female with her legs together is beautiful."

"I think they are beautiful. I like the way the pubic hair curls and the smell of the secretions; the colours of the skin, the shape of the lips."

"Women seem to me to be more sexually curious and freer than many men. They like smells and gushiness more."

"Beautiful. I think they smell great. I resent that we've been made to feel dirty and bad-smelling."

"I used to think my genitals were ugly but one day I realized that I only thought they were because I was supposed to feel that way. From then on I admitted that they were quite functional, graceful, and handy. Beautiful, like a person you know well becomes beautiful."

"At fourteen I decided to cut off one labia which hung lower but after getting the nail scissors I lost my nerve."

"Basically ugly, but I'm struggling like mad to get rid of that."

"Pleasantly homely, interesting, and complex."

"I like most parts of my body. Those parts I don't think are attractive, I'm fond of."

"Neither. Good if clean. But can I consider any part of me beautiful at fifty?"

"BC (before cunnilingus) I thought they were disgusting. But, since I love *hers*, I now love mine too! Smell too."

"At first, when I had not looked at adult vaginas, they looked ugly. Now okay."

"I only looked recently; I like the hair and sometimes brush it after a bath. The lips look funny."

"I used to think I was horribly ugly and deformed until I saw some porno and saw I looked like other women. Now I think all female genitals are ugly."

"Lovely, all the little folds and holes and juices."

"They just 'are.' I wish I were a man."

"I've been told they're pretty, but don't believe it."

"I sense that men think that while they're blessed with a wondrous organ, women are cursed with something downright repulsive."

"Plain, but with charisma."

"Ugly. I pulled one of my labia minora when I was masturbating when I was eleven. It got long and I thought that was the reason. The other got almost as long, later. I always thought I was supposed to look like a nude little girl, except with hair. My mother said my labia majora were separated because I had 'touched' myself. So I had a big guilt about how I deformed myself. I have had to get other ideas piecemeal, for the anatomical drawings of women's genitals look more like little girls' genitals with a scrap of pubic hair than like mine. The SF *Chronicle* has or had (I don't see it any more) a Dr Hip-Pocrates, who gave straight answers. He said something once about a woman who had lips four inches long not being abnormal. Another time he mentioned the fact that the lips of a brunette are brownish. *Lolita* taught me when I was about thirty that someone else's crotch smelled, for HH smelled the acrid crotch of Lolita's panties. All my life I had tried to get the courage to ask a doctor what genitals should look like, but I never dared, even through two births! Finally at forty-six I asked a doctor if mine were normal, and his answer was, 'I'm not much of a judge.' I did it again at forty-seven but this time I asked a woman doctor at the college and she was magnificent. She said it was an important question and she was glad I had asked, that women don't have the opportunity men have to compare genitals because women's are hidden and they have a tradition of modesty, in contrast to the male tradition of comparison. She said that my genitals were normal, but I was hairier than normal. I was glad to receive a straight answer. I am comfortable naked with another person, if I am intimate with him and we love each other. Then I don't mind my hairy (or prickly) legs and my ugly crotch, because he doesn't. Other than those things I feel proud of my body and take pleasure in its strength and competence and good looks. I have had fantastic breasts—full and high—that I never liked when I was in girls' schools because all the girls made fun of them. When I was young and interested in gymnastics, I wanted to cut them off. When I was older and a good modern dancer, I'd come across the floor and my roommate would say 'jello again.' When I finally got into co-ed college, I learned they were as beautiful as any breasts in the world. Part of feeling all right about myself, I taught myself by becoming an artists' model— seeing that artists found me beautiful made me feel more assurance (but I tried not to show my crotch and comb my pubic hair over the split in it). I am not comfortable naked with people I am not intimate with. I went with my children and another woman and her children to the wilderness where they all skinny-dipped. I didn't want to. I thought about my dreams of going naked and it was all right; and now I wanted to wear clothes and have it be all right. I don't like encounter groups either—instant intimacy of any sort turns me off. I have no desire to embrace strangers and fondle their faces. It's too good with someone you love. Now I am sorry to see my body age. My breasts are lowering a little, my skin is losing its firm under-layer and discolouring, I am out of shape and somewhat overweight. I used to take such pleasure in my body that I am sorry to see it go, and I'm just hoping my mind will hold out, so that I can do for myself in old age what I never did when I was young—learning music, languages, math, chess, writing, writing songs, etc."

One reason women like cunnilingus so much was that they felt that for someone to want to put his or her mouth there was very meaningful. It implied a special kind of acceptance:

"The fact that someone can love 'that' part of me means a lot."

"I enjoy cunnilingus immensely for the obvious physical reason, and for a mental reason as well. The male is exhibiting positive feelings to my femaleness. Its particular odour and architecture is as attractive to him as it is to me. He feeds at the font of my biological femaleness. His penis becomes obsolete inasmuch as it is not needed for cunnilingus. Therefore he is offering me something besides his tool to please. It is infinitely easier for him to offer his penis as it offers him release in using it, but for him to declare by action that the penis isn't necessary for my orgasm is to offer himself as a human being first and a male second. I have thought about my partner's reluctance to practise cunnilingus and maybe this holds true for other like-minded men. If I have an orgasm by cunnilingus it negates the power of his penis. He feels like a pseudo woman, a crippled man perhaps. Nevertheless, the few times I have cajoled him to do this I reached near orgasm in half the time and was going wild with delight. He, sensing the nearness of the orgasm, withdrew, however, and proffered his non-obsolete tool."

"It seems more intimate than the sex act. It's as close as one can get physically to another."

"I like to see his face and mouth down there and know that he's exploring me—with his tongue, his mouth and eyes. And I consider a man to be a *real* lover if he eats me during my period!"

"Men have gotten me very excited that way but I have yet to get over inhibitions making me feel they are doing me a favour, that they don't like doing it, that they will stop soon—now! It is, of course, an act of extraordinary intimacy (to put your head *there!*) and if I don't feel that intimate with the man, it can seem quite embarrassing and inappropriate and fail to get me off. But in most cases it is a real, even a terrible turn on because of the softness of contact, and above-mentioned intimacy, and perhaps the *verboten* thrill."

In the same way that men seemed to resent manual clitoral stimulation, many men also resented or felt awkward during oral sex.

"I enjoy oral sex, but it never leads to orgasm. My partner doesn't like it (or he doesn't seem to). I like it because a tongue/lips are soft and moist and warm and feel good on my soft warm sensitive genitals. I like to just lie back and enjoy—feeling good—not feeling like I have to do anything. But I'm always waiting for my lover to stop too soon."

"Now take cunnilingus. The thing to do is to lie back, stretch out, let fantasies take over or whatever, and don't rush! If I know the man will do it only so long, and will think it's weird and perverted even though it excites him, and will then look up bravely, spitting a pubic hair out of his mouth and run to the bathroom to wash his face . . . yes I felt guilt and who needs this stuff? I've got to feel my partner is psychologically into the activity."

"Sometimes during cunnilingus I notice him watching TV out of the corner of his eye. That is a turn-off!"

And as with clitoral stimulation by hand, women often felt they shouldn't need it, they *should* be able to orgasm during intercourse:

"I feel perverted that I can't have orgasms during intercourse and need to have cunnilingus to make me come."

Another objection to cunnilingus was that even though it felt great, many women didn't want to be obligated to perform fellatio—or "69"—in return especially to orgasm/ejaculation.

"I only dislike the slight twinge of guilt I feel about not reciprocating."

"I don't care to do this to my spouse because he usually doesn't smell too great. Also I am afraid of ejaculation in my mouth and I have an excellent gag reflex."

"I like cunnilingus when freshly washed, and when I can succeed in not feeling guilty about not liking fellatio."

"I just don't feel comfortable, especially knowing he expects me to respond likewise."

"I dislike an unskilful partner, and don't like to have him come in my mouth."

"Cunnilingus seems too detached, and one has to reciprocate and that's a bore."

"I guess it's a hang-up, but I feel personal distaste for doing it to my partner."

"I like everything about cunnilingus except my having to do fellatio at the same time does cut down on my concentration, but you can't have it all your own way."

"Sometimes I feel that it is selfish on my part because my partner cannot enjoy it *that* much, and I do not like performing fellatio for him. But he says he enjoys it anyway."

"Do you enjoy fellatio? To orgasm?"

"Sometimes I like fellatio although I'm not wild about swallowing semen—it burns my throat. Sometimes, though, it makes me very excited."

"I don't mind doing it, sometimes I really enjoy doing it. I know it makes my partner feel very good, which I like doing."

"I hate to go down on a guy unless I care for him a great deal. Or if I can't have sex (don't want it because I am menstruating or have a vaginal infection or am too pregnant) and he needs relief. The penis is too big for my mouth and I choke. I do it as a present for someone I love. Otherwise I hate it. I don't mind the semen so much, someone compared it to the white of an egg."

"To orgasm is fine as long as the semen does not end up in my mouth."

"I do it to orgasm, but avoid swallowing it."

"With a new partner, I have a problem about what to do with the 'come' in fellatio. I don't like to swallow it but with a new mate I'm embarrassed to spit it out."

"I enjoy it a short time, but don't like him to come in my mouth. I like fellatio mixed in with a lot of body play, not as the main event. My partner really likes it; often I do it mostly to please him. I have never had sexual contact with women, but I think if I did, cunnilingus would be more pleasant than fellatio—I wouldn't feel invaded."

"Fellatio feels like my face is being raped."

"The orgasm feels like big blobs of thick snot being shot down your throat."

"You should perform fellatio and cunnilingus several times in order to condition oneself before deciding against it."

"Fellatio is okay but my mouth gets tired of being stretched open."

"I'm sure I would choke to death! Cannot stand the idea of sperm in my mouth, and I'm sure he'd urinate."

"My feeling is that I would consider sucking a cock with a loaded gun at my head. No other way."

"He doesn't go down on me during my period like I wish he would. I love his sperm. I love to swallow it and rub it on my face, my breasts. I wish that he found my blood as beautiful and delicious."

"I don't usually mind fellatio. At times it seems a chore, and I have to stop in the middle, but usually when I do it's because I want to. It's often fun. I like it when he comes in my mouth. I like the taste of semen and think the protein does me good. I have never performed cunnilingus, and the idea of it revolts me. And the idea of it revolting me revolts me even more. I hope I'll grow out of this perverse attitude liking it to be done to me but not being able to imagine doing it."

What kind of cunnilingus do women like?

What are the best "techniques" for cunnilingus? Once again, there are individual preferences, and much depends on the situation, mood, and feelings of the person doing it.

"Massages like licking or sucking are great because they involve a constant breaking of contact, which keeps the sensation from being too monotonous. Every time the tongue touches, it is a new and pleasurable sensation, which eventually leads to orgasm. Any great change in position would be distracting, but the slight breaks and expectations are exciting."

"Starting in the lower folds, with your lips and tongue work upwards from side to side opening me fully; when the apex of the folds are reached, go all around the clitoris with a simultaneous stomach and buttock massage, then put my clitoris between your lips for my climax."

"Oral stimulation should include the nose, mouth, and chin. The tongue should *not* be flexed and pointed!"

"I like oral stimulation to be soft and delicate but it must be constant."

"I love being eaten with a very rapid licking tickling tongue on my clitoris, accompanied by slurpy noises and throaty sounds."

"Since she has learned how to exert heavy pressure with her jaw to bring me to orgasm if I have trouble with light pressure, I *always* orgasm. Also, her tongue can touch more area than her finger, which helps."

"I lie on my back with my partner between my legs, flicking his tongue very gently over the same area, over and over. I like not doing anything else except concentrating on the sensation until I orgasm."

"I dislike it when my partner's tongue digs too close to the clitoral nerve inside the hood—it really hurts."

"Orally, he vibrates his tongue very fast (great!)

and/or sucks. He also blows air into my vagina, which is strange, yet exciting."

"I like a slow, steady rhythm, very gentle and circular in motion, right at the front part of my private parts, then moving down to my opening, with a deep penetration of his tongue just before I come."

"Nibbling and nuzzling on the clitoris, like simulated chewing is good—but gently and tenderly."

"I like soft gentle kisses above the hair and between my legs. Long laps of the tongue up and down my vagina and anus. Should be moist and with sound."

"If my partner will apply clitoral stimulation with his tongue, and at the same time gently rub my nipples, I can achieve an orgasm within a few seconds. Some men try to stimulate my *vagina,* but that really does very little for me."

Quite a few women mentioned that oral stimulation was better than stimulation by hand:

"A tongue is much gentler than a finger usually and also involves a bigger area."

"The tongue is warmer, wetter, and softer than a penis or finger and makes more delicate motions."

"Oral stimulation is best, mainly because most men do not have a clue what to do manually and are often too rough, whereas the tongue is more gentle."

"The tongue moulds to my shape the way fingers can't."

"I prefer the tongue because it's smaller and more versatile than the penis."

"I like it because it is less painful and abrasive than manual stimulation. A tongue feels more alive and direct, not just power and pushing."

"Oral stimulation is better than manual because manual is sometimes too intense, giving more sensation than pleasure feelings."

"I like the tongue's mobility and sensitivity and constant lubrication. I like that it's possible for my clitoris to be directly touched with tongue or lips without causing pain, and because during it I feel completely open and vulnerable to my partner. It symbolizes my being known completely, being accepted and seen openly."

But one drawback was the inability really to caress the other person, because she/he was of necessity too far away.

"I dislike not being able to feel my partner's body next to mine and his lips on mine. I like the fact that he wants to do it to me and the feeling of his mouth and breath there."

"I feel disconnected from him, as though I were alone."

"I like to have my partner's body close and enveloping during orgasm—which is possible in this position."

"It *works* fine, but I feel isolated since she is so far away from my head."

"I miss my lover's head . . . nothing left to kiss."

Did "69" solve this problem? Not very well.

"We tried '69' a few times but each of us felt distracted by too much going on at once."

"I know cunnilingus is not *his* favourite position, but since he likes fellatio, we usually do '69'. But I have trouble concentrating on the feeling this way, because I have to worry about pleasing him. I like to be on top in '69' because I can control how much cock gets into my mouth. On the bottom, I always get choked."

"I really cannot have a good orgasm myself if I am involved in his at the same time."

"On the subject, I don't enjoy '69' at all for many reasons: first, the positions we must assume are unsatisfactory. If he is on top of me, he tends to choke me by thrusting too far into my mouth. I like to have control over my movements when I go down on him. I am not comfortable being on top of him—I can't get used to the idea of shoving my vagina in his face, and I don't like having to have that much control over it. On our sides, my legs are uncomfortable, as well as my head. I also don't like the idea of our noses being in each other's assholes (I realize that's an exaggeration, but that's what I always think of in that position). And I forgot the most important thing—in this position I can't get the kind of clitoral stimulation I need. I like stimulation that concentrates on the 'underside' of my clitoris—and in the position of '69' the stimulation is either too much on my vaginal area, or on the top part of my clitoris."

Is cunnilingus a passive activity? Not necessarily. Some women described moving during oral sex:

"I love rubbing my clitoris on his mouth with him sucking it and rubbing his tongue around."

"I sit on his shoulders while he's lying down, with my legs apart. But near orgasm, I begin to close my legs a little. I like to move myself against his tongue, up and down, but I don't move *very* much. *I hate* a man to throw my legs around or move me very much when he's giving me head. I've been with some guys who push my legs up like I was in stirrups ready to give birth, I resent their trying to play a manipulative role like that. They've got to let *me* do it!"

"I would like to try it standing up, with the man on his knees (reverse blow job) but men seem to find this position demeaning."

"I also like cunnilingus because I usually get it sitting up, which lets me be more in control than lying down."

"I like him to grip my ass hard, suck on my clitoris, and just let me *move!*"

Remember how beautiful and enthusiastic the language was that was used to describe intercourse and general arousal? But notice how spare and tight, unenthusiastic and secretive the language has become here. Obviously women do not feel proud about clitoral stimulation in any form. Our culture had discouraged clitoral stimulation, even to the point of not giving it a name. "Cunnilingus" at least is a name, even if its meaning is not clear to everyone, but "manual clitoral stimulation" is just a phrase that is used to describe an activity that has no name. Our language for, as well as our respect for, clitoral stimulation, is almost non-existent. Our culture is still a long way from understanding, not to mention celebrating, female sexuality.

"Do you ever find it necessary to masturbate to achieve orgasm after 'making love'?"

	Q.I	Q.II	Q.III
Yes	120	170	55
Sometimes	90	117	29
Rarely	35	41	11
No	275	349	73
Used to	19	23	11
Would like to	20	22	19
Yes, with partner (or, he does it)	12	25	1
Would be embarrassing	6	20	2
I don't bother	2	5	6
It wouldn't be right	1	3	
It doesn't work	6	6	
Do it during intercourse!	1	5	
For an extra orgasm	5	2	
Total	592	798	207

"I never felt I had to, but maybe it would be a good idea and not so hard on the nervous system!"

"Yes, except when a man has been awfully rough or clumsy or thoughtless, and masturbation wouldn't even help afterwards."

"Sometimes, but I usually masturbate at other times,

so that making love with my partner is for me a friendly rather than a sexual act anyway."

"No. If I don't have an orgasm, I generally feel that he's been selfish and using me which makes me feel *shitty and awful* and I'm much more upset about my emotional feelings and his than attaining an orgasm by masturbation."

"Sometimes I do unless I'm afraid I'll be caught doing it."

"No—I just take a cold shower!"

"Yes—sometimes *several* times after intercourse!"

"I never have. I'd feel very self-conscious and insulting if I did."

"Yes, with some regularity. Since I lie fairly still, most of them don't know what I'm doing till I come, and then in wide-eyed surprise they ask me if I just jerked off. After that they sometimes get apologetic like, 'Oh, why didn't you *tell* me? I'd have eaten you out for hours,' or some such nonsense."

"I've never tried. I think it's cheating."

"Yes, I did sometimes after my ex-old man had gone off to sleep, slobbering and snoring."

"No, never. With a man like this, I would scream and yell and break things, but not masturbate."

"Sometimes. It's frustrating because he rolls over and goes to sleep, after he's had his orgasm."

"Yes. That was how I masturbated for the first time."

"Sometimes. Usually I just forget about it. It seems such a cheap thing at that time."

"Sometimes I would really like to, but it's quite a difficult thing to do if you are still in the man's company. You might feel embarrassed and create strange feelings between both of you."

"Frequently I would like to, but I don't for fear of embarrassing or revolting my partner."

"I feel like it but don't get up the courage."

"No, because it just makes me feel more frustrated."

"Yes, sometimes to re-enact the act after he has left."

"Sometimes I do. My husband seems to understand, but I know it makes him feel he's sort of let me down."

"I've never dared."

"No. It doesn't seem right or fair to the guy (even if he doesn't know). (Brainwashed, brainwashed, brainwashed.)"

"Yes, but I do it by lying on top of him and rubbing up and down."

"Sometimes, but I feel ashamed."

"Yes, but if I do, I don't think we have 'made love'— I think he has masturbated in my vagina."

"Sometimes it helps to run a spray of warm water on myself when I haven't had an orgasm."

"Sometimes, but then I never sleep with *him* again."

"Not in front of my partner."

"Yes. Most men are lousy lovers."

"I have thought of it at times, when intercourse had ended, when I was just on the verge of an orgasm, but I never did so out of consideration for my partner's feelings!"

"Sometimes when he's not with it I get frustrated so I cut off the session and wait till he's asleep to masturbate and have an orgasm. It makes me either mad or sad."

"Yes, but like a fool I sneak out into the living room so he won't know. Then I hate myself for not telling him he's a lousy lover."

"Sometimes, when I'm alone. I don't know what to do about it. Should I tell him I do it?"

"Yes. Sometimes. I don't want to tell my partner about my need to masturbate during intercourse so I get left out."

"I used to do it secretly in the bathroom. Now my partner does it for me."

"I did it one time then hid in the bathroom crying afterwards. I never thought sex could be so disappointing."

"When I haven't come and I still want to, I have

masturbated on occasion. Also I've done deep breathing and relaxation exercises to let go of the sexual tension."

"I've tried (secretly) a few times, but somehow I come down with him *enough* so I can't get up again right then even if I'm disappointed about not having had an orgasm."

"Yes, once in a while. Other times I grin and bear it."

"Yes, sometimes I do. Most of the time though I'm either too exhausted, or so emotionally satisfied that I don't need to masturbate."

"Sometimes I would like to do this, but there is no way to do it without being noticed.

"Sometimes I wish I could but it would be too insulting to the man I'm with. I sleep with him afterwards so there is no chance of being alone."

"I first masturbated when I was extremely frustrated because I'd been aroused by the man I'd just had sex with, but hadn't come. He'd left the room. It suddenly occurred to me that I could do to myself what he'd been doing to me. I had never thought of doing that before. The thought surprised me. So I locked the door. I touched myself with great hesitation at first—feeling distaste. (Now it's hard for me to imagine that because I like to touch myself—and the smell from the sexual juices, too.) I remember the thought that passed through my head as I came, 'My God, this is better than with a man.' The thought surprised me as much as the orgasm."

"In fourteen years no partner has ever masturbated me after he had orgasm from intercourse (when I did or didn't) and I have always been too inhibited to ask. I am too inhibited to do it in front of my partner and if I go to the bathroom, I usually feel resentful and thereby tense and just push aside my feeling."

Is it bad for women not to orgasm during sex? It is obvious that it doesn't feel *good*. As shown in the orgasm chapter, most women felt that after a certain degree of stimulation, orgasm became more or less necessary, or else they were left with feelings of discomfort and irritability.

"Orgasm is especially important if I am aroused to the point where my genital area feels bloated."

"Physically, orgasm is not always necessary, but if I am close to orgasm, then I feel a crampy tightness and I don't feel like moving freely if I don't have an orgasm."

"Sometimes it's okay without until I reach a certain level of arousal; then it's either orgasm or a crying spell or a fight."

Are there any physical effects on women who become aroused and don't orgasm? If this is a pattern that occurs on a regular basis over a long period of time, chronic/pelvic congestion can result. Sherfey defines it as "chronic passive congestion":

> *An abnormal amount of blood in the vessels of any part of the body due to increased influx and/or inadequate drainage. In women this condition is caused by enlarged varicose veins of the pelvis; it is the usual byproduct of two or more pregnancies and, to a lesser extent, of frequent prolonged sexual stimulation. Vessel relaxation may then render adequate expulsion of blood during orgasms impossible or completely prevent orgasms. This, in turn, increases circulatory stagnation, enhancing the varicosities. If severe, the pelvic congestion contributes to many disorders and may block venous return from the legs. This places increased strain on the heart. In this condition, all the external genitalia become swollen, waterlogged, and purple; this condition is very uncomfortable, and the sensation of unrelieved sexual tension readily passes into cramps and pain.[1]*

Of course, congestion is not commonly found in the extreme form described, since most women can and do masturbate to orgasm, even if they are not regularly having orgasms with their partners. However, Masters and Johnson have also described women who are not able to orgasm as irritable, emotionally disturbed, and complaining of pelvic fullness, pressure, cramping, moments of true pain, and a persistent, severe low backache.

However, the worst effect not having orgasms can have on women is psychological. What lesson do women learn as they watch a man enjoying his orgasm, secure in the knowledge that it is his right—every time? This is a perfect object lesson to women that they are inferior, oppressed, and *less*.

Of course this does not mean that the solution is for both men and women to always orgasm every time as the goal of sex. It means that sex and physical relations must be redefined in a way that ceases to reflect these oppressive and outdated cultural stereotypes.

Conclusion

The reproductive model of sex exploits women.
It is very clear by now that the pattern of sexual relations predominant in our culture exploits and oppresses women. The sequence of "foreplay," "penetration," and "intercourse" (defined as thrusting), followed by male orgasm as the climax and end of the sequence, gives very little chance for female orgasm, is almost always under the control of the man, frequently teases the woman inhumanely, and in short, has institutionalized out any expression of women's sexual feelings except for those that support male sexual needs.

Many women expressed their frustration about this:
"I don't quite understand why for men, orgasm is
presumed to occur each time, but for women it must be
'worked at.' Sex as it is defined between men and
women is male sex." And, "I think most of the writers
I've read don't understand women at all, sexually. They
regard sex as an activity engaged in by two for the
satisfaction of one. The current writers are worse than

the older ones, because they stress the whore-like sexual techniques used by women for men. Women's needs are less and less emphasized, except by female writers."

The reproductive model of sex ensures male orgasm by giving it a standardized time and place, during which both people know what to expect and how to make it possible for the man to orgasm. The whole thing is prearranged, pre-agreed. But there are not really any patterns or prearranged times and places for a woman to orgasm—unless she can manage to do so during intercourse. So women are put in the position of asking for something "special," some "extra" stimulation, or they must somehow try to subliminally send messages to a partner who often is not even aware that he should be listening. If she does get this "extra," "special" stimulation, she feels grateful that he was so unusually "sensitive." So all too often women just do without—or fake it.

Do it yourself

But we can change this pattern, and redefine our sexual relations with others. On one level, we can take control over our own orgasms. We *know* how to have orgasms in masturbation. How strange it is, when you think about it, that we don't use this knowledge during so much of the sex we have with men. Why, in our pattern of sexual relations, does the man have charge of both his stimulation and ours? A man controls his own orgasm in the sense that during intercourse he thrusts his penis against the walls of the vagina in ways that provide the best stimulation for him; this is not considered "selfish" or "infantile" because there is an ideology to back it up.

However, women do not usually, are not supposed to, control their own stimulation:

"I have never tried to stimulate myself clitorally with a partner—I have always been afraid to."

"It seems too aggressive when I act to get the stimulation I want."

"During sex, I must depend on a man's willingness

to do an aggressive action for me, while I am passive. (Passive about my *own* stimulation; moving for *his* pleasure doesn't count.) Whereas during intercourse a man climaxes through his own aggressiveness."

"When you're young, you masturbate/touch yourself instinctually, then you stop when you hear it's 'wrong' and 'naughty,' and then you try the rest of your life to get other people to touch you the same way, only they hardly ever do it right!"

"I always dreamed of the ecstasy of physical love. I have never been able to reach this kind of feeling with another person. The sensations, the orgasms I can give myself, are more than just in the sex organs, they are feelings of relaxation and pleasure throughout the body, mind, and soul. A sort of sailing feeling, a flowing, rich in colours, rich in well-being, joy. They are 'multiple orgasms,' each richer than the previous one. A *whole, complete* feeling. I can have orgasms with a partner, but not these complete intense sensations."

But why can't we touch ourselves? Why can't we do whatever we need to make orgasm happen? Although sharing sex with a man can be wonderful, why does "sharing" for a woman mean that the man must "give" her the orgasm? Why can't a woman use her own hand to bring herself to orgasm? In sex as elsewhere, women are still in the position of waiting for men to "mete out the goodies."

We have the power to make our own orgasms, if we want. You can get control of your own stimulation by moving against the other person, or by stimulating yourself directly in the same way as you do during masturbation. Although this suggestion may sound strange at first, it is important to be able to masturbate with another person, because it will give you power over your own orgasms. There is no reason why making your own orgasms should not be as beautiful or as deeply shared as any other form of sex with another person—perhaps even more so. The taboo against touching yourself says essentially that you should not use your own body for your own pleasure, that your body is not your own to enjoy. But we have a right to our own bodies. Controlling your own stimulation symbolizes owning your own body, and is a very important step towards freedom.

5 Lesbianism

"Neither male nor female sexuality is limited by 'genital geography,' and it has been one of the greatest public relations victories of all time to convince us it was. The very naturalness of lesbianism (and homosexuality) is exactly the cause of the strong social and legal rules against it. The basing of our social system on gender difference, biological reproductive function, is barbaric and should be replaced by a system based on affirmation of the individual and support for all life on the planet."

"I think we are all born 'sexual'—that is, we are each born with natural desires to relate to all other creatures—animals, plants, ourselves, women, men—when we feel love or communication with them. But society teaches us to inhibit all of these but desires for partners with whom it is possible to procreate, and then works up our enthusiasm for the 'act' by pushing the ideal of romantic love combined with marriage down our throats until we can't think of anything else."

It must be clear by now that female sexuality is physically "pan-sexual," or just "sexual"—certainly not something that is directed at any one type of physical organ to be found in nature. There is no organ especially concocted to fit the clitoral area and the kind of stimulation we generally need for orgasm. From the point of view of physical pleasure, we are free to relate to all the creatures of the planet, according to their individual meaning for us, rather than their specific classification or gender.

Of course it goes without saying that as we move towards a more equitable view of life, the right to love other women will be taken for granted. However, the general villainization of homosexual contacts in our society has a long history. As Kinsey explains:

The general condemnation of homosexuality in our particular culture apparently traces to a series of historical circumstances which had little to do with the protection of the individual or the preservation of the social organization *of the day. In Hittite, Chaldean, and early Jewish codes there were no overall condemnations of such activity, although there were penalties for homosexual activities between persons of particular social status or blood relationships, or homosexual relationships under other particular circumstances, especially when force was involved. The more general condemnation of all homosexual relationships (especially male) originated in Jewish history in about the seventh century B.C. upon the return from the Babylonian exile. Both mouth-genital contacts and homosexual activities had previously been associated with the Jewish religious service, as they had been with the religious services of most of the other peoples of that part of Asia, and just as they have been in many other cultures elsewhere in the world. In the wave of nationalism which was then developing among the Jewish people, there was an attempt to disidentify themselves with their neighbors* by breaking with many of the customs which they had previously shared with them. Many of the Talmudic condemnations were based on the fact that such activities represented the way of the Canaanite, the way of the Chaldean, the way of the pagan, and they were originally condemned as a form of idolatry rather than a sexual crime. Throughout the middle ages homosexuality was associated with heresy. The reform in the custom (the mores) soon, however, became a matter of morals, and finally a question for action under criminal law.*[1]

Kinsey (who was originally a biologist) also tells us that other mammals and other animals routinely have lesbian and homosexual relationships:

The impression that infra-human mammals more or less confine themselves to heterosexual activities is a distortion of the fact which appears to have originated in a man-made philosophy, rather than in specific observations of

---

*Especially their non-patriarchal neighbours.

mammalian behavior. Biologists and psychologists who have accepted the doctrine that the only natural function of sex is reproduction have simply ignored the existence of sexual activity which is not reproductive. They have assumed that heterosexual responses are a part of an animal's innate, "instinctive" equipment, and that all other types of sexual activity represent "perversions" of the "normal instincts." Such interpretations are, however, mystical. They do not originate in our knowledge of the physiology of sexual response, and can be maintained only if one assumes that sexual function is in some fashion divorced from the physiologic processes which control other functions of the animal body. It may be true that heterosexual contacts outnumber homosexual contacts in most species of mammals, but it would be hard to demonstrate that this depends upon the "normality" of heterosexual responses, and the "abnormality" of homosexual responses.[2]

Kinsey mentions that lesbian contacts have been observed in such widely separated species as rats, mice, hamsters, guinea pigs, rabbits, porcupines, marten, cattle, antelope, goats, horses, pigs, lions, sheep, monkeys, and chimpanzees. And, he adds, "Every farmer who has raised cattle knows . . . that cows quite regularly mount cows."[3]

The arguments over whether lesbianism and/or homosexuality are biological or psychological in origin (the origin of the "problem," as it is usually put) are still raging in some quarters,* but the "answer" hardly matters any more. Homosexuality, or the desire to be physically intimate with someone of one's own sex at some time, or always, during one's life, can be considered a natural and "normal" variety of life experience. It is "abnormal" only when you posit as "normal" and "healthy" only an interest in reproductive sex. Discussions of why one becomes *heterosexual* would come

*A good summary of the arguments can be found in Edward Brecher's *The Sex Researchers*.

to the same non-conclusions. To consider all non-reproductive sexual contact "an error of nature" is a very narrow view.

Not being "allowed" to really touch or be in physical contact with anyone other than a sexual partner—since it might "imply" a sexual connection!—is depressing and alienating. Specifically, *vis-à-vis* women's connection with one another, this ban on physical contact is oppressive and has the effect of separating women. The dynamic works something like this: you may feel a sudden impulse to kiss or hug a friend—or you may feel subtler desires for greater closeness or contact of which you are unaware—which you must stifle and repress. But when a natural impulse is stopped and is not consciously recognized, it can cause feelings of conflict, guilt, and anxiety. Such repression can then lead to half-conscious feelings of rejection, which engender feelings of distrust and dislike for the same person to whom one was originally attracted. This, of course, is a well-known psychological phenomenon, and commonly happens on a subtle level between friends. The point here is that this prohibition on the exchange of physical contact *(of any kind)* between women is bound to increase the level of hostility and distance between them.

One of the best descriptions of how we more or less "unconsciously" select our sexual partners on the basis of gender (and screen out those of the "wrong" gender) has been given by Pepper Schwartz and Philip Blumstein.* To begin with, they explain that given a state of physiological arousal for which an individual has no immediate explanation, "he will 'label' this state and describe his feelings in terms of the cognitions available to him . . ." They continue, "the sources of arousal are likely to be more diverse than the sources to which it is attributed by the most astute laymen," and, "the greater the confidence in, or need for, a

---

*"Bisexuality: Some Sociological Observations," a paper presented at the Chicago Conference on Bisexual Behavior, 6 October 1973, Department of Sociology, University of Washington.

heterosexual identity, the more likely that ambiguities will be resolved in a heterosexual direction. When one has strong suspicions about one's homosexuality or has taken on gay identity, then the interpretation is likely to go in the other direction." In other words,

> . . . homosexuality—like heterosexuality—becomes self-fulfilling. This is especially so since the free-floating arousal levels early in one's sexual development tend to be channeled and shaped by sexual experience and strengthening sexual identity. So we believe that untapped or uninterpreted homosexual arousal cues tend not to arouse as one takes on a more firm heterosexual identity and engages in more heterosexual behavior. Likewise, untapped or uninterpreted heterosexual cues tend not to arouse confirmed homosexuals. Our dichotomous views of our own sexual identity thwart any possibility of bisexuality.[4]

With specific reference to women, Schwartz and Blumstein state that:

> Women have a different arousal system from men. Their arousal is a total body response, rather than a genital one. While some women may feel "horny" (i.e., feel sexual tension in the genital area, or lubricate during an exciting encounter), all of these signals are less visible than their counterpart in the male. To put it very simply, a woman can reinterpret her excitement; a man cannot miss noticing his sexual arousal and labeling it as erotic . . . If a woman has sexual tension in an inappropriate environment such as during a softball game, a mother-child interaction, etc., she has more freedom than a man in how she can label that excitement.
>
> Likewise, in female/female relationships, the cues that a woman receives from another woman are more subtle than the cues men give each other. Apropos of our discussion of erection, two women do not have to explain away an erection should one of them get excited while they were

having a tête à tête and talking about their sex lives. If they are getting excited, and they want to communicate sexual interest in one another, they have to rely on eye contact, intensified attention, and other kinds of interpersonal connections to convey their meaning. The problem, however, is that these kinds of cues are confusing, they are usually associated with heterosexual negotiation and since they seem inappropriate or unreal in a same sex encounter, may be reinterpreted to mean friendship or non-sexual affection. Women may be afraid to believe—even if they want to—that another woman is giving sexual cues to them. If they were coming from another source their intent would probably be unmistakable; but since they come from what has in the past been an asexual source, the receiver may tend to doubt or reinterpret the most direct of signals.

Because of this obfuscation of cues—and because women are not used to being wooed by other women—nor are they trained to do the aggressive part of sexual pursuance—it may be hypothesized that women rarely activate erotic responses to women simply because they do not realize how often the excitement they feel is mutual and has a possibility of being reciprocated. Furthermore, since no sexual negotiation is apparent, women may not realize or admit to themselves that they have been in a sexual encounter, thereby allowing all such attractions to die out. One final hypothesis along these lines follows this same theme of unapparent passive aspects in the female sexual tradition. That is, that since women have been taught to eroticize people who eroticize them—i.e., interpret their worth and sexuality by the way men "turned on" to them, many women discover their own sexual feelings when they are approached by a man. When they see someone sexually aroused and interested in them, then they decide they might be sexually interested in the other person. To some extent, this seems to be true for both sexes—people start to get sexually aroused when someone begins to show sexual interest, begins aggressive moves and makes the other person feel desirable. Sexual tension begins to build and soon the

*two people must acknowledge its presence (even if they
choose not to act on it). With women, this sexual tension
may not get a chance to build because each person is
embarrassed, unpracticed and unsure about the validity of
the encounter as a sexual experience. Unused to taking the
lead (or the responsibility) for such situations, they may
back off rather than try to chart something they are
unprepared for and unused to. It may be hypothesized that
same sex relationships between women will not occur unless
at least one person in the dyad is able to take on an
aggressive sexual role and dare to make ambiguous cues
explicit. If both women are unable to take this role, the
relationship may never become articulated.*[5]

"Do you prefer sex with men, women, yourself, or not at all?"*

In this study 144 women (8 per cent) said they preferred sex
with women. Another seventy-three identified themselves as
"bisexual," and eighty-four women had had experiences
with both men and women but did not answer as to preference (another 9 per cent).

In addition, fifty-three women in this study said they
preferred to have sex with themselves, and seventeen
women preferred to have no sex at all. Another fifty women
had had no sexual experience with others yet, or had had
such extremely limited experience that they felt they could
not answer the question. All the remaining women said
they preferred men, although many stressed that they did
not prefer "men" but rather an *individual* man.

It is impossible to know what relation there may be
between statistics and how many lesbian women there may
be in the United States population, since, due to the fear of
persecution, no one knows how many lesbians, or bisexuals,
there are. Kinsey estimated that perhaps 12 to 13 per cent

*See appendices for UK, Australia and New Zealand statistics.

of women had "sexual relations to the point of orgasm" with another woman at some time during their adult lives, and that between 11 and 20 per cent of single women and 8 to 10 per cent of married women in the sample "were making at least incidental homosexual responses, or making more specific homosexual contacts" between the ages of twenty and thirty-five. This research would roughly indicate similar percentages. Dr Richard Green, of the University of California (Los Angeles) Gender Identity Research Treatment Program, commented that there may now be an increase in bisexuality and/or lesbianism among women "partly for political reasons"—as one of the ways women can "disassociate themselves from the extraordinary dependency they've had on men all these years."

At the same time, it is important to note that preferences can change during a lifetime, or can change several times; what is called "gender identity" is not so cut and dried as the preceding statistics might seem to imply. As Kinsey explained, there are not two discrete groups, one heterosexual and one homosexual; in other words, the world is not to be divided into sheep and goats. "The living world is a continuum in each and every one of its aspects," and homosexuality and heterosexuality are only the extreme types sitting at the poles of "a rich and varied continuum." In fact, "lesbian," "homosexual," and "heterosexual" should be used as adjectives, not nouns: *people* are not properly described as homosexuals, lesbians, or heterosexuals; rather, *activities* are properly described as homosexual, lesbian, or heterosexual. In other words, it is really only possible to say how many persons have had, at any particular time, a given type of relationship, and that is how the figures in this study should be viewed.

Many women say they might be interested in having sex with another woman.

One of the most striking points about the answers received to the questionnaires was how frequently, *even though it was not specifically asked,* women brought up the fact that they might be interested in having sexual relations with another woman, or were curious. This interest was usually mentioned in connection with the question on sexual preference (above), or with the question "What would you like to try that you never have?" Some of these answers follow:

"I have been married for twelve years, but I am not happy with it. I've never had a physical relationship with a woman but I feel it would be more satisfying than with a male. I don't know how to relate to another woman physically, as I've never had the opportunity to do so. There is a woman whom I'm attracted to and feel is the same as me but I am afraid to approach her."

"How I wish I could have a relationship with a man the way I have with my closest woman friend. I want to be honest and giving, caring, loving, supporting, and supportive. I want to be cared about, thought special and worthwhile. That I am a person who has lived through things. I want to be able to say 'I love you' and 'I want you' without the other person feeling threatened."

"I've only had sex with one man—the man I'm with now. He felt like a close friend for a while. I found I wanted to talk to him and be with him in times of happiness and crisis. The relationship has progressed from friendship to 'being in love', back to deep friendly love. Right now my head is in a place where I would like to be in a relationship with a woman as well as keeping my relationship with this man. I am in the process of changing my entire life and feelings about my sexuality."

"I have always admired beautiful women, but have never had a homosexual experience. So far I've loved fucking. But women excite me more and more."

"There are times when I feel such a warmth from my best friend that I experience it sexually and almost desire her. But I have never let her know I have this feeling, because it might make her afraid of me."

"If my parents had not put so much pressure on me to find a good man and get married, I might have continued the relationships I had with other girls in grade school. My best friend and I, at about eight, used to play doctor and touch and examine each other. Then at twelve she and I would spend the night and take off our clothes under the covers and kiss and mess around, and take turns being on top, trying to figure out how men did it with women. We were horny and curious! And we loved each other too. I still write to her (she's married too)."

"I have been brought up to believe women are more attractive and more beautiful and I am beginning to believe it."

"I'd love to massage a woman I liked and was turned on to, and then gradually arouse her sexually through massage and then slowly make love to her and then stop and talk, then love again, then sleep together. I'd like with her to know myself better. But I'd never have the nerve!"

"I would like to have a sexual relationship with a woman. There is one woman I am sexually attracted to but I would never approach her in a sexual way because that would be imposing on her heterosexuality. We are very good friends and her non-sexual friendship is more important than her sexual friendship. It is a new experience for me even to consider lesbianism. Until two years ago, I barely recognized this facet of sexuality, never consciously thought about it, and when I did I thought it was 'disgusting.' I have never met a woman who was a lesbian to my knowledge, although one doesn't broadcast this proclivity yet in this repressive society. Women, even feminists, are sometimes uncomfortable talking about lesbianism, so I have little idea what their fears and unconscious desires are concerning their sisters *vis-à-vis* themselves as sexual partners. One must grapple with many possibilities before embarking on a sexual relationship with a woman. 'Am I doing so because men have disappointed me?' 'Am I running from a threatening situation and thus avoiding confronting the problem where it stands?' 'Am I having sex with a woman who cannot handle guilt associated with "deviant" behaviour?' 'Am I exploiting her as I was exploited by men?'"

"In school, I had lots of hopeless crushes on boys I wouldn't look at now. I also had lots of crushes on women—friends and teachers which I'm only now acknowledging as sexual. I also really wanted someone to be close to but I thought I wanted a boyfriend, which is not necessarily the same thing."

"I would like to have sex with women. I think I am a lesbian, which is not too helpful since I'm married, and don't feel capable of a divorce at this point, and living on my own, etc. However, someday it'll probably get to be too much, and I'll have to."

"I haven't had sex with another woman, except verbally—I think women often make love by talking a certain way, at least I do."

"I want a woman lover—or more. I generally want *closer* relationships with women; I want to do all the things only *men* are supposed to do! I want to explore!"

"I never thought of women as such interesting people before this revival of the women's movement. I enjoy their company so much, and we are able to work together with real pleasure. I suppose sex, in another lifetime, would have been a part of this."

"My experience up until now has been with men, but I would welcome a love affair with a woman. I would want to question myself very strongly as to the genuineness of my feeling for a woman, however, because, knowing me as I do, there is a danger that I might enter an affair merely from sexual curiosity. Somehow I wouldn't feel too bad about going with a man out of that motivation, but I would feel rotten if I used a woman that way."

"I've never had sex with a woman but I would like to—although I'm not sure about whether to orgasm or not. I have, after a good deal of thought about things like the fact that I *have* had many deep relationships with women, come to the conclusion that I am, for the time being, at least, straight. The thought of performing cunnilingus doesn't turn me on, and although I have been physically attracted to women friends, it has not been particularly sexual—just wanting to cuddle, hug, etc. Another difference—I can be attracted physically to men I don't know, but I feel physical attraction only to women I love."

"I have never had sex with a woman and can't imagine it, but that is because of my conditioning. I can see why women would want other women, and can accept it. I don't know any lesbians that I know of. I have a close girlfriend who is divorced and we have discussed this a little and it seems we are both 'straight' but I notice we never touch each other. Are we afraid we might be gay and couldn't handle it? Sometimes I think I would like to try but then I realize I'm fairly happy the way things are."

"I guess I still feel strange when I take the initiative, though I don't think it's right that I don't initiate sometimes—I guess I have become very used to having things done to me. I think that's the main reason why I haven't had sex with women too—that we are accustomed to not initiating sex and so no one does! That's a hard bit of conditioning to overcome—it's the gap between believing something is right and actually *feeling* good about it, too."

"I have only had sex with men and with myself— more with men than with myself. Sex with women appeals to me, but I think mainly because of curiosity, because in my closest relationships with women I love, sex doesn't seem to come 'naturally.' I still consider myself rather inexperienced in sex."

"I was married for seven and a half years. I didn't like being married, except at first when it was like a new toy, sort of like playing house. Our sex life was disastrous. I had no extramarital experience during marriage. I am now single, and enjoy it, but it is difficult. I do not have sexual experiences as often as I would like. When I was about fifteen, I had what you might call a crush on a woman. She was about twenty-one, I think. We were friends, and I discovered that if we touched (by accident), I liked it. I began to speak of love. We spent a lot of time together, until one day she told me that her father thought she ought to see less of me and concentrate on her studies. Naturally, I didn't believe a word of that, but it was pretty much the end of the relationship. Then, about three years ago, I had a sexual experience with a woman. All we did was lie in bed together naked, and touch and caress each other all over. I liked it very much, though I was a little afraid. Apparently she was even more afraid, for later she sort of pretended that it had not happened."

"I have several friends who are lesbians, and superficially I have no strong feelings about that one way or the other. However, when they talk about their relationships, I find myself becoming rather defensive; it seems I do have very deep and complicated feelings about it, both positive and negative."

How do women relate physically?

"As far as how we relate to each other physically—we hug a lot and kiss and caress each other. As for 'technique,' we masturbate each other with our hands and fingers and orally, as well as combining both. Also, mutually masturbate, with other parts of our bodies. Basically, the same things a man and woman can do without a penis, and *usually don't!*"

"I've made love with a woman only twice, the first time was a year ago—don't think I know enough to tell you exactly how. The basic difference with a woman is that there's no end, where you have orgasms and end—it's like a circle, it goes on and on."

"Some times I think I could go straight from deep mouth kissing to clitoral stimulation to have orgasm. It depends on my state of 'readiness.' I like also to have my lover touch me very lightly, with her tongue and hands, all over my body, especially my buttocks and lower abdomen. There is no one 'best' way of clitoral stimulation—when she uses her mouth it's different than her fingers. Sometimes I like her mouth at first and then her finger, and the other times, just her mouth. Either her tongue gently flicking my clitoris, or her mouth sucking me hard, or her finger moving right above my clitoris in an increasingly rapid up and down movement, usually makes me orgasm. Sometimes she pushes her mouth hard against me and shakes her head rapidly from side to side—I orgasm this way also. No one way works best all the time; different ways at different times work marvellously well. One thing, I guess it's easier for me if we start love-making with our clothes *on* and do not have more than a minute's interruption for removal of clothes. Otherwise I get a little self-conscious."

"There is always a great deal of touching and affection, fingers run over each other's bodies, legs entwined, and a great deal of kissing all over our bodies. Then we get into oral sex, mutual or sometimes one person at a time. Sometimes we rest for a while and then start up again."

"Sex is slow with long preliminaries and explorations, conversation, gentle mutual stroking and then clitoral stimulation in unison. Great! It's great to do and feel the *same* done to you."

"She's soft and gentle, knowing exactly how to rub my clit and what pressure to use—taking as long as we want coming—coming—*coming.*"

"Once, recently, when my lover and I had been making love for hours, I felt that she was beginning to feel frustrated (I had not yet learned her 'style'), so I guided her hand to her clitoris, so I could learn from her what pleased her."

"The women I've been with so far have been more on an affectionate love basis than sexual. I have yet to be more sexual with a woman. The women I've been with have kissed me and I them, we have hugged and gently touched each other; just having our bodies together and being warm sends a fire surging through my body. One woman sat on my pelvic area lightly, with her back to my face, and stimulated me vaginally/clitorally with her fingers, very gently, taking her time and not at all concerned with getting me excited but more exploring—which releases me to take my time and do the same. I enjoy all of them very much and hope to see that I make women a more active part of my life. I am doing this by seeking them out by going to women's and lesbians' activities and putting myself in a position to meet them for the conscious purpose that I want to make love to a certain kind of woman that I love."

"Love-making with a woman is always more variable than with a man, and the physical actions are more mutual. While the same places are kissed and touched with a man, the whole feeling is heightened for me when the lover is a woman, and it is so different because of all the psychological and emotional factors involved. The touches become different, the kisses different—the whole aura is different."

"Sex with a woman includes: touching, kissing, smiling, looking serious, embracing, talking, digital intercourse, caressing, looking, cunnilingus, undressing, remembering later, making sounds, sometimes gently biting, sometimes crying, and breathing and sighing together."

"Liz, my roommate, and I have oftentimes made love when one of us has emotional problems—the love of friends. In this case, Liz had a bad experience and I made love to her. I first kissed her forehead, then her lips, and then very gently massaged her breasts. Gently kissing and rubbing them, sucking her nipples. While doing this, she usually either squeezes my breasts or rubs my shoulders. I then caress her vagina and perform cunnilingus on her. I then take the position of the man and let her kiss and hug me. This is when the emotion comes out. If she wants to, she then makes love to me."

"To relate to another woman physically, you just caress her body the way you like to be caressed and/or the way she indicates she likes. You explore love-making together and find out what works. I don't know how to answer more specifically. I don't think there are any 'cookbook' approaches that work in all situations—thank goodness. For me it comes more naturally than it ever did with men."

"Technically, women together do what male and female together do—touch and kiss and caress one another, except there's no penis. (And I've yet to meet a lesbian who uses a dildo. I think that is one great big male porno trip.) I earlier mentioned mutal breast playing. Sometimes it feels good to put my nipple into her vagina, or vice versa. Cunnilingus is beautiful too, either as participant or recipient. I don't enjoy '69', however—it's too distracting, too much happening at once for me to concentrate on either of us. When I perform cunnilingus, I like to not only stroke the inner lips and edges of her vagina with my tongue, but I also like to suck her clitoris. This excites me very much and my partners always seem to enjoy it. I also enjoy tribadism. I enjoy just holding each other very closely, our thighs pressing against one another's genitals; or lying diagonally with each other, our legs in a 'V' sort of scissors around each other's torsos, our vaginas warm, moist, happy, touching, our hands holding."

"Our relationship works on a pretty equal basis, with both of us the initiators at various times, with both of us taking different positions in tribadism, the '69' position, mutual masturbation, rubbing breasts, or breasts against clitoris. There are no particular patterns, except we usually achieve our orgasms during tribadism, which we practise most frequently."

"Sex with a woman for me has involved kissing, feeling one another completely, and *basically* humping—pressing mound of Venus against mound of Venus or each other's leg. Also cunnilingus and manual and even anal lingus! Pressing against her backside, riding her, which feels *good.*"

"It's most stimulating to be in a sitting position facing my partner. She also sits and presses her hand gently into me. This way I can determine the speed and intensity of the movements. And we can see each other, kiss, talk, and feel each other's breasts."

"Usually with the one woman I've gone to bed with we would spend *ages* on foreplay and *finally* when we *absolutely* couldn't stand it any longer, we would manually bring each other to orgasm—or else I would perform cunnilingus on her, even though she didn't on me."

"My best sexual experiences were with the first woman I ever loved. I had been married for a thousand years and she was a total virgin. We didn't even practise cunnilingus, yet they were powerful sexual encounters for both of us because they were a dream come true emotionally. We were mad for each other and that's why they were my best sexual experiences."

"I become very aroused by caressing my female lover's breasts and clitoris and vagina and get so hung up on her body that she need not do anything to me, the mere touch and taste of her body is all the stimulus I need. Arousal (and orgasm) is a very emotional experience because somehow it communicates all the love I feel for her."

"Finally, now with my present female lover of two months, I have orgasms. A person's understanding of the clitoris's stimulation, foreplay, cuddling, display of other intimate expressions of caressing and deep kissing are important. She and I spend anywhere from two hours to six hours in caressing, touching, cuddling, hugging, lip kissing, deep kissing and intimate conversation before, in between, and after sex, lying in bed. This is very important!"

And one woman gave a long answer:

"My lover is very sensitive to what I want. But she asks me, and I tell her, too, because it is better to communicate your desires. Like the other night when she was being gentle and I wasn't responding much and I said, 'I want you to be rough' and so she was and it was strong and wonderful. We like to stimulate ourselves and neither of us minds this or feels embarrassed. Sometimes, usually, if she comes before I do, she keeps making love till I come but if she doesn't then I masturbate and she holds me while I do and it's just the same as making love.

"She is always emotionally involved. Sometimes her mind wanders, like once we were hugging and kissing and starting to make love and all of a sudden she says, 'What part of the world do armadillos live in?' Really, she was serious, and we laughed a long time.

"I must be lying face down to have an orgasm. I must be rubbing my clitoris against a part of my lover's body or a soft object. (Before getting in this position, I like my breasts to be sucked. I like that the best. I also like manual clitoral stimulation and oral.) Then I get in a face-down position. Sometimes my lover lies on top of my back and I rub against a pillow or soft blanket and sometimes (usually) I lie on her back and she stimulates herself manually and the feeling of the waves in her hips and legs and my thighs and clitoris moving against her brings me to orgasm.

"I like non-genital sex as well as or better than genital. I like hugging and kissing (we don't usually have big deep penetrating kisses, but when we do it's nice, but mostly little wet ones in nice places). I like talking and laughing and being silly, and just looking at her face and body in the moonlight. I like it when she lies on top of me and looks down into my face. She looks loving and proud. Once my heart had an orgasm when she was hugging me and looking at me and saying how she loved me. Hers did too. It felt like it just jumped up and had a wave like my body does when it comes. I like smelling a lot. The first woman I was in love with (when I was twelve) had a smell like wild woods and autumn leaves, and I loved it. I like to smell my lover's hair and her breast and her melt. I like to suck her breasts and I like her to suck mine. She does all kinds of new and wonderful things to me. I never felt like I do with her. I like the little things she does better than all the orgasms in the world."

"Being together with a woman is one of the most beautiful things on earth. Recently, on the giant New Year's Eve Millennium celebration, I booked a hotel room and invited my girlfriend. It cost me a bit, but then what the hell . . . We checked in (or I did, not sure about their gay-friendly policies at posh hotels—she came along later), washed up and settled in, then went down to dinner in their lavish dining room, but by 11 p.m. we left to go up to the room. We gazed out the window at the stars, then kissed very deeply and declared our love (mostly she declared her love to me), and I carried her to bed. (I lift weights.) I undressed her slowly, playing with each part of her body and telling her what I was going to do to her, while she moaned and pretended she didn't want anything so violent . . . I told her I was going to rape her, and she would have to just take it, no matter what I put inside her nor how hard, that she was lucky to be fucked by me and should keep quiet. This made her moan all the more (what I wanted) and I tied her arms together above her head (while she protested). This gave me free access to her body, to touch it and look at it any way I wanted. I went down on her and kissed and licked her crotch until she couldn't take it any more and begged me to make her come with my hand. I ignored this and started to pull and tug at her nipples (I know she loves it), then she yelled at the top of her voice demanding I fuck her with the candle I kept holding and showing her—so loud I had to put my hand over her mouth and 'threaten' her with 'punishment' if she tried that again . . . Soon I couldn't resist coming so I stood up and made myself come in front of her, then fell on top of her . . . anyway, this gives you some idea. I love her a lot."

"I'm pregnant and I'm living with a woman. Everyone asks me, doesn't she mind that you're going to have a baby? They don't realize, of course I didn't have sex with him! It's all done outside the body, he's just a friend (for a long time). She's keener than me for the baby, it'll be our baby not 'mine'. It'll have two mothers. I feel fine, I'm just like I normally am, just that I have a bump in my tummy. Sexually, I don't have any problems either, no big ups or downs and I like sex as much as I normally do with her. It's so beautiful to explore her body and feel her exploring mine, with all the changes. The other day she was lying with her head on my stomach when we were in bed, her fingers inside me, I was coming and she was listening to see if the baby could feel our happiness. We are very close."

"The first time she held me down and more or less raped me with a big dildo, also using a bottle in my ass, I didn't know what was happening. I was on my back looking up at her, I felt incredibly turned on. I came and came and came. Another time she pinned me down holding my arms with one hand and clamping her other hand over my mouth while wearing a dildo that she fucked me with . . . She was looking down at me daring me to scream or cry out. I didn't but my mouth was open and gaping. She can really get me going!"

Women explained some of the reasons why they preferred to relate sexually to women.

"I have been relating sexually to women for over four years. I have always had strong, warm, loving relationships with women—ever since I can remember. My feelings of sympathy, compassion, and understanding have always been more strongly directed towards women. In other words, women have mattered and do matter to me more than men, and even though I've had more sexual relationships with men in the past, they have not compared in depth emotionally to my relationships with women, sexual or non-sexual."

"I am a lesbian. I had my first feelings of sexual desire for another woman eight years ago, when I was fourteen. We both got scared after that (terrified would be much more accurate) and tried to convince ourselves we were heterosexual. In that next three and a half years I slept with seven or eight men but never was very satisfied with the relationships emotionally, sexually, etc. They weren't satisfying because I just don't feel the *complete* relationship—emotional, spiritual, etc. Besides, I like women's bodies much more. When I was nineteen I fell head over heels in love with a woman and realized that I couldn't kid myself any longer. I knew then that I was a lesbian. She was much more afraid than I (this was the first time she had realized that she felt this way about another woman), and our sexuality was not expressed with each other very frequently for that reason. I was in love with her for almost two and a half years. About a year ago I saw my first lover again (from freshman year in high school) and we began to sleep together. In the year since then I slept with two other women before I met my present lover. We've been living together now for three months and we both expect it shall be for a long, long time. We are extremely comfortable with each other in all ways. Neither of us wants to sleep with anyone else (at least right now). I am now twenty-two, she is twenty. She has been out since she was thirteen though she too slept with some eight or nine men in the first few years of her sexual experience. Neither of us would ever get married, even if we weren't lesbians. The political implications are too large and damaging. We live with two other women and really enjoy collective living."

"I believe that this is true for countless millions of wives, in spite of all the claims to orgasm, that they really don't know what orgasm is. Almost no one is willing to admit to not having orgasms—what, me frigid? I used to say, during my marriage of thirty years, and quite sincerely, believe it or not, that yes, I had orgasm almost every time. But then, taken by surprise in a lesbian relationship, I experienced real, buffola total eclipse orgasm for the first time. Wow! I'd never felt anything like *that* before. Suddenly I understood all kinds of strange masculine behaviour. The rather pleasant, generalized sensations I was accustomed to feeling with men—vaginal stimulation—were in a class with sensuously warm oatmeal. No wonder women have never made such a big thing out of sex—it's nice, really, but one can do without it. I believe that most women who claim orgasm without having experienced the clitoral detonation are speaking in ignorance."

"I was divorced in September 1974, after being married for thirty-five years, no extramarital experiences, only had intercourse with one man ever—I just didn't like it. After thirty-four years I tried a woman and loved it, so I got divorced. I think I had always been attracted to women but the women's movement and a less inhibited lifestyle, thankfully, caused me to come out. In junior high and high school I had 'crushes' on girls, but I was too young and stupid to know what was going on and what to do about it—information regarding lesbians was practically non-existent then. I also had scrapbooks of Dorothy Lamour (boy that dates me!) and other women stars—Pat Neal and Lauren Bacall. I am fifty, and I am very enterprising and very resourceful, and run a business of my own."

"I think I've had a lot of experience for being eighteen. A lot of it was bad, but I learned from it anyway. I've slept with about twenty men and one woman. I found the woman much better sex and better love. She was warm and tender. This is because we were friends for five years before sleeping together. Until men understand me as well as she does, I prefer to sleep with her above anyone. I would like to have more experience with women I know. The most important thing involved in good sex is being honest. If you dig another woman, let her know—she may very well feel the same. If it freaks her out, talk to her about it—she needs to loosen up.

"Personally I like girls better, they are more tender and loving."

"I have orgasms—always multiple—in masturbation, but I do not have them too often with my husband. I fake them at times, but at times I don't even bother to do that because it's only for his gratification. I am in my forties—in the past year for the first time I have been involved with a woman. It is entirely different and I always have orgasms."

"My best sex experiences were with my woman friend, not because I was orgasmic, because I generally wasn't, but because 1) she was a woman and it's much easier for me to give myself emotionally to a woman, to surrender my ego; 2) her skin was so soft and smooth, the vulnerability sent me; 3) the opportunity to act the aggressor and the lover was wonderful; 4) love-making was so mutual, endless, unhurried, she didn't quickly tighten up into a ball of sweat and demand the old in and out; 5) I didn't worry about coming, there was no programme; 6) I didn't worry about my body, whether it was 'adequate'; and 7) I didn't worry about her sexual-moral judgement, where I was going to be placed on the spectrum of female frailties (angel or whore?)."

"My best experiences were this past year with my girlfriend. Once we made love in my parents' bed in candlelight and discovered our love for each other as sexual women. Also once we made love all night in great passion and were soft and silly and warm, and great love was built that night. The difference with boys is it is much shorter."

"Sex is not just sex no matter whether hetero or homo. As any lesbian (or bisexual) will tell you, sex is a very different thing with men than with women—a completely different experience which encompasses more than the fact that most women who have sex with other women like women better than men. It has to do more with the way men are brought up to regard their bodies, touching and sensuality, versus the way women learn to do this. All of which is summed up by the phrase 'make love *with*' instead of make love '*to*.'"

"Men were mostly concerned with their own pleasure rather than mine. I found no emotional love, just physical love. I find women better lovers; they know what a woman wants and most of all there is an emotional closeness that can never be matched with a man. More tenderness, more consideration and understanding of feelings, etc."

"With women there is a lot of hugging, kissing, caressing, i.e., a lot more touching and affection. There is not any particular procedure, only there is usually either finger-clitoral stimulation or cunnilingus to produce orgasm at some point. Women are warmer, more mutual, careful to see how I'm reacting, as opposed to most men, and sex is much slower. Women consider the whole body erotic since there is no one concentrated 'tool' for pleasure."

"Women seem to have a more sustained energy level after orgasm, and are more likely to know and do something about it if I'm not satisfied. It isn't all automatically 'over' because somebody orgasms."

"There was clitoral manipulation by hand and mouth, with much more kissing and holding than with men, and much more concern for my pleasure. I felt greater, much more free, than with men."

"I have been a lesbian for two years, and I'm living with the woman I love. Both of us hope this will be a permanent situation and we are happy, comfortable. I don't consider it a marriage, and by my definition of marriage I don't think I'd like to be married. Physically, sexual relationships with women have been *much* more pleasurable than with men. Psychologically too, because the women I've had sex with have been my friends first, which was never the case with men. Being friends sets up a trust that I think is essential for satisfying physical intimacy. Relating to another woman physically seems to me like the most natural thing in the world. You've already got a head start on knowing how to give her pleasure. Gentleness seems to be the key, and is the main difference between relating to men and women. Just follow the golden rule."

"When I first had sex with a woman, I thought, there's something very weird about going to bed with a girlfriend, your best friend and making love to her. 'God am I a *lesbian?* I must be *sick!*' But then, you know you aren't really sick at all. I found out that it's a new experience to make 'love.' It's a different sort of sex when there's emotion behind it. Both are good—yet they are different."

"The first time I made love with a woman, who was my best friend, was a good experience in that I had been waiting to touch her for so long, and finally when I told her how I felt for her she gave me a back rub which led to sex and I was surprised how natural a woman's body felt, and what a rush it was kissing her—it felt pervertedly good—I mean it was supposed to be so perverse but it was great. The sex itself was not too good—we were both freaked out, especially me, and I was afraid to do anything. And we never talked about it."

"I've only been out since early this year. I had chosen a woman to talk my feelings out with and went to her house and realized that considering my emotions, it was ridiculous to talk so I said, 'I want to hold you,' and did. When I kissed her neck I was shocked and delighted to find how easy it was and how good it felt. I am still and probably will always be amazed at how easy it is for me to feel desire or to excite another woman, and how natural it is to act on it."

"Sex is better with women physically and emotionally. Women are much more sensitive to other people's needs probably as a result of our servile programming. However, the benefit is a tuned-in lover! Also, I like the fact that women can't rape each other. I also like the aesthetic symmetry—'twin' aspect—as well as the power symmetry"

"At seven, I used to become highly aroused fantasizing kissing a certain girlfriend. By about twelve, I was fantasizing necking with both sexes. By about fourteen, I wanted to fuck; or, more mysterious and exciting and forbidden, do whatever it was the lesbians did! Now I do and it's great."

"My love affair with a woman (a good friend) was beautiful, even though neither of us came to climax, she because she couldn't, I because I knew how that felt for her and said I wouldn't."

"Most of the men in my heterosexual career (from age twenty until I was twenty-eight) wanted oral stimulation from me of their penis, after which they would mount me and reach their climax. After their ejaculation they would ask, 'Did you come?' In general, my female lovers have taken far more creative and varied approaches to love-making. All of them, however, began by being incredibly gentle and aware of my needs, as well as theirs. The women did not act as though I was a 'masturbation machine' for them, nor did they fall asleep when it was over. No woman ever asked me, 'Did you come?' They knew. My love-making periods with women have always lasted much longer than they ever did with men. Twenty minutes for a man, at least an hour with a woman, usually more. I hope the day will come when heterosexual couples can universally boast of having the kind of good sexual encounters I am having now."

"Lesbian sex is very different from sex with men. It is

not an 'exchange' or a 'trade' of services, it is not physically awkward, it is not something done *to* me (despite the best will in the world men still made me feel I was being acted *on)*, it is not demand (orgasm) oriented. It is wonderful. I can be both passive and active, relaxed and demanding. There is no anxiety that anything will stop our love-making except exhaustion. I enjoy what I do to her almost as much as what she does to me; we make each other's feeling possible by revealing our need and pleasure to each other. I have somewhat forgotten the panic I used to be in about orgasms and I am angry whenever I feel pressure from that kind of memory. I'm not even sure if I answered the questions about orgasm 'right' because I've stopped thinking like that because now the act is not pleasurable, and besides I don't have to make sure I have an orgasm so I won't feel left out and cheated when he has his. It is good simply to be with women. I could not have written that five years ago. I hated women, believed affection was male (!) and looked like a fairly successful imitation of a Barbie doll. Except that I kept rejecting Kens."

What is "different" about sexual relations between women is precisely that there is no one institutionalized way of having them, so they can be as inventive and individual as the people involved. Perhaps the two most striking specific differences from most heterosexual relations, as defined in the clitoral stimulation chapter, were that there were generally more feelings and tenderness, affection and sensitivity, and more orgasms. This higher frequency of orgasm in lesbian sexuality has of course been remarked on by other researchers going at least as far back as Kinsey. Also lesbian sexual relations tend to be longer and to involve more overall body sensuality, since one orgasm does not automatically signal the end of sexual feeling, as in most of the heterosexual relations described earlier.

What types of bisexual answers were received?

"I think my background has a lot to do with the way I feel about sex. I was brought up middle class with parents who taught me that sex was bad unless you were married—period. A girl should never go to bed with a man unless he was her husband. So I'm still struggling with some guilt feelings. It hurts me to think how it would hurt my mother if she knew some of the things I've done, but I just couldn't live my life just for what she wants. I had sex with a woman for about two years and it was really a fantastic experience. I have never felt so close to anyone or so loved. I used to think I would always prefer sex with a woman, but now I find I like sex with a man I care for too. Both are really great if the caring is there. I guess I feel more relaxed with a woman because I know about her body and seem to be more in touch with her feelings. At present, I am only having sex with one man but if the opportunity presents itself, I will have sex again with a woman."

'The first time I fell in love was with a woman who had been a close friend for several years. We joined a consciousness-raising group together, which is where we first discussed the possibility of sexual relations with women. We were then apart several months during the summer, and when we got back together she told me she had slept with a woman. Our relationship after that got more and more intense, and several months later we started sleeping together. Falling in love with her was totally unexpected—I had known her for years, but it really changed. We talked all the time, about everything under the sun. We grew to know and understand everything about each other. I am still very much in love with her, and still get chills of anticipation when I'm about to see her. Even though we're apart most of the time, at school, we still share all our thoughts and I've never felt so close to anyone on any level. We understand each other on all levels, and satisfy needs no one else has even realized were there. Since our falling in love, I've also fallen in love with two other people, both male. One was gradual, the other was instantaneous. I feel that somehow, my love for her makes me much more open and able to have intense feelings for others too?'

Lesbianism can be political.
Besides the increased affection and sensitivity and the increased frequency of orgasm, some women felt that sex with another woman could be better because of the more equal relationship possible. Sex with women can be a reaction against men and our second class status with them in this society:

"Sex with a man is often the beginning of a political education. Sex with a woman means independence from men."

"Because of my own tremendous conditioning, which I believe is almost universal, it is almost impossible for me to have a truly healthy sexual relationship with a man—probably for any woman."

"Sex with women is more of a communion with self, although society makes it more complicated. But men are usually juvenile in some way and so one gets emotionally wasted with them."

"I am currently thinking of lesbianism as an alternative to abstinence, and to men in general, because they are not very liberated sexually or emotionally or any other way, and I can't stand it any more."

"You can have sex with everybody and say 'up yours' to morality, or, you can have sex with women and say 'up yours' to men and the society that puts you down. Lesbianism in my view is a far-out alternative to always being underneath some man and being a baby machine."

"I see lesbianism as putting *all* my energies (sexual, political social, etc.) into women. Sex is a form of comfort and to have sex indiscriminately with males is to give them comfort. I think it should be seriously considered."

"Is sex political? Of course. When I quietly parted from my last male lover (for women) I suddenly, for the first time, moved into my own space, my own time zone, and my own life."

Janis Kelly has had some interesting things to say along these lines in *Sister Love: An Exploration of the Need for Homosexual Experience:*

> *All heterosexual relationships are corrupted by the imbalance of power between men and women. In order to maintain superiority, males must feed on the emotional care and economic servitude of women. To survive in a male-supremacist social order, women must cripple themselves in order to build the male ego. Due to the stifling effect of this culture and to the damaging roles it enforces, women cannot develop fully in a heterosexual context.*
>
> *Love relationships between women are more likely to be free of the destructive forces which make [these] defenses necessary. Institutional norms and the restraints of a power-oriented culture have, of course, also influenced women; nevertheless, the domination-subordination patterns women sometimes bring to lesbian relationships cannot overshadow the essential equality of the persons involved. In addition, many of the responses nurtured in females are extremely conductive to non-exploitative interaction. Sensitivity to the feelings and moods of others, caretaking, and gentleness are among the qualities more encouraged in women than in men . . .*
>
> *Because men occupy a superior social position and are schooled to covet power over others in order to maintain that position, they can rarely accept others, especially women, as equals. Human contacts must be arranged hierarchically, and women must be on a lower level. Tension is inevitable when a woman refuses to accept this*

position and must be "put in her place." In contrast, women are able to start from a foundation of equality and devote their energy to growth and creativity rather than to struggling to maintain identities against the destructiveness of the traditional female role.[6]

It is important for women to recognize their own potential for having sexual feelings for other women. If we want to grow strong, we must learn to love, respect, honour, and be attentive to and interested in other women. This includes seeing each other as physically attractive with the possibility of sexual intimacy. As long as we can relate sexually only to men *because they are "men"* (and as long as men can relate only to women because they are "women"), we are dividing the world into the very two classes we are trying to transcend.

Any woman who feels actual horror or revulsion at the thought of kissing or embracing or having physical relations with another woman should re-examine her feelings and attitudes not only about other women, but also about *herself.* A positive attitude towards our bodies and towards touching ourselves and towards any physical contact that might naturally develop with another woman is essential to self-love and accepting our own bodies as good and beautiful. As Jill Johnston has written: ". . . until women see in each other the possibility of a primal commitment which includes sexual love they will be denying themselves the love and value they readily accord to men, thus affirming their own second class status."

6 Sexual slavery:

Intimidation, economic and emotional blackmail

What is sexual slavery?

"I have wanted to have orgasms with a man for years—
about twelve. Seems like the impossible dream. I can be
a loving eunuch with him, but only a full sexual person
by myself."

Why does this woman say this? Why, if she can be "a full sexual person" by herself, can she be only "a loving eunuch"
with a man? This woman's comment points up a dilemma
that has become clearer and clearer throughout this book.
We have seen that heterosexual sex, even today, usually
involves the general pattern of foreplay, penetration, and
intercourse ending with male ejaculation; often the woman
does not orgasm. But women *know* very well how to orgasm
during masturbation, whenever they want. If they know
how to have orgasms whenever they want, why don't they
feel free to use this knowledge during sex with men? (Why
do they feel freer to express themselves with another woman
or alone?) *Why do women so habitually satisfy men's needs
during sex and ignore their own?*
   The fact is that the role of women in sex, as in every
other aspect of life, has been to serve the needs of others—
men and children. What could be called "sexual slavery" has
been an almost unconscious way of life for most women,
though this may be changing now. As we have seen, however (in the intercourse chapter), our model of "sex" is *culturally* (not biologically) defined, and can be redefined—or
undefined. We need not continue to have only one model
of physical relations—foreplay, penetration, intercourse,
and ejaculation.
   Women are sexual slaves insofar as they are (justifiably)
afraid to "come out" with their own sexuality, and continue

to satisfy others' needs but ignore their own. As one woman put it, "Sex can be political in the sense that it can involve a power structure where the woman is unwilling or unable to get what she really needs for her fullest amount of pleasure, but the man is getting what he wants, and the woman, like an unquestioning and unsuspecting lackey, is gratefully supplying it." The truth is that almost everything in our society pushes women toward defining their sexuality centrally as intercourse with men, and toward not defining themselves as equally important or full persons in sex with men. Lack of sexual self-determination is another sign of the oppression of women.

This, of course, is not to say that women don't like sex, or that they don't enjoy intercourse in many ways. When asked if they enjoyed sex, almost all women said yes, they did. Furthermore, there was no correlation with frequency of orgasm: women who did not orgasm with their partners were just as likely to say they enjoyed sex as women who did. And women who never orgasmed during intercourse were just as likely to say they enjoyed intercourse as women who did. However, the important question is: What is it that women enjoy about sex/intercourse, and what do women mean when they say they like them?

Feelings about sex and intercourse

"Is having sex important to you? Why? What part does it play in your life, and what does it mean to you?"

The overwhelming majority of women answered that sex meant a great deal to them, because it was a wonderful form of intimacy and closeness with another human being.

"You can be as close as possible with another person. During sex I feel so at ease, and the time before, during, and after I can really enjoy how close we are."

"Sex is beautiful because such a complete contact with another person makes me feel my being is not solely confined to my own body. It is one of the most direct ways to get beyond the barriers between 'them' and 'me.'"

"Sex plays a very important part in my life because at this point it is a symbol of the love I am sharing with my man. I know it is his way of showing he loves me. Many times I do not have an orgasm but I still feel a great deal of satisfaction. The closeness and feelings are what is important."

"Sex is primarily important as a vehicle for intimacy, a way of showing my deepest love. It is the very essence of my life with my husband, not in the sense of a transitory emotion resulting from some form of personal satisfaction, but because of its symbolic meaning that we share."

"I become very emotionally involved in my sexual relations. I think I have sex almost always to consummate a bond, to develop and perpetuate closeness.

The more sex I have with someone, the closer I feel to them. I love my sex partners more than I would if I wasn't having sex with them. Is this true of other women? of men? Sex is very important to me for this reason."

"Sex is very important because it is the most intense pleasure, the closest you can be to another person—the one time we express ourselves fully. We drop all barriers and truly communicate as human beings."

"Sex brings me closer in spirit to others in ten minutes than I can get in ten years to people I do not share sex with."

"Do you like vaginal penetration/ intercourse? Physically? Psychologically? Why?"

Since 87 per cent of the women in this study answered "yes" to this question,* this includes most of the women who never orgasmed during intercourse. Clearly, there was no automatic connection between not having orgasms during intercourse and not liking it. In fact, even women who did orgasm during intercourse most frequently gave affection and closeness as their basic reason for liking intercourse, rarely mentioning orgasm.

The most frequent reason given for liking intercourse by far was that it is a time of great affection and closeness.

"I love intercourse. Even when I'm not getting off at all or don't really love the man, I still love it (unless actual pain is present), because we are so close at that time— closer than at any other time. Even *with* orgasm, I would have to say that this is over half the pleasure of intercourse for me. There's just something about it that brings you closer."

*See Appendix 3 for the feelings of women who did not like intercourse.

"Yes, I like intercourse, even though I don't have orgasm. It shows affection or the illusion of it—when people are at their most vulnerable moments. Physically I like the total closeness and the sensation of wrapping myself around him."

"Yes, it feels warm, like being hugged more closely than ever. I feel accepted and giving at the same time."

"Physically, I love having his penis inside my vagina—which kind of caresses the penis and hugs it. Emotionally, I feel it all through my body and spirit—I feel that we two are merging as one. I feel very alive, very vital. I feel very fulfilled, and I feel as if I hadn't a care in the world, just the supreme ecstasy and happiness of being one with him."

"During intercourse I feel very close and somehow entangled and united with another human being, which I cannot realize in any other way. It is like holding your first new-born baby—someone else is part of you."

"Intercourse is good, warm, close, a reaffirmation of love, an ultimate sharing, and special intimacy—a very private spiritual thing."

"Intercourse is profound—a sense of merging your individual identities and becoming one."

"Yes, the idea of union, both physical and emotional, with another is exciting and satisfying. We are joined in love."

"Psychologically I feel I am truly communicating with my partner—getting as close as one can get, both physically and spiritually."

"Yes, I like intercourse—especially psychologically, due to the closeness and intimacy, and the sharing, hugging, and togetherness. It is totally satisfying."

"During intercourse I feel secure and wanted—whole, warm, loved, womanly."

"During intercourse I feel secure, assured of his love, and protected. It feels good to my mind, body, and heart."

"I like penetration physically because it feels warm

and sweet and mutual. Especially his chest against mine is great! Psychologically I feel more complete, and fulfilled and needed."

"It is an affirmation of love, warmth, and caring, and makes me feel alive and human. My face is near his and I can feel his breath."

"The touching and tenderness then makes me feel warm and secure, safe and close."

"I love it. Feeling your man's penis deep within you, thrusting even deeper, is ecstasy. Psychologically it is warmly intimate—becoming one. It's really tender, acting out our physical love for each other."

"It is a oneness that transcends all else. I feel overwhelmed and in a grand passion, and very close to the person I love."

"Yes, it is the most beautiful thing two people in love can share. Frequently at the moment of penetration there is a tremendous feeling of relief, of becoming one together."

"Yes, I like it, because of what it represents—the ultimate unity of us. It's an inimitable closeness, one is kind of enfolding the other person."

"It is the ultimate of physical and psychological fulfilment. The act is something only God could have imagined that is so beautiful."

"Intercourse is the total integration of two people in love. Didn't you know?"

In addition these answers very frequently included specific reference to feeling sure of the man's attention and affection at that time.

"I love intercourse. It feels really close, like he is really mine, and cares for me."

"I love the intimacy of it because for those minutes the man is totally mine and I am loved, happy, fulfilled, high, needed—and sometimes adored."

"The greatest pleasure in sex is simply feeling very special and very close with someone. The greatest displeasure is anxiety about the relationship."

"I like intercourse because it is a time when I get his undivided attention, and feel very loved and secure."

"Intercourse shows my husband loves and wants me."

"The greatest thing is the security I feel when I'm in bed with a man. I feel loved and wanted and powerful."

"Yes, during intercourse I feel a sense of euphoria—I am successful, competent, beautiful!"

"I feel that when he's inside me, I really 'have' him as opposed to always wondering if he cares or what/ who he's thinking about."

Similarly, answers to "Is sex important to you? What does it mean to you, and what part does it play in your life?" contained references to the reassurance sex gives about the over-all emotional relationship.

"Our sex life together is important because it makes me feel secure and wanted, and proves he loves me."

"Sex is to please him. What I like is the feeling of security I get when he holds me tight after. It makes me feel accepted and attractive."

"Sex makes me feel I am a woman to my husband instead of just a live-in maid."

"I get self-confidence because my husband desires me."

"Sex is the biggest part in a relationship with a man. If he doesn't want me, I feel something must be wrong with our relationship."

"It reassures me I'm desirable, gives a deeper bond to a relationship."

"My entire marriage revolves around making love to my husband. It makes me feel loved and wanted."

"It keeps me close and affectionate with my husband, and gives me a feeling of security."

"Maybe I like it because when I have sex the other person is focusing all his attention on me, and I feel important and wanted."

"Sex is important to me as a reaffirmation of my worth that a man would take the time to be gentle with me."

"Sex tells me where I stand with my man. It allows me to ask nitty-gritty questions I wouldn't be able to feel I could without being close. I feel loved."

"To me, the moment he comes inside me, I feel like all my worries and fears are forgotten, I'm in ecstasy, I'm one with him, things are wonderful and I'm not afraid of anything. He says for him too it symbolises Us."

Another frequently stated reason for liking intercourse involved identification with male pleasure, giving the man pleasure.

"I like the closeness and definitely the pleasure I'm giving the man. I like the feeling the man seems to feel."

"I never had an orgasm this way, but I love to hear him panting, groaning, moving, getting crazy. I like the feeling of closeness it produces, and I am excited by my partner's excitation—the sound of his breathing, the feeling of his excitement through the stiffness of his penis and the way he moves."

"Yes, I like intercourse. I like men, their bodies, and pleasing them."

"Yes, intercourse is a lovely way to share passions, love, devotion. And there's a feeling of power in it—the power to give a man a pleasure that is very important to his feeling of well-being."

"Psychologically I like being in control and having power, feeling close to him during his orgasm—giving the most valuable and personal pleasure possible to my man."

"I like it because I feel very close to my partner. He has an orgasm and I'm very glad to watch him and help him—we do it together and I feel very good. I would like to have orgasms then too and I'm hoping that sometime I will."

"Sometimes it is enjoyable in itself, but usually I

enjoy it because I am giving pleasure to my partner. I like the idea of having his penis inside me, although I don't usually need the accompanying *movement*. However, it gives him pleasure."

"Intercourse is something I'm finally good for and the only way he can satisfy his desire."

"No, not for its own sake, but during intercourse I get to have him in the most intimate way, and to be a part of his body."

"During intercourse I constantly think about if he's enjoying it, if I'm tight enough, what he's thinking about, and I try to keep my vaginal muscles contracted. I guess I like it okay."

"It's only good for me psychologically—I'm too much involved with making sure the man is having a really good time. Mainly I worry about whether he will lose his hard-on if my vagina squeezes his penis too much."

"Yes, I do like intercourse very much. The only way I do not like it is politically, because I do not like being as vulnerable as I am, just physically, not to mention other ways, which are probably more important. But I love to feel the man that I love, or even a man that I just want a lot, come into me. I love to enclose him, give him pleasure, feel his body all over, wrap my legs around him, and to feel his strength and show him mine. Love to feel him come, and hear his heart beat, and whatever craziness he has to say at that moment. That, in itself, is a trip."

Another reason sometimes given for liking intercourse was habit or "conditioning."

"It has never led to a climax for me. I guess I enjoy it because I have been conditioned to view it as 'normal sex.' Not enjoying it at all, or not having orgasm during intercourse, threatens my concept of myself as a 'normal' woman."

"Yes, I like it, especially when I want it. Probably I

like it because I've been conditioned to find it pleasurable."

"Yes, I like it in all ways. I feel more at home with this type of stimulation."

"Psychologically intercourse may be more enjoyable because of all my hang-ups with masturbation."

'Yes, I like it in all ways, but probably more psychologically than any other. I think I like it partly because of fantasies that are a result of reading, seeing films, etc., etc., and all the other attempts of society and the media to make this a 'great' thing."

"Yes. I like to give him pleasure, and also maybe I like it because it's so familiar."

"Yes, especially psychologically because 1) we're sort of brought up to think it fulfilling (I don't know whether it is *per se*), and 2) because I know I've got a vagina."

"Intercourse is fun—sort of like a carousel ride where you've gone to all the trouble and paid your twenty-five cents and you might as well get a kick out of the prescribed number of ups and downs and the colour and glamour and all the pretty lights and people watching you . . . and besides, it's the only game in town."

Intercourse also seemed to make sex "official."

"I feel I'm not really having sex without penetration."

"Yes, I like intercourse in all ways. To go through all the actions without penetration seems like you're leaving something out."

"I love it; to me nothing else is really 'sex.' I love the feeling of our bodies united and confused at their most sensitive points."

"It's okay physically but it's especially valuable psychologically because it makes sex 'official.' No relationship could last for long without it."

"Until a man is inside me, no matter how much we fondle and play around, I don't think I have officially 'had sex' with him. He hasn't 'had' me, and I am not yet 'possessed.' Is this a cave man-woman handover?"

Some women said intercourse made them feel "more like a woman."

"During intercourse I feel whole, like a woman."

"I love intercourse because during it I get wild and free. I'm a sexual woman, and I enjoy feeling passionate."

"Yes, I like it, especially the initial penetration. I feel I am fulfilling the reason for my womanly existence."

"Yes, I like it in all ways because my cunt is *there* to receive the male organ and naturally it feels good. I feel renewed as a woman."

"Physically it's healthy, psychologically I require it. It's a basic requirement of a healthy physical woman."

'Yes, I like it. What healthy American woman doesn't? It's a normal process."

"Intercourse is beautiful, God-given, necessary to my happiness, and my physical and mental well-being as a woman."

"Yes. I am a woman, he is a man, and it was meant to be this way. It's instinct. Also sometimes I have a tender thought of possible impregnation."

"I don't know, but I sure have a surge of hormones with fucking. After, my skin looks better, I feel a special glow about being a woman. I'm proud—well, not if he acts like a shit, but if he's my boyfriend it's like that."

Why don't women create their own orgasms?

We have seen that the basic value of sex and intercourse for women is closeness and affection. Women liked sex more for the feelings involved than for the purely physical sensations of intercourse *per se*.* As most women's answers in the preceding section reflected, it is the emotional warmth shared at this time, and the feeling of being wanted and needed (not the plain physical act) which are the chief pleasures of sex and intercourse.

Sex in our society is an extremely important way of being close—almost the only way we can be really physically or even spiritually intimate with another human being. And sex is one of the few times we tangibly feel we are being loved and demonstrate our love for another person. And yet, in another, as yet unborn (uncreated) society, it would not be necessary to define "sex" in such a closed and rigid way. It would not be necessary for women to accept a ritualized set of events that leads to male orgasm more often than female orgasm ("sex" defined as we usually know it) in order to get closeness and affection.

It is not the fact that women don't want or don't like intercourse that makes them sexual slaves (since they do like it), but rather the fact that they feel they have few or no alternative choices for their own sexual expression and satisfaction. Sex is defined as a certain pattern—foreplay, penetration, intercourse, and ejaculation—and intercourse is always part of that pattern, indeed, intercourse *is* the pattern (at least insofar as it ends with male ejaculation, and

---

*As far as the physical sensations themselves are concerned, the moment of penetration was by far the favourite sensation mentioned by most women. What sex researchers call "proprioceptive feeling"—pleasurable physical sensations having nothing to do with orgasm—were very rarely mentioned.

this ends sex). This pattern is what oppresses women, and in fact it oppresses men too, as we shall see later on.

But the original question of this chapter is still not answered—If women know how to have orgasms, why don't they use this knowledge during sex with men? Why don't they break out of the pattern? There is no reason why using this knowledge and taking the initiative in new directions would diminish the warmth and closeness of sex. Or is there?

Habit

On one level, it could be said that we think of "sex" as we do—as "foreplay," "penetration," and intercourse followed by male ejaculation—because we are taught that this is what sex is, because we are taught that these are the proper physical relations between people, and that this is what you are "supposed" to do. Our idea of sexual relations is structured around reproductive activity, which is defined as "instinctual." Although sexual feelings of pleasure are instinctual, or at least innate, intercourse is not, strictly, their instinctive or innate goal. One of our society's myths is that it is "nature" or our "instincts" that make us have "sex" as we do. Actually, most of the time we do it the way we do because we have learned to do it that way. Even chimpanzees and other animals must learn to have intercourse (Yerkes; Harlow and Harlow; H. C. Bingham). Sex and all physical relations are something *we* create; they are *cultural* forms, not biological forms. Most often, however, we do not think of ourselves as free to explore and discover or invent whatever kinds of varied physical relations we might want, or which might seem natural to us at any given time, corresponding to our own individual feelings and needs. Instead, we tend to act as if there were one set formula for having intimate physical contact with other people (who "must" be of the opposite sex), which includes foreplay, intercourse, and male orgasm.

From this point of view, the answers women have given when asked if they like "sex" can be seen as reflecting their feelings about this standard definition: if intercourse were instinctive, and if the way we have sex were nature itself, how could anyone (who is not "neurotic") say they don't like it? Or how could anyone say they would like to change it? Sex is sex, and either you like it or you don't. However, as we have seen, the more specific questions did bring out all kinds of satisfactions and dissatisfactions with sex as we know it.

There is great pressure on women in our society to say they like "sex." As one woman put it, "With the current spotlight on sex, the knowledge that I have a good sex life protects me from damaging doubts about myself every time I read an article about sex." Women *must* "do it right" and especially they must enjoy it. Any woman who says she does not like sex is labelled "not modern," "has problems," "weird," or "sick," by colleagues, counsellors, even friends. Women, for all kinds of reasons (just look at any woman's magazine), *must* like "sex." This means, essentially, that women must like heterosexual intercourse.

In fact, to even hint at questioning the glory and importance of intercourse as a primary value is like questioning the American flag or apple pie. One is not even allowed to *discuss* feelings about intercourse, or whether one likes it, etc., without arousing a strong emotional reaction in many people, who feel you are attacking *"men."* But this is not true. The fact that it is so perceived is merely another indication of how stereotyped our ideas about physical relations are and, further, how emotionally and politically sensitive a topic sex is.

To reinforce in us these ideas of what sex is, and especially that heterosexual intercourse is *the* high point in every case, all kinds of people—from physicians to clergymen to self-styled sex experts in books and women's magazines to our own lovers—instruct us in what sex is, and in the proper ways of having it. But, how can there be a "proper way" of touching another human being? Sex manuals tell us with mechanical precision where to touch, how to touch, when to orgasm, that it is bad not to orgasm, and so on. Especially, we learn that no matter what else, intercourse and male orgasm *must* take place. Although this subject will be pursued further in a later chapter, it is important to stress here that, although sex manuals can be helpful, it is *we* who know what we want at any given time, and we who can create sex in whatever image we want. There is no need to follow any one pattern to be close to another human being.

Love

But somehow, the truth is more complicated than the simple idea that women are oppressed in bed as elsewhere out of "habit"—simply because "just as women are used to serving men their coffee, so they are used to serving them their orgasms." It is still remarkable how easily we bring ourselves to orgasm during masturbation, and how totally we can ignore this knowledge during sex with another, especially a man. It seems clear that we are often afraid to use this knowledge during sex with men because to do so would be to challenge male authority. Somehow it is alright for a woman to demand equal pay, but to demand or create equality in sex is not considered valid.

Why are women afraid to challenge men in bed? First, they fear losing men's "love." The question of what love is, of course, is very complicated,* but it is clear that as seen throughout this chapter, the importance of sex for women is inextricably bound up with love:

"Sex for me is a very private and almost sacred thing. To me sex means the supreme proof of love."

*This book has purposely refrained from bringing these feelings into the discussion, since the politics of love still remain to be analysed. If you would like to contribute, please send an email to info@hite-research.com, or c/o this publisher, for a copy of the questions on love and personal relationships.

"'In my own case, I desire happiness, togetherness love, etc., and I know that if for no apparent reason I kept refusing sex, I would lose some of the happiness in my life, and I might lose the love my man has for me. He would assume that something was wrong and make changes, perhaps excluding me from his life.'"

"It's a trade. Like my mother says, men give love for sex, women give sex for love."

It does seem to many sex therapists that fear of losing a man's love *is* holding many women back from having orgasms with men. According to Helen Kaplan in *The New Sex Therapy*:

> . . . *the frank reaching for sexual pleasure may mobilize unconscious fears (in a woman) that she will be abandoned. She may be afraid that her husband will get tired of 'catering' to her. Or, if the patient assumes the superior position in coitus, she may be afraid that her husband will find her unsatisfactory sexually because she is unattractive in that sitting-up position. These fears may have some basis in reality. The husband may, in fact, become impatient or rejecting. Moreover, if he feels that his sexual role has been pre-empted, this experience may give rise to anxiety in the husband as well, and in that event he may defend against this anxiety by behaving in ways that repel or frighten his wife.*[1]

Similarly, Fisher found that the *only* difference psychologically between those women who were able to orgasm with their husbands (his sample were all married) and those who were not, involved love. As Fisher reported:

> . . . *the prime difference between women who are high and low in orgasmic consistency is their alarm about losing what they love. The low-orgasmic woman feels that persons she values and loves are not dependable, that they may unpredictably leave her. She seems to be chronically*

preoccupied with the possibility of being separated from
those with whom she has had intimate relationships.[2]

In addition, he remarks:

It should be pointed out that this fear of loss of love object
bears a remarkable resemblance to a type of anxiety that has
been found to be particularly characteristic of women . . .
women have been observed in several studies . . . to be
especially sensitive to potential separation from those with
whom they have close relationships."[3]

In his epilogue Fisher says:

The psychological factors—for example, fear of object
loss—which my work suggests may interfere with orgasm
attainment in many women may exemplify at another
level the general cultural feeling transmitted to woman
that her place is uncertain and that she survives only
because the male protects her. *The apparent importance*
of fear of object loss in inhibiting orgasm can probably be
traced to the fact that the little girl gets innumerable
messages which tell her that the female cannot survive
alone and is likely to get into serious trouble if she is not
supported by a strong and capable male. It does not seem
too radical to predict that when women are able to
grow up in a culture in which they are less pressured to
obedience by threats of potential desertion, the so-
called orgasm problem will fade away.[4]
[Emphasis mine.—Author.]

It is heartening to note that, since the research in this book,
and the increased numbers of women in the workforce,
more women than previously now take action to create an
orgasm for themselves as well as their partners. Although
Fisher, as a psychologist, tends to see these fears of loss of
love as emanating from childhood experiences, it is obvious
that they also can be reactions to very real current, adult

conditions, such as fears that as you get older the man you love will stop loving you, that he needs you less than you need him, and so forth.

Economics

Not only may a woman be afraid of losing a man's love, if she asserts herself, or "challenges" him sexually, but all too often economic intimidation is also involved. This can take many forms, some subtle, some overt. The most obvious form of economic intimidation occurs when a woman is totally dependent on the man with whom she has sex for food and shelter, and has no economic alternatives such as being able to get a job herself if she wants—that is, marriage as it was traditionally defined. We have all seen the connection between affection and economics in a mild form on "I Love Lucy,"* where affectionate words and embraces were always a standard part of talking Ricky into a new sofa, a new hat, or a vacation. Some of the women in this study also mentioned the connection between sex and economics in their lives, in answer to *"Do you feel that having sex is in any way political?"*:

"In my circle, generally the man makes twice as much money as the wife. That means if you like your lifestyle—your swimming pool, leisure, shrink, dishwasher, neighbourhood—you don't chuck it all to run off with some surfer. I see a lot of marriages held together not with a genuine desire to share a life, but with a need to keep things financially secure. When women make as good a living as men do, there will be far fewer of these feudal relationships."

"My husband has on occasion threatened to withhold money or favours—that is, permission of some sort or another—if I do not have sex with him. So I fake

*A 1950s US television soap opera popular fom South America to Europe to the Middle East until the late 1970s (in re-runs).

it. What the hell. When the kids are older—I just might lay my cards on the table."

"I'm not sure if it's political, but it's economic. I really felt I was earning my room and board in bed for years, and if I wanted anything, my husband was more likely to give it to me after sex. Now that I am self-supporting, I don't need to play that game any more. What a relief!"

"I think it is used for 'horse trading.' I know I have used it that way, and I think most women have been forced to use it that way (for bargaining purposes and to gain economic support) at one time or another, although this is gradually changing as jobs become open to us."

"With my husband, I sometimes feel obligated because I'm his wife and, after all, he does pay for everything. That's why I enjoy extramarital affairs (although I haven't had one in some time)—it makes sex special and exciting."

"There are times when I feel I'm discharging an obligation, like washing the dishes or doing the ironing Then I feel like a prostitute."

"For me, I'm glad to have lived long enough to see the light out of the tunnel—the hope that women some day will get an equal shake. Can you imagine what a brainwashed era it was forty years ago? You had to consider yourself lucky you had a husband, and most of the time you were sure something was wrong with you, and you just spent your life catering to men and your children and you touched your forehead to the floor that he didn't beat you—that he provided for you, and all you were was an unpaid domestic. His death freed me, and I discovered a career and life for a woman. Some of my peers died without ever knowing that there was hope for the female—died ignorant of the whole thing."

Anyone who is economically and legally dependent on another person, as women traditionally were, and in the many cases still are, is put in a very vulnerable and precarious position when that person expects or demands sex or affection. Although the woman may genuinely want to please the man, still, the fact that she does not feel free *not* to please him, and that she puts his satisfaction before her own and keeps secret her own knowledge of her body, reveals the presence of an element of fear and intimidation. Clearly, if a woman is financially dependent on a man, she is not in a good position to demand equality in bed. Economic dependency, even if you love someone, is a very subtle and corrosive force.

Until quite recently and still in most countries of the world, *legally* in marriage, a woman *must* have intercourse with her husband.* As Kinsey explained it:

> *Both Hebrew and Christian codes have emphasized the obligation of the wife, and to some lesser degree the obligation of the husband, to engage in coitus with the lawfully wedded spouse . . . The position of the wife in a marriage is reflected in the traditional attitude of English and American law which rules that she, in consenting to marry, has thereby given her irrevocable consent to accept coitus under any conditions from her husband, even though he may use extreme force or violence to achieve his ends. Even under present-day American penal codes, a husband's coitus with his wife can never be interpreted as rape, no matter how much the coitus may be against her wishes and no matter how much force he may use.*[5]

Even the position most commonly used today—the man on top of the woman—is a legacy of ecclesiastical law. Kinsey was writing in the 1950s, but most of these laws are still on the books today. Although they are unevenly enforced in various places, in general, they still are very much in force.

Of course, it is not marriage itself that is at fault—that

---

*Germany, France and other EU countries as well as the UK, passed laws prohibiting rape in marriage during the 1990s.

is, the idea of two people wanting to share their lives in common goals. Marriage in the sense of a *real* love contract could be wonderful. However, the reality of marriage now for many women is economic and legal dependency. This dependency can keep women from feeling free to explore and discover their own sexual feelings with their husbands.

Women who are not married can be economically intimidated in other, more subtle ways. As one woman explained her situation:

"From early childhood, I felt I was programmed by my family background and society to become a wife and mother with a fallback on a meaningless job. Therefore I graduated with high grades in nothing subjects and went on for one year to a community college to study to be a secretary. For the next five years I worked as a secretary (still am one). During this time I have felt very inferior about my position in life and I am sure this carried over into my sexuality and feelings about myself. In the last three weeks I have made the decision to quit my secretarial job and return to school full-time. This decision has worked miracles for me. I have a higher opinion of myself and feel totally unwilling to become involved in any kind of relationship (sexual or other) that is destructive in any way for me. I feel free to enjoy my body on my own terms, and not as some preconceived notion of some sexist man. I do not hate all men at all—I feel my attitude is very healthy and will not hinder me from developing good relationships with men."

On another level, even a woman who is only on a "'date" with a man can be made to feel that she "owes" him sex:

"I hate Disneyland dating—the old 'I-took-you-here-and-spent-$$$-so-now-you-go-to-bed-with-me.'"

"There were times when I was in school I would go out to dinner with a guy just for the chance to eat

something besides spaghetti—I was very poor. I knew
they usually wanted sex, and the less I was able to afford
the dinner he was paying for, the more I felt I owed it to
him. The more grateful I felt. Isn't that awful? It was
terrible, but I couldn't help it."

As Dr Pepper Schwartz has pointed out, even when women
are no longer economically dependent, they are still

> . . . used to modifying (their sexual) desire to fit their more
> important needs: food, shelter, protection, and security, and
> most have ceased to be analytical about their sexual
> situation. Even when the situation arises that makes them
> independent of such considerations (personal wealth, a
> successful career, and a bevy of admirers, etc.) they are so
> used to having other exigencies define their sexual and
> marital structure that they do not re-evaluate their life style.
> They believe the myths they have heard about their
> emotional and sexual needs.[6]

There are also economic pressures on single women to get
married—leading to the same financial and legal dependency discussed earlier; as one women, age twenty-seven, working in an office, explained her situation:
    "Even with the jobs I can get—and I'm a good
secretary—I still can't afford to pay my rent. I'm forced
to move in with a man, or else have roommates.
Roommates do not give you any privacy, and living with
some guy—first one guy and then, after a year or two,
another guy, and so on—is a horrible way to live. You
feel like an itinerant worker, moving all your belongings
from place to place. It's humiliating. So you have the
pressure to get married and settle down and forget it.
And—(!!) if you are just living with a man on a
supposedly equal share-the-rent basis, guess who still
gets to clean house and cook? And be loving and
affectionate and always ready for sex? And if, God
forbid, you just don't feel like it for a while—out you go!

So—you wind up thinking you'd be better off married."
As the Redstockings put it,

*For many women marriage is one of the few forms of
employment that is readily available. Not marrying for
them could easily mean becoming a domestic or factory
worker or going on welfare. To advocate women "liberate
themselves" by giving up marriage reflects a strong class bias
in automatically excluding the mass of women who have no
other means of support but a husband.*[7]*

Of course this is not to say that love (for husband and children) cannot also be involved. Unfortunately, however, economic dependency can eventually corrode and subtly undermine the most beautiful feelings, or even go hand in hand with those feelings, leading to a kind of love-hate situation. Marriage could become a *real* love contract (either heterosexual or homosexual) if laws that make women legally dependent are changed and when women have a real chance for economic autonomy.

The negative effect of economics on women's freedom, both sexual and otherwise, is widespread. According to the US Department of Labor, in 1975, women who worked full-time year round (40 per cent of American women) still earned only about 60 per cent of the wages of similarly employed men. In 1995, over half of American women were employed, yet still only earned 75 per cent of men's wages. Women, despite their education and qualifications, are still largely absent from higher management and corporate executive suites—though there is some hope that this is

---

*Dorothy Tennov, in *Prime Time* (a journal "for the liberation of women in the prime of life"), has looked at it another way: "Those who recognize that wives who remain in marriage for economic reasons are, in fact, selling sexual services may condemn the practice on the basis of the male-serving edict that there is something wrong with selling sexual services. The thing that is wrong with the wife's situation is not that she gets paid for her services—sexual and others—but that she receives so little for what she provides that she remains dependent."[8]

changing. Women in the US have won back-pay discrimination law suits against employers like Texaco and Ford. Still, women's financial independence is fragile.

In other words, as Ellen DuBois of the State University of New York at Buffalo, has written:

> *An erroneous and dangerous assumption is that the only thing that stands between a woman and "satisfactory" sex is her realization of her own physical needs. As an oppressed people, what we women lack is not knowledge . . . but power, social power, economic power, physical power. To put it another way, it is not our ignorance that has condemned us to sexual exploitation and dissatisfaction, but our powerlessness.*

7 The sexual revolution

"What was the "sexual revolution"—and how do women feel about it?"

> "If the Sexual Revolution implies the attitude that now women are 'free' too, and they can fuck strangers and fuck over the opposite sex, just the way men can, I think it's revolting. Women don't want to be 'free' to adopt the male model of sexuality; they want to be free to find their own."

"Did the sixties' 'sexual revolution' help women or rip women off?"

The "sexual revolution" of the 1960s (with whose legacy we are still living) was a response to long-term social changes that affected the structure of the family and women's role in it. Contrary to popular opinion, the "sexual revolution" was not the same thing as the "women's liberation movement". In fact, also contrary to popular opinion, the birth control pill may have been more a technological response to these same historic social changes than their cause. Up until the second half of the twentieth century, a high birth rate was considered of primary importance, and the larger the population, the wealthier the society would be, and the stronger the army. Modern technology, however, ended the need for huge work-forces, while nuclear power and technology are far more significant militarily than massive human armies. Large populations are valuable principally as consumers.

Children used to add to the family income by working, and they assured the parents of support and protection in their old age. Socially, male children continued the family name, and increased the family's social prestige. Today these assets are considered negligible: children cost a great deal, their education is prolonged, and after the second or third child, a couple's standing in the community diminishes rather than rises. In addition, most men no longer feel that carrying on the family line is a matter of primary importance—

although they may very well enjoy having children. All this meant that childbearing was no longer so crucial or necessary: women could be "allowed" sexual "freedom."

This "new freedom" of the pill was double-edged. Insofar as having many children became less important, women's status declined. That is, since women had traditionally been seen almost completely in terms of their childbearing role, they themselves as a class became less respected when that role was no longer so important. At the same time, it was said that, now that women were "free" from their old role, they could take up new roles and be "sexually free like men," etc. There was some truth to the idea that new possibilities for female independence *had* opened up. However, since women did not have equal opportunities for education or employment, they were stuck in their traditional role of being dependent on men. These women found dating and having relationships with men an area of great confusion, like quicksand. While marriage had offered some forms of protection, for some women, the new free-floating relationships often increased insecurity, as reflected in the childlike, baby-doll fashions of the 1960s—short little-girl women's dresses, long straight (blonde) hair, big innocent (blue) eyes, and of course always looking as young and pretty as possible. The change in men's attitude towards women (from mother to sex object) is summed up in Molly Haskell's title to her 1970s' book about women in the century's movies, *From Reverence to Rape.* This situation eventually led to the women's movement of the early 1970s, which began working to implement some of the positive potential in the change in women's role, to make women truly independent and free.

In conclusion, what we think of as "sexual freedom"—the 1960s' movement giving women the "right" to have sex without marriage, and decreasing the emphasis on monogamy—was a function of the decreased importance of child-bearing to society. Although labelled "sexual freedom," in fact it did not fully allow much real freedom for women (or men) to explore their own sexuality; it merely put pressure on them to have *more* of the same kind of sex.

The ambiguity of the "sexual revolution"

"What do you think of the sexual revolution?"

Answers to this question varied, including the following range of opinions:

1. I like it, because it allows more openness. It is basically a good thing, healthy and necessary.

2. It is long overdue, but not over yet and has a long way to go.

3. What revolution? There has been no real revolution. It makes women feel they *have* to have sex and can't say "no."

4. It is a male rip-off and exploits women.

5. It came along too late for me, but is probably fun. I wish I'd been born later.

6. Mixed emotions. I don't understand what it's all about, and sometimes it seems to go too far.

7. I don't believe in it; it is bad and leads to promiscuity, etc.

During the 1970s more women expressed the first opinion—that increased openness is good—than any other.* However, they often shared some of the doubts of other women. Many married women and older women in particular, who had not experienced "sexual freedom" personally, took this long view of the change:

---

*In this chapter, unlike the earlier chapters on physical stimulation for orgasm, or the later chapter on more abstract theory, differences will be noted between statements received for this study in the 1970s and those made or received between 1995 and 2000.

"It's highly important and the only sensible way our society can go. Future young people—my grandchildren—will reap the benefits of it. The sexual revolution is one more step to humanity's adulthood, but it has been exploited and needs refinement."

"I really hope that people are becoming freer and more tolerant of both their own and others' attitudes. I hope we can pass it on to the next generation. Our sexuality is so integral to our everyday lives, that I hope I can see progress in other areas, socially, politically, and intellectually, before I die, as well."

"It's about time we are able to be human and feel normal instead of some quiet closet pervert. Now people can discuss freely many things which years ago were considered vulgar. Women now are beginning to have a say if they want instead of acting like quiet little girls; they can express themselves and their feelings, they can now begin to learn a lot about others and themselves."

"People are finally acknowledging that they have penises and vaginas and that they enjoy using them. I think it's healthy and helps us do away with our cramping inhibitions."

"It's marvellous, because it finally allows those of us who grew up in the 1950s to break out of that horrible inhibition, guilt, and unnatural 'respect' for our bodies."

"The sexual revolution (if you could call it that) has brought sex and body communication out into the open a little more than before, along with attempts to make it more natural and better understood. People are just as hung up as always—but at least they are talking more and realizing they aren't alone with their problems."

"It's good for the most part, especially less guilt about masturbation and more acceptance of sex as a part of life—a healthy reconsideration of our customs and values."

"I think it is great because a lot of people are finally learning to become comfortable with and accept their own sexuality for the first time in their lives. The young ones coming up will not have all our hang-ups to get rid of in the first place."

"It is good that more people are talking about sex and I think that more women are recognizing themselves as sexual beings—not passive objects waiting for a man's arousal. I don't think that my mother ever enjoyed sex though she is beautiful and a strong woman. She doesn't talk about it or read about it, to my knowledge, and I think that she has always depended entirely on my father for sexual feedback. I think that it was always an in-the-dark, under-the-covers ordeal that she tolerated out of a sense of duty. This could have happened to me also if times were not looser now. I am glad for a greater sexual freedom, but see too many women fucking out of a sense of obligation and exploiting themselves, using their sex to manipulate men. It seems to be the only hold we have over them at times."

"No love is 'free'—there are always consequences. But I do approve of alliances outside of marriage so long as children are not involved. I really believe fifty-year marriages are over—especially the gritted teeth till death kind."

Some of these women, although they thought the sexual revolution was good in general, worried about its effects on their daughters.

"The sexual revolution today is men acting haughty, knowing women will be there, available, desperate to please them, trying to get them 'to love them' or 'in a relationship', thinking they are kings. The ironic part of it is that today's lads—especially the young skinny ones in T-shirts and hip suits with punky hairdos (gel, you know what I mean)—want to have it both ways: they are the New Men, with it, 'hey man, women are cool, I don't have a problem, guys in my generation don't have those old hang-ups'—but at the same time, they are the same ones who usually expect to spend the night with

my daughter or her friends, expecting her to have a
fridge full of food (food I brought her for HER) and
nice, clean sheets and towels (she brings them over here
to use my washing machine once a week) to make their
Sexual Event Evening a pleasant one . . . I see her being
exploited but I don't say so, she would just say I didn't
understand and was being critical, but I worry about
her, especially with AIDS. I know she thinks her
boyfriends are fun and great, but I doubt if she really
makes them wear a condom—'after the first time, when
I know them, it's okay, mom, really it is, trust my
judgement!' It's useless for me to tell her, 'But knowing
they are okay as people doesn't mean even they know if
they have HIV without a test, don't you realize that?'
She looks at the ceiling like I'm hopeless, and I drop the
subject, just help her stock the fridge. What else should
I do?"

"I don't really know—I think that if people feel
more, that is great. I have three daughters, twenty-four,
twenty-three, and eighteen—and they all have had good
sex experiences, which I am quite happy for, although I
am concerned a bit about the wisdom of sex so young."

"It's mostly a good thing, though sometimes I think
if I see another *Playboy* spread on sex in the movies I'll
scream. I still have an old-fashioned streak. One of my
daughters recently had an abortion (at sixteen) and
hastened to assure me that the boy who had
impregnated her was not her best boyfriend; she didn't
want me to be mad at *him!* Well, I wouldn't have been
mad at him—to tell the truth, it would have just made
the abortion hard to take, because I like him so much I'd
have had an awful time signing the papers to condemn
the potential baby to oblivion. On the other hand, I
found myself feeling regretful that she was having
relations with other boys, even though this is acceptable
in her crowd. I would have preferred to think the boy I
care for is the only one."

"If you mean the free-wheeling 'easy' sex present

right now, I worry about it because of a sixteen-year-old daughter and a ten-year-old daughter. I see notes my sixteen-year-old writes back and forth with friends and it upsets me very much. She is presently a virgin and I want her to stay that way."

"I think the sexual revolution is basically good. My only hesitations are 1) an almost inevitable development of guilt feelings in those who do not feel 'with it.' Eventually these reactions should subside but I feel sorry for those who will suffer for it. 2) I also am concerned that young people have not been prepared for this. I would categorize this group as those between eight and twenty who have been or will be influenced greatly by traditional attitudes and at the same time by the current new ones. Their traditional upbringing and current level of experience are not sufficient to help in the decision-making process they will inevitably encounter. The traditional viewpoint says 'don't' and the new revolt says 'do.' They are not experienced and frequently cannot accept their personal decision because of the tug of war of the old versus the new viewpoints."

Only a very few women totally accepted it for their daughters.

"I'm all for the sexual revolution. I think a good many of my children's generation are benefiting from the breakdown of many crippling taboos about sex. I like the fact that my children now in their early twenties have good relationships with young people I like; that I was able to speak very candidly and openly with my daughter, answer all her questions about sex long before she had her first experience, and that sex seems to be a healthy part of their lives, not something secretive and apart."

"It is amazing to me that it's this easy to write about these things and yet I never discuss them with women. I recall finding my fourteen-year-old daughter asleep in bed naked with a young man one morning and smiling and tiptoeing out. But I couldn't ask her about her experience, nor could she tell me about it (with a view of comparing notes, giving advice, etc.). However, I told her about this questionnaire and she wants to answer it too. I'm not at all sure she wouldn't think I was pushing for unwanted intimacy if I photocopied this and let her read my answers."

"My nineteen-year-old daughter was encouraged by me to have her young man spend the night at our house—rather than 'play games' and pretend it was not happening—and that worked fairly well for us. I never worried about it much with my kids—let them go on camping trips, etc. with their peers and just trusted their judgement, which they seem to have; however, at twenty my daughter did get pregnant and had an abortion (from the same young man) and I supported her through it—feeling proud of her judgement but irritated and concerned that she somehow deliberately (??) let herself get pregnant and now still wonder why—and she hasn't figured that one out either."

Many of the answers reflected strong reactions against the so-called sexual revolution. Many women felt there was no real revolution.

"I think there is a lot of talk about the 'sexual' revolution but I don't think there has been much change in attitudes. Just having left my husband of eight years, four months ago, I am somewhat shocked by the fact that men still want to play games, that they can't accept me as a person when I am strong, intelligent, and have as much will and strength as they do. It has me quite worried actually because I know in order to relate to me sexually, they also have to accept me as a person—and there aren't many men around who do not feel threatened by strong women."

"It's got a long way to go. If the crap in *Playboy* or *Penthouse* is anybody's idea of a sexual revolution then it's revolting all right. As long as women are exploited sexually, viewed as sex objects and raised from the cradle to accommodate men, the sexual revolution is meaningless. It seems to me that the sexual revolution has just given the con men the chance to sell douches and razors, but that you don't see much in the way of real free expression and happiness, or joy in the body and in sex."

"I think the *idea* of a sexual revolution is very good, but I think that some people are out in left field in their interpretation of what needs to be done. *Playgirl* is no better than *Playboy* and they're both disgusting, and demoralize both men and women."

"Is there one? I hardly noticed. Talking a lot about sex hardly constitutes a revolution. Most 'swingers' are non-swingers. Most men have hardly heard of the clitoris. Boys are constantly looking to get laid, girls are constantly getting hurt—what else is new? Girls are going to bed somewhat more than they used to— nothing revolutionary about that—just a different way of handling a problem one still does not understand."

"What is it? Some journalist's expression? I think that wife-swapping, porno movies, etc. are not necessarily freedom but obsessions."

"It's just words. The 'sexual revolution' has been stimulated by advertising and by the ethics of competition and consumption, etc. It opened up a whole new market. Mini-skirts are not a revolution!"

"I'm not thrilled by it. People have sex more often with more people but the *kind* of sex most people have is still unhealthy."

"Baloney! Men get to look at women half-dressed or undressed more, there are more 'free fucks' around, and there are *more* women faking orgasms."

"The so-called sexual revolution, from my point of view, did nothing to liberate women or men. Men got a screw for free and it was done out in the open and under the liberal-radical guise of a revolution against anti- quated sex attitudes. Women still wanted those men for lifetime companions because they found their identity in the man instead of in themselves. Men still maintain the top position in the job market, in women's magazine stories, in bed, and in the mind of the female psyche. So really the sexual revolution advertised something I already knew: women are treated as objects. Only in this 'revolution' the oppressed didn't gain a thing. The oppressor began the 'sexual revolution' through rock music, the cosmetic market, Hugh Hefner, etc., but we weren't liberated from our roles, only more objectified. It also backfired on the patriarchy, by leading (indirectly) to the women's movement."

"I think it's got a long way to go before it's a real revolution. It's causing harm to women as it is now, especially young women. For older ones, too, I suppose, because the older men are, by and large, not liberated and still operating out of their *pig* assumptions—and we all assume older women aren't very sexy, so they are never asked to sleep with anyone and are considered neuters, expendable."

"The sexual revolution was late '60s bullshit. It was about *male* liberation, women being shared property instead of private property. And we know which kind of property gets better treatment."

"Men have reaped glorious benefits from the sexual revolution, but have acquired no more sense or sense of responsibility. My feeling is, 'Whatever happened to the good night kiss??'"

The crux of the matter—the effect of declaring sex healthy and necessary, and women "free" to do it—was to take away women's right *not* to have sex. Women lost their right to say "no."

"To me, the sexual revolution is just a simple reversal of the pressure I grew up with to be chaste—now there is another one path for all to follow, and it makes just as little sense. Both enforced sex and enforced abstinence are bad."

"I think the 'sexual revolution' basically pushes many women towards having sex more often and with more men than they want to. Now that women are supposed to enjoy sex as equally as men, they are considered 'square' or 'frigid' if they don't rush into bed, etc. I don't think men's attitudes have changed towards women; they are still threatened by aggressive women and they may dig a sex trip with a sexual woman, but not necessarily want a relationship with her."

"The line I hate the most is, 'You won't ball me because you're hung up,' which is what the sexual revolution has used to scare women with."

"Now men feel it's *expected*, the cherry on the sundae. When some of those men I've slept with call me they give their first and last names, thinking I do it with everybody, I guess—incredible!"

"I think it's destructive and a lot of bullshit. Not that I have anything kind to say about the Victorian idea of marriage either. But a woman retains less independence and integrity when she feels she has to screw every slob she runs into or risk not being a 'hip chick.' The whole freaked-out scene is some dude who's got his dope and his chick, both possessions for his pleasure. You go to a party and you're expected to ball because everyone balls at 'hip' parties. Well, maybe I just don't happen to feel like it. Or maybe I might feel like it after a while but I don't see sex as a prelude to getting to know each other as people. I think the most triumphant moment of my life was finally being able to get up out of bed as we were going through our preliminary rolling around, announcing 'this is a pile of shit,' and walking out of the room, not giving a damn whether I hurt his little ego or not, because suddenly my own ego and integrity were more important. It took me a long time to get to that place, a lot of trying to explain to guys why I don't want to screw them and really wanting them to understand. I now feel that if I go to bed with somebody it's because I want to and because the liking is mutual. It wasn't easy, but it feels good."

"The sexual revolution tells me I am abnormal if I don't desire to make it with every Tom, Dick, or Jane that I see. I am only free to say yes."

"I think sex is great but I don't want to sleep with everyone or anyone that comes along. There has to be a special attraction. There shouldn't be insinuations like if you won't sleep with a black guy you're a prude or scared or prejudiced."

"Indiscriminate sex is irresponsible. Loving your body and your feelings is beautiful. Guys looking for a girl 'who screws' is revolting."

"Some of the sexual revolution is okay. But when we like guys and say no to sex, the guys get all pissed off and will drop the girl. I don't like to be called a whore. If we don't give men the sex they want they call us sluts or bitches or anything else rotten they can think of. There is this girl I know and used to be friends with. She's sixteen. She had sex with one guy. This guy told all the guys at school and now when she doesn't give a guy what he wants, he'll beat her up just to get a good hard fuck."

"When I was a freshman (freshwoman!) at college (1968–69) I thought that a 'liberated woman' was one who could, as freely as men did, pick men up and have sex, with no emotional strings attached. Then I saw how shallow that was, and I got involved in women's liberation. Now I try to live my feminist politics in bed as well as elsewhere. Women sometimes feel they have to submit to sex with men, to keep them around. But I reserve the right to say 'no.'"

"The sexual revolution liberated a vast amount of masculine bestiality and hostility and exploitiveness. Some (few) younger women seem to know how to say no; the others have lost some protection. On the whole, there is a lot of mess revealed as prohibitions disappear; people are then free to be louses in a way they weren't before. It's something one must fight, but expect."

"Most men didn't give a damn about whether I wanted to have sex with them or not; if I didn't want to screw them, they would make a moral thing out of it, and try to lecture me into being 'free.'"

"I've opted out. The only sexual revolution I like is the one that gives equal time and freedom *not* to do what you don't want to do."

"Basically it's progressive but women still get *fucked*—literally, because now you have to prove how liberated you are and men use that."

"I personally have greatly benefited from the women's movement, which is a sexual revolution for me. I'm not sure whether the 'sexual revolution' is really that at all, and I hope women don't end up in general being even more exploited by it. If a sexual revolution means that either sex has the privilege of initiating and having sex whenever and however they want (between consenting adults) and people are aware of the intricacies of 'choice' and 'consenting' and no one is exploited, then *great!* However, I think we are a long way from that, and I think, as much as I hate to admit it, that among the majority of the population, a lot of guys are getting 'laid' a lot easier, and their responsibility towards the act and the relationship hasn't changed all that much. I think it is the minority of the population that is really involved in a true sexual revolution and I hope it spreads."

Many women, when asked "Were you ever afraid to say 'no' to someone for fear of 'turning him off?'" said they felt like cowards.

"I was afraid to say no and hated myself for being weak and submitting. Afterwards I thought, how can anyone like me or me like myself, if I can't say what I feel and not be threatened?"

"Yes, and afterwards I felt like a dead lump. A hole. A cunt."

"When I was younger I did. I felt like hell—angry and unhappy, and just plain powerless. Infuriated."

"Yes, I felt used, and later just disgusted with myself. I hope I have the strength never to let it happen again."

"Yes, when I am afraid. I feel lonely afterwards."

"I couldn't wait until intercourse was over and the

pain gone, but my feelings toward my partner make me feel that it would be unfair not to satisfy him physically."

"Powerlessness at not being able to say no and experiencing the development of something I don't want. It's harrowing."

"I never believed in the oft-quoted marital advice to a wife that she must always accede to her husband's demands. When I was first married, sixteen years ago, I made the headache excuses, etc., but now I just say 'not interested.' Sometimes I go along with his demands to keep peace in the relationship. On the other hand, if I want sex and he doesn't, that's a bit more difficult; he feels his time is too valuable to interrupt."

"I've never been raped but I've often had a combined feeling of unwillingness and accession."

"Very rarely have I had sex without wanting it. Sometimes I've had my doubts, and in the course of 'fooling around' have been turned on, begun intercourse, and then wished I hadn't done it—my emotional reluctance was strong enough to recur fast— then I wish I could just get up and leave the room, sorry, goodbye. But I stay, politely, like a hostess, and wish to hell the guy would disappear afterwards so I could go to sleep alone. But I act like a "nice person.'"

"My husband has a defensive personality. I have a horror of offending him. I always accommodate him, though it gives me no pleasure. Before, during, and afterwards I think, how can I remedy this situation?"

"Sometimes I hesitate to say 'no' when I would really like to. When I don't, then intercourse is not enjoyable to me. And I want it over with as soon as possible. There is not the feeling of closeness that I value and it leaves me feeling distant afterwards."

"I have never said 'no' to sexual overtures when they occurred during a continuing relationship. I resent my own passivity very much."

"Yes. Stupid. Disgusted, with my lack of spine."

"Sometimes I have been afraid to say 'no' to someone

for fear of spoiling what relationship we did have—the trouble is, I often don't know whether I feel good about them sexually till they are worked up, and by then it doesn't seem very fair to say 'no.' But I really hate sex if I don't feel like it, feel a bit revolted physically and very resentful of the person. Afterwards I feel very miserable and usually want to cry."

"Yes, at eighteen a man whose wife had just died used to come over. One day when no one was home he started touching my breast and suggesting more. He may have kissed me. I felt like protecting him from rejection rather than myself and then felt very guilty afterwards, and it caused me to cut off almost all sexual feelings for quite a while after that."

"When I was fifteen, my cousin told me that when a man gets a hard-on and doesn't come, it's the most painful thing in the world. I believed that till last year. I believed that if a man got turned on by me, it was unfortunately my responsibility to keep him out of his misery. So I'd be with Professor X or radical student Z who'd suddenly be standing there naked and hard and I'd say to myself, "Oh shit, oh no, I might as well go through with it and never see *him* again.""

"We were all taught that he can't control it! *He* is in pain! Shit! It's the same old martyr bit."

Questionnaire IV asked: "Have you ever been afraid to say 'no' to someone for fear of 'making a scene' or 'turning them off?' If so, how did you feel during sex? Would you define this as rape?"

"I never knew how to say no. I was brought up that nice girls were treated like ladies, and men behaved like gentlemen with them. I never knew girls were supposed to say no, that they were in control of the situation. I define as rape someone you don't know who attacks you. I never defined it as someone you go out with or someone you know. If you define rape that way, every woman has been raped over and over. In that situation feelings vary, from obligation to might-as-well to hatred for that one, or all men, to self-contempt—never any good feelings."

"I have been afraid to say no for fear of incurring a major hassle (if I was just afraid of 'turning them off' I would probably have said no anyway). Sex wasn't much fun on these occasions, as I was plagued with guilt and anger at the partners, and afterwards with shame. I guess these weren't technically rapes except when I feared physical harm, but I think any sex not wholeheartedly engaged in is rape. Even if the wholeheartedness is wholehearted jealousy, or something. The important point is that one makes love because that's what one wants to do, for whatever reasons, without reservations."

"Yes, cold, used, and hateful. I didn't then, but I do now, call it rape."

"Yes, once: I was afraid I was over-reacting if I just left, and he kept subtly making further and further advances after persuading me to stay over and promising me my own bed. Eventually I got tired of listlessly fighting him off in bits and pieces and thought okay, let him have his stupid orgasm and leave me alone. I had *no* feeling at all—not even a physical realization of the slight penetration, and did not believe him when he told me he'd been inside. Later, I discovered he had been right; I got pregnant. I used to think it was rape, because he knew my consent was not involved, but no one else seemed to think so."

"I have been afraid to say 'no.' Then if I give in and this person ignores me after sex, I feel angry and sad and humiliated. I don't know if this is rape."

"I was 'ripped off' by my boyfriend when I was a virgin. He really raped me, but not in the legal way. I couldn't prevent him, in other words. As a result I got pregnant and had a child. I gave the child away. This has caused a deep, deep feeling of resentment and bitterness which I can never get rid of. I think this colours my sex life. I have become more enlightened by the new books that I have read—*Free and Female, Sexual Politics, The Female Eunuch*, etc., and now realize how conditioned I am in regards to sex. I am trying very hard to undo all the damage."

"Oh yes. I went to a New Year's party with one guy once and crashed there. I said I didn't want to sleep with him and he said I could have the sofa. I felt I should be more relaxed, and I said no, I'd sleep on the floor too. Then he talked me into a corner: Why was I so afraid of touching? Afraid of sex? We didn't have to ball after all, we could just hug and touch. What, my God, why didn't I have orgasms? What was wrong with me? etc. etc. I felt raped even though we never had intercourse; we had oral sex. He didn't know my cunt from a hole in the wall. If this happened to me now I would have acted totally opposite but this was two years ago and I didn't really know that I could actually say no, and not have to prove that I was a 'woman.' This has been a major change in me—knowing I have the right to say no!"

"Women aren't always free to not have sex. The time I was beaten up by a strange man in a strange city, the police wouldn't do anything—they tried to say that he was my boyfriend, even though I didn't know him and he was trying to rape me. If you don't submit, you can be beaten, killed, and nothing is done. Under less severe circumstances, you don't want to yell and scream, especially if you know the guy, even if you don't want to sleep with him. Some guys understand if you don't want to have sex, or if you don't want to at a certain time; but most think they have a right to have sex with every woman just because she's there."

"Only with my husband. It was a condition of our marriage as it developed, that if I refused him sexually he was insufferable. I think this is a common degradation of women in marriage. But rape is too strong a word, as force was not involved. I felt I was prostituted, being used as a whore, with no regard for my desires. I think it is a barbaric tradition, that men cannot be refused by women in marriage, and this led to my finding my husband sexually repugnant."

Does this same amount of pressure exist today on women? Yes, but in a different form: although some men still pressure women by implying the woman is psychologically impaired if she doesn't want sex, or "old-fashioned", it is more common now for men to imply they are "too good for the woman," but might consider doing the woman the favour of making love to her once or twice—the woman, thinking she can change him, get through to "the real him" on a deeper level . . . that he is "only afraid of his feelings" trick.

How strong is the male "sex drive"?

Combined with this scenario is a further pressure: the idea that a man's need for "sex" is a strong and urgent "drive," which, if not satisfied, can lead to terrible consequences. As one woman phrased it, "Men being sexual animals, at least to my way of thinking, their bodies drive them to the culmination of sex, the climax, ejaculation, and depositing of their seed. I feel that most of them could gladly do without foreplay. At times I have felt guilty, especially if waiting for me has robbed my partner of some of the intensity of his climax."

This particular stereotype of male sexuality is extremely commonplace in men's minds as well as women's and reflects the picture most   frequently presented by sex manuals, psychologists, physicians, men's magazines, and many others. Typically, the male "sex drive" is seen as a constantly surfacing and demanding feeling; as Theodore Reik expressed it in *The Psychology of Sex Relations:*

> ... *the crude sex drive is a biological need which represents the instinct and is conditioned by chemical changes within the organism. The urge is dependent on inner secretions and its aim is the relieving of a physical tension.*
>
> *The crude sex-urge . . . is entirely incapable of being sublimated. If it is strongly excited, it needs, in its urgency, an immediate release. It cannot be deflected from its one aim to different aims, or at most can be as little diverted as the need to urinate or as hunger and thirst. It insists on gratification in its original realm.*[1]

This glorification of the male "sex drive" and male orgasm "needs" amounts to justifying men in whatever they have to do to get intercourse—even rape—and defines the "normal" male as one who is "hungry" for intercourse. On the other hand, the definition of female sexuality as passive and receptive (but since the sexual revolution, also necessary for a healthy woman) amounts to telling women to submit to this aggressive male "sex drive." Especially since the 1940s the glorification of male sexuality has often been justified as a kind of natural law of the jungle (the product, we are led to believe, of cave-man hormones), even by some of the most serious social scientists. Actually, the information available does not warrant such conclusions. This idea of male sexual "right" (via biology) is not much more scientifically based than the old idea that kings were monarchs by the grace of God and natural law. Just as kings said that any other political model (like democracy) would be unnatural and would not work just so men now say that if women are aggressive sexually (i.e., anything but passive), sex will be unnatural, they will become "impotent," and sex will be impossible.

What *is* "sex drive"? asks Lester A. Kirkendall, in "Towards a Clarification of the Concept of Male Sex Drive":

> *As the term "sex drive" is now used, it has become a blanket*

*term which obscures the components with which we are
actually dealing. We should distinguish between sexual
capacity, sexual performance, and sexual drive . . . that is,
what you can do, what you do do, and what you want to do.*[2]

Kirkendall explains that although capacity ("what you can
do") has a biological base, sex drive ("what you *want* to do")
"seems to be very largely a psychologically conditioned
component . . . Sex drive seems to vary considerably from
individual to individual, and from time to time in the same
individual, and these variations seem related to psychological factors." In other words, sex *drive* (not capacity) is more
a function of desires than "needs."*

A further point along this line is that even if a man has a
strong physical desire for orgasm—an erection, for example—there is nothing in nature, nothing physical, that
impels him to have that orgasm in a vagina. The stimulation he feels is linked to the desire for *orgasm,* and not to
any desire for intercourse *per se.* The physical "urge" a man
feels is a desire for further stimulation of the penis, or for
orgasm—not a desire to penetrate a woman's vagina. There
is no "beeper" or sensory device on his penis that makes
him seek a vagina in which to put his penis. This pleasurable connection is *learned,* not innate; as mentioned earlier,
even chimpanzees must learn to have intercourse, although
they masturbate on their own from early childhood. The
definition of male sexuality as being "instinctively" drawn
to heterosexual intercourse is only another example of the
way we define sexuality as reproductive activity.

Finally, there is not even a medical term for the colloquial
"blue balls." Contrary to popular opinion, it is no harder on
a man not to have an orgasm than on a woman. Men feel no
more "pain" then we do. Kinsey gets right to the point:

There is a popular opinion that the testes are the sources of

*For a discussion of possible hormonal influences, see John Money and Anke
Ehrhardt's* Man & Woman, Boy & Girl.

the semen which the male ejaculates. The testes are supposed to become swollen with accumulated secretions between the times of sexual activity, and periodic ejaculation is supposed to be necessary in order to relieve these pressures. Many males claim that their testes ache if they do not find regular sources of outlet, and throughout the history of erotic literature and in some psychoanalytic literature the satisfactions of orgasm are considered to depend upon the release of pressures in the "glands"—meaning the testes. Most of these opinions are, however, quite unfounded. The prostate, seminal vesicles, and Cowper's are the only glands which contribute any quantity of material to the semen, and they are the only structures which accumulate secretions which could create pressures that would need to be relieved. Although there is some evidence that the testes may secrete a bit of liquid when the male is erotically aroused, the amount of their secretion is too small to create any pressure. The testes may seem to hurt when there is unrelieved erotic arousal (the so-called stoneache* of the vernacular), but the pain probably comes from the muscular tensions in the perineal area, and possibly from the tensions in the sperm ducts, especially at the lower ends (the epididymis) where they are wrapped about the testes. Such aches are usually relieved in orgasm because the muscular tensions are relieved—but not because of the release of any pressures which have accumulated in the testes. Exactly similar pains may develop in the groins of the female when sexual arousal is prolonged for some time before there is any release in orgasm.[3]

In other words, if a man's desire for intercourse is not shared by a woman, there is no reason why masturbation or other stimulation will not provide him with an equally strong or stronger orgasm, although the psychological satisfaction may not be the same. Or, there is no overriding reason why he must have an orgasm at all. The point is that there is no

*"Blue-balls."

physically demanding male sex *drive* that forces men to pressure women into intercourse. Women need not be intimidated by this argument. As one woman answered, when asked "Have you ever been afraid to say 'no'?", *"No. This is my body, my breasts, and my cunt, and they are my territory and if anyone, even my husband, tries to take what I do not wish to give, it's WAR, baby."*

Of course, today the pressure on women and men to "have sex all the time" has lessened somewhat because of the tragedy of AIDS and HIV; one can always refuse sex "for health reasons". On the other hand, the man can offer to use a condom. This research does not show a particular increase in monogamy since the ravages of AIDS became apparent, media reports to the contrary.

One woman speaks for many:

"Pressure? Sex is so expected now that it goes beyond pressure, it's already internalized as Every Modern Girl's own identity. 'Hey, isn't it the twenty-first century? Women like sex too, don't they?' Never mind that there are still attitudes judging women negatively for being 'too sexy,' 'not really serious.' It hasn't been unheard of for a man to say to a woman after sex, 'You've got a lot of experience, you must have done this with a lot of guys.' (How about 'That was wonderful, I'm crazy about you,' this would be better.) My head is full of all this every time I get the hots for somebody. I'm already twenty-eight and I don't know how to find guys who are not like this."

The double standard: The continuing idea that there are "two kinds of woman"

"I think the sexual revolution is very anti-woman: men are telling women they're free to fuck around with whomever they want. But the catch is that the double standard is still employed. A man who has many lovers is 'sowing his oats'; a woman who has many lovers is a 'prostitute' or 'nymphomaniac.'"

The 72 per cent of women responding voiced this complaint.

"Several partners castigated me for indulging in sex with them at the conclusion of the act. This has left me somewhat fearful of rejection."

"Most males still have the feeling of wanting to conquer and win me. Therefore they try much harder to be nice and to please me before I agree to have intercourse with them. Then afterwards they are never as excited or as anxious to please as that first time (not just in sexual dealings either)."

"I started out when I was very young being open, natural, warm, spontaneous, uninhibited. In ten years I've become bitter, cold, cynical, angry, resentful, hateful, frightened, suspicious. I don't like it but that's where I've ended up."

"I suppose I should be totally against sex. I was fucking *many many* guys when I was young because they wanted me to and I couldn't refuse. I've been pregnant twice and have gone through much shit for abortion money, etc. I suppose I hate men except the man whom I live with. I think if we ever split I would be alone. I am pretty dried up and old for twenty-one but maybe I'll die young. This world's really fucked up."

"I just can't take the attitude that men put into women through the sexual act. When I find *the* rare man whose head is relatively okay I'll really try to hang on to him. Men have been raised in an environment where sex is seen as something they *need,* and that they must trick and seduce women into letting them have, against the woman's better judgement. Thus when a woman really chooses to have sex with a man, he doesn't see it that way. Rather he thinks he has won something, and proceeds to use it. Afterwards he doesn't care what happens to her. This is a terrible down for a woman—

although I'm trying to say, 'That's his problem, not mine,' and go my way."

"However casual sex is, it can still be friendly and constructive, which is how I want it to be. Boys have had casual sex with me and have then ignored me or thought less of me. I've been hurt, but in the long run what are they saying about themselves and their own attitudes? If they think sex is wrong and dirty and are disgusted with themselves for having it, all right, but please don't project your disgust onto me. If their semen is 'dirty' and I as the spitoon am therefore dirty, that's their problem. People may try to make me feel guilty, but I don't think I've done anything wrong."

"They generally pretend to care, to be enraptured, and talk bed talk till it is over, and then it's back to reality. The important thing is to not believe these lies, not get involved, just realize it is bed talk and you won't be hurt."

"It's great if you can just take as much of it as you want or need. Men who play off of it to be bigger schmucks than they already are hopefully will suffer appropriately in hell. I mean the type who say, 'Sure women are liberated now! Liberated to get laid . . .' Nobody should put up with that shit. Release your anger and tell that insignificant idiot what you think of him."

"There are too many men who still think 'loose woman, easy lay' and all kinds of other derogatory thoughts. Even if you are aggressive enough to get what you want, the whole double standard is still in effect, hidden under a surface of phoniness and pseudo-hip liberalness, it always comes out in the end."

"The sexual revolution is the biggest farce of the century for females. Before at least she had the right to say 'no.' Now she is a prude or worse if she doesn't put out whenever asked. And if she does have many short-term sexual encounters, she is considered a whore. The sexual revolution is a male production, its principles still concentrated on male values, e.g., why get married any more, since we have our pick of slick chicks."

"In high school, my favourite masturbation fantasy was to imagine that a pornographer was filming my masturbation and directing me. He'd tell me which way to turn, what to masturbate with. While stripping before a mirror, I'd imagine I was stripping for a camera. Later, when I was twenty I started to model. I'd meet men hitchhiking and ask them if they'd be interested in taking pictures of me nude. Soon I was making fifteen dollars a half hour—working at home. Then I got into pornography—fucking for cameras. I made a porno film for some men who own an 'adult bookstore.' We spent six hours making the film. I fucked several men— including the cameraman. I spent about two hours giving blow jobs to the men. By that time, I had not only lived out my every masturbation fantasy, but also over-lived every fantasy. The next day my muscles ached, my jaw was sore. My vagina was irritated from so much fucking—with men and wine bottles. Burned out. Satiated. For two weeks, the thought of sex made me tired. By the way, I only got thirty-five dollars for making that film. The men who made it never paid the rest which they previously promised. They knew I had no legal power—for I had signed no contract. I didn't think I needed a contract because they were so friendly, they smoked dope, they had long hair . . ."

"Incredible as it may seem, there is still a strong double standard. Although people practise sex more, they still have large remnants of their childhood prejudices and sexist ideas of sex. This makes it very hard to freely experience sexuality without fear of censure. Although I live at a college campus which is considered nationwide as a place of avant-garde sexual and intellectual ideas, it is not. Men here still disrespect women who have sex with those they're not 'in love with,' and if a woman cares about her esteem, it is only safe to have sex with either a male who cares about her so he won't make her feel bad and talk about her to other men so they disrespect her—or else with a person no one finds out about (like flings at ski resorts or vacations, etc.). One male, considered a leading radical here, was talking to a supposed female friend of his the day before Hallowe'en. They were invited to a costume party and she, having trouble deciding what to wear, asked him, 'What do you think I should go as?' Very cruelly, he replied, 'Why don't you go as a virgin? I'm sure nobody will recognize you!'"

"At a dinner party in Leeds, where I live, Sir Freddie (one of those businessmen, a stockbroker, I think or something in banking) was at a party at my parents' house. He started talking about a woman he knew, bragging, carrying on about so and so, 'she's been his mistress for ages', etc., etc. I didn't say anything, then later he kept throwing into the conversation bits about other women, whether they wore bras and whether you could see their nipples, and other nonsense like that, until finally I couldn't stand it anymore—such a big demonstration of male privilege, a monster ego that needed a big bang. So I stood up and said, in front of all present, 'If a woman is a man's "mistress," then what does that make him to her? Is he her "mister"??!' He looked at me, blinking, 'Huh?' I was furious but tried not to show it. 'If you say "his mistress",' I said condescendingly, looking at him like he was a small fly on the table, 'when there is no counterpart terminology for use in reverse, such as "he's her sonny-boy or something", then you are discriminating against women and making them look like things to be had.' And I sat down. The women there practically cheered, and several were giggling, trying to repress laughter. My parents were terrified the party was ruined, but he recovered himself, 'Quite right, my dear. I hadn't thought about it like that. I shall reconsider.' I was sure he wouldn't (he would stop saying 'mistress' for the next hour, but not 'nipple' and so on, probably), but still I felt I'd won and improved the tone of the party, by the way."

Be a "good girl"!
("You don't want to
get a reputation, do you?")

Almost all the women in this research study had been
brought up to be "good girls."* And the youngest girls, still
living at home, were, for the most part, *still* being taught to
be "good girls." Though sex is continuously talked about,
girls are often judged negatively, even today, by their families if they are "overly sexual" or "experimentally active".

"Sex was never talked about—what us kids knew
about sex was from what we heard or read. My sister got
pregnant at sixteen and from that time on my parents
were watching me so close, especially my Dad. Every
time I would say 'Can I talk to you' they'd always reply
'Are you pregnant?' When I'd ask if I could go out on a
date my Dad always had some nasty remarks about
getting laid or knocked up. Believe me I was thankful to
get out. I dated a lot and loved it. But I treated the guys
terrible because I always felt they wanted me only for a
bed partner."

"I was never told that sex was bad or dirty, although
my father used to freak out at my sexual activities with
boys, and he was constantly warning me that they
wouldn't respect me if I let them 'do things' with me. I
believed this. When he found out I wasn't a virgin at
sixteen, he wouldn't speak to me for months. I'd
forgotten this until now because the values they
mouthed were contradictory to the way they must have
felt. I think of them as liberal because they said they
were liberal, you know?"

"My mother is afraid of sex, I always knew that, but
I was shocked and saddened to learn finally that my

*There is an in-depth development of this point in Dr Leah Schaefer's work
Women and Sex (New York: Pantheon Books, 1973).

father is also ashamed of his own desire and does not want me to have sex because I am female. In a rare moment of opening up to him once, I asked him if, when a girl refused to kiss him goodnight, he would think that maybe she didn't want to. His answer was, 'No, I would think she was a good girl.' I can't tell you the agony that answer created in me. Probably the only fear I have left about sex now is that men will despise me if I let them make love to me because of their own fear and disgust, but any man who loses respect for me because I like sex and give myself to him—that is a man I don't want. Sometimes I even go so far as to think that if men got more satisfaction in bed, more real satisfaction— and that means honest, free giving on both sides and real, openly expressed joy in orgasm—there would cease to be wars. But perhaps that is wishful thinking."

"One experience which I think affected me deeply was my parents finding out I was sleeping with my lover. I was living at home for the summer. My mother read my diary. I'm sure not three days went by without intense fights, battles, pain, name calling, whore, slut, etc. Five years have gone by; we don't fight any more but we are not close. I've been a lot more frightened—and less spontaneous in all my relationships since that time."

"I lived at home until the age of twenty-three, and the sexual repression was incredible. My father freaked out every time I as much as mentioned such things as lipstick or dates or dancing. Once, I was about eighteen then, I think, my mother and I went shopping and I bought a beautiful purple velvet cape at a sale. I showed my father the cape, and he called me a prostitute ('street girl' was the expression he used; I think what he had in mind was the Biblical 'harlot'). The next day I gave the cape to the Salvation Army."

The "sexual revolution" simultaneously brought the problem of child sexual molestation out of the closet, and made it worse ("it's good for kids"):

"My first experience that I remember was when I was in the third grade. One of my girlfriend's fathers while I was at her house sent everyone else out of the house—or they were in another part of the house—and he took me in the bedroom and pulled my pants down and looked at my vagina and touched it and told me it was pretty. I knew it was wrong so it took me about a week before I told the girl what her father did and she didn't believe me and yelled that I was a liar, so I didn't tell anyone else. A year later a friend of my father did it (at our house). I can remember it really felt nice. My mother found out and he didn't show up any more, but right after that my sister and I started touching each other. That lasted about six months and we stopped that probably because we were afraid of getting caught by our parents."

And one woman described how her parents used religion to portray her as a "bad girl":

"When I was four I was told I had to accept Jesus or go to hell. I questioned it then and all my life. I wonder why I did and my sister, cousins, parents didn't. The mutant me. I had very strong sexual fantasies and along with them masturbation, as a kid and now, and all in secret but they helped me for I accepted them and enjoyed them even though when I was younger I suffered guilt feelings. But I've always been independent minded and when my dad hit me or screamed or my mom did, I kept it in and decided they were wrong. My mom has very warped views of women and they're shared by my dad. As I don't shave my legs or armpits my mom and dad inform me that it's nauseating, etc. My mom's always pleading with me to wear make-up on my eyes and to curl and comb my hair like my sister's. I keep it clean and long and that's me. And I have pride in my body. I don't like girls who dress like dolls and only for guys for I think clothes are for self-expression . . . my mom instilled fears in me by telling me when I was too young about perverts, etc. A release for her but a millstone around the neck for me for I couldn't handle it and I still suffer from them . . . man, the saddest thing is that they don't know and couldn't possibly understand. They don't even realize what they've put me through! I've tried to explain some minor stuff and get met with blank stares and Jesus-preaching . . . I remember a time when I was still a virgin and my father didn't take to something, maybe it was my clothes, and he called me a slut and a whore and every name in the book . . . said I opened my legs to every guy who came along. I was very sensitive about my self-respect as far as guys saw it. Everything was embedded in guilt . . . Then I was birthed and I've emerged an Amazon, and he still bellows, but, babes, he knows he's lost me and it's his biggest pain for he loves me and receives none back."

Sex and emotions

Today, the "Back to Basic Values" movement has stressed the connection between love and sex.

Some of the sexual revolution ideology stated that it was old-fashioned to want to connect sex with feelings—it meant you weren't "hip." Not only marriage but also monogamy and love or even tender feelings were often considered to be something only "neurotic" women wanted. The idea during the 1970s was that "people should spontaneously have sex and not worry about hurting each other, just behave freely and have sex, no strings, anytime with anybody, just for pure physical pleasure." But almost no woman in this study wanted that kind of sexual relationship very often—although a few thought that they *should:* "I saw a TV show the other night and this guy said we need to separate sex and love and I think he is right—that is why women get hurt so much because men for some reason seem to be able to do this while we have a great deal of trouble separating them. At least I don't seem to be able to." During the 1980s, the "Back to Basics" movement became popular, preaching a return to "love and marriage." But even in the 1920s, women had found the "sexual revolution" lacking in feelings during sex, according to this research.

Overwhelmingly, women wanted sex with feeling.
"I think the sexual revolution has totally distorted the place of sexuality to the point that it has become an end in itself, an escape, or a desperate attempt to achieve love. Writers like Rollo May (*Love* and *Will*) and the women's movement have helped me to value the integration of love and sex as opposed to casual encounters with partners who do not value me."

"Well, I like being able to have a sexual life even

though I am not married. But I do not like the casual and 'cool' sort of relationships as well as what used to be called 'romance.' I like to feel involved with someone."

"I approve of the acceptance of sexual desires and relations. But personally I still believe it is most desirable to have a personally intimate and close relationship, not a casual one."

"Where I see trouble is in people of my generation, many of my friends. In their attempts to be freed by the sexual revolution they have undertaken sexual practices they are not psychologically equipped to handle. In joining group gropes and multiple sexual encounters they seem to mess up their lives . . . leave their partners and families for all the wrong reasons . . . become middle-aged hippies, as though we could ever be twenty again. They seem confused and definitely not content. This older group has simply forgotten that sex should be a thing that fits in nicely with a lot of other things like a good nourishing one-to-one relationship, work, personal growth, strengthening friendships, going fishing and watching sunsets. I get the feeling they've thrown out all commitments, not just the bad ones. The sexual revolution has permitted me to share home and life with a man without marrying, and it gave me the right to choose my way of life without having to be a flag-carrying rebel about it, but if I were not to pick and choose within this revolution to suit myself, to avoid damaging myself . . . then I would not have been freed, and I feel the people I am talking about have not been freed by the so-called revolution either; they've just exchanged one kind of slavery for another. Without doubt though, more good than harm has come of it, and my generation will pass out of it in time anyway."

"I like sex a lot. But it can only supplement a warm, affectionate, mutually respecting, full personhood relationship. *It* can't be a relationship. It can't prove love. It can't prove anything. I have found sex with people I don't really like, or whom I'm not certain will really like me, or with people I don't feel I know well, to be very shallow and uncomfortable and physically unsatisfying. I don't believe you have to be 'in love' and married 'till death do us part' but mind and body are one organism and all tied up together, and it isn't even physically fun unless the people involved really like each other!"

"Because I'm very sensitive and afraid of getting hurt (I'm only eighteen), I still imbue intercourse with very strong emotional meaning. It upsets me and leaves me unhappy to be with someone who views intercourse casually and feels no meaningful tenderness afterwards."

"My emotions play an enormous part in sex for me—maybe too much for my liking. I sometimes feel that I'm too 'particular,' or selective or delicate—I have to be feeling very intensely, or in love, or overwhelmed by sexual feelings in order to enter a deep sexual encounter. Sometimes I worry about whether the man will expect too much from me, sometimes whether I will expect too much from him. Sometimes I worry about whether I won't feel enough, or will be disappointed afterwards. At times I have gone out to have a totally casual encounter just to avoid these complications. Most of my relationships—maybe all—begin with a combination of the physical and emotional. I can't get turned on to a partner without an emotional or mental factor being present, even if not primary. And sometimes it is primary, and the physical secondary."

"I think the sexual revolution has caused a lot of suffering. People use it to avoid commitment; they refuse to work at a relationship, preferring to search for the 'perfect' love. They fantasize their way through relationships, always seeking perfection, running scared at the first sign that work is needed to keep two people together. No one knows where the other person is at, and what attracts one may turn off another. Everyone wants to try everything, but not stick at any one thing, so they change from day to day, and are bewildered by the way they and their friends reverse options and trade partners. I'm not saying the old way was better, but I'm afraid of what kind of life I can look forward to. I'm not married, but even if I do get married it seems that my marriage has a small chance of surviving. And I don't see the advantages of this style, frankly."

"I'm confused as hell about the 'sexual' revolution.' My husband and I lived and slept together for over a year before we were married—and that was fine. We loved each other and there was some kind of commitment between us. The summer before I was married, my (then) fiancé was away and I slept twice with another man because I was curious. But extramarital sex, after a man and woman have made a big commitment to each other—I can't buy. I moved out on my husband when he took on a girl friend because I couldn't stand the pain. A year later, right now, we're negotiating. I hate to think of myself as behind the times, but I just can't hack anything but monogamy."

"I still believe the greatest sexual satisfaction comes from having a partner you care about. I've gone through stages of having several lovers and thinking I was really liberated. But I'm much more fulfilled now with one caring partner."

"It's an over-reaction and after years and years of the old double standard, of women expected to be pure and virginal for marriage and to always set the limits, society has overturned itself. Now women are supposed to be willing, ready, and able to have sex with anyone, anytime, no strings attached and so on. Out of the latter swing of the pendulum have come some good opening-ups of certain repressive taboos. But women, and men, remain oppressed by these roles. I have found that I *can't* detach myself from sex and still enjoy it. I can't make love with someone I'm not supposed to trust—and feel good about it. These attitudes don't treat me like a whole person either. Too much mind/body separation results in either compulsive screwers or strained virgins!"

Many women mentioned these same feelings in answer to 'What is it about sex that gives you the greatest displeasure?"

"The absolute worst was all the hassle I used to go through in New York with guys who abused me, who didn't know me and didn't like women, and considered it their prerogative to get laid. I minded the ordinary abuse more than the time I was raped, as the rape I could excuse on the grounds of psychological disturbance."

"One thing that makes sex so pleasurable is being able to share such an intimate part of someone. It is like being in a world with just you and your partner, everything else becomes unimportant at that moment. Then comes the moment when it must stop and after a while, after he goes home, then the total separation things sets in. I don't know, I get kind of depressed after it's over. But it is only slight depression. I suppose I feel that way not knowing if I will see him again."

"My greatest displeasure is feeling myself to be simply a substitute for his hand, a dish of mashed potatoes, or any warm place he can stick it into and come."

Birth control

The pill itself did not bring about "sexual freedom," as mentioned earlier, but did offer a new kind of protection from pregnancy. However, it (ironically) also had the effect of pressuring women into having more intercourse.

> "The pill doesn't lead to greater freedom but perhaps to greater availability to men: 'Well, baby, as long as you use birth control pills, this ain't going to matter.' "

Although there is no space to delve into the subject of birth control here, it is important to note that many women are dissatisfied with current forms of birth control, for a variety of reasons:

> "I feel free to enjoy sex although now I worry about the dangers of the pill instead of worrying about pregnancy. I have tried a few other methods but was terrified of becoming pregnant. I also feel extreme anger that I should be completely responsible for birth control and risk all the dangers."

> "The pill liberated men from condoms. I demand a return to the old way."

> "I think that if there is such a thing as a sexual revolution going on it is, for the most part, to the detriment of women. Men expect that a woman will consent to having sex more often and with less commitment. Men very rarely take responsibility for the birth control and it angers me that women have to be prepared every day for a man's sperm. Women are really wreaking havoc on their bodies and mainly for the

*For further reading about birth control pills, see *Doctor's Case Against the Pill* by Barbara Seaman (New York: Peter H. Wyden, 1969). See also Barbara Seaman and Gary Hull, 2000.

explicit pleasure and convenience of men."

"Contraception was a hassle till my hysterectomy. He didn't like his 'sensations' dulled by a rubber. The diaphragm hurt me; the coil caused constant bleeding and pain, and the pill had enough side effects to have probably caused the hysterectomy. I was very bitter that I had to endure all of these gadgets with rarely an orgasm while he could always come even when 'dulled' by the rubber."

"The birth control pill allows a woman to control her fertility but also forces her to take all the responsibility for birth control and to risk her life and health and future fertility."

"Contraception is a pain in the ass to me. I feel very frustrated and oppressed when I think about how relatively unreliable and/or unsafe or what nuisances they all are. I took birth control pills before and after we were married for about a year, then went off them as the doctor I had wouldn't let you use them longer than that if you never had used them before. I never went back on them because I discovered that they seemed to have had a bad effect on my vaginal secretions and made intercourse more painful because I had less lubrication—I still have that problem somewhat but then it was much worse. They also gave me breast pains that felt like someone was sticking pins in my breasts for about a week before the time you went off them to have a period. Because of that and all the studies that have been done on side effects (my family has a history of heart trouble, and cancer on both sides) I didn't feel very safe about using them. After that we have used condoms and I have used foam but don't really trust it and find it always seeps out and is a nuisance therefore. So mostly we use condoms, which I don't really like either, as I like to feel his penis. I am thinking about asking for a diaphragm the next time I go to the gynaecologist."

"The medical establishment, overwhelmingly male, has both not bothered to investigate 'female complaints' and also has withheld information about our bodies and our sexual functioning, plus spreading myths about menopause and vaginal infections (they may be caused by cunnilingus, etc.). *We* must be responsible for birth control, no matter how hard on our bodies, so men can be free to ejaculate into our vaginas; and we have no control over methods of birth, and are usually put to 'sleep' while male doctors do whatever they want with regard to the birth. Having a baby and a D&C and a cervical biopsy made me afraid of my reproductive organs for the first time."

"Contraception or lack of it affected my sexual life as food or lack of it affects a human's chances to survive. I used the rhythm method for five years, complete with temperature taking, chart keeping, and calendar eyeing, turning the bedroom into a laboratory. After my third unplanned baby was born in as many years, I desperately wrote a letter to the good Bishop inquiring if there had been any change in Vatican policy (what a fool I was). He directed me to the local Rhythm Clinic. What a joke that was! After the priest (male) sang the praises of rhythm, a doctor (you guessed it, male again) proceeded to confuse the safe days with the unsafe days. Upon leaving, and this is funniest of all, the priest gave us poor souls a gift—a thermometer wrapped in a baby blue and pink box. I stood on the street corner and laughed hysterically for minutes. The thermometer seemed the final indignity. I never got a chance to use the blessed thermometer as I was already two weeks pregnant with the fourth. My husband was wild with disgust by now and insisted he'd divorce me if I didn't get an abortion. Now, how could I consider abortion at that time if I couldn't even use any birth control! . . ."

"Contraception is a very sore spot with me. For two years I held off with my first lover because I was afraid of birth control and was too chicken to get the pill. I clearly remember the first time I got the pill at age nineteen. I had to go to this dingy-looking doctor in an old health clinic that didn't even examine me and sent me away with three months' supply of pills. At the beginning of every month I was on them I threw up, and since I have a very sensitive stomach, felt sick the first week of every month. Not until a year later did I connect the throwing up with the pill—I always thought I had the twenty-four-hour flu or food poisoning. I also remember crying constantly during that time. I went off them and did not go back on them till six months later. I vomited again, and tried eight different pills altogether. Two more made me vomit, one gave me break-through bleeding, one gave me severe periods that lasted two weeks, one gave me tender sore breasts, some made me gain weight, and I cried constantly on most of them. My sex drive also seemed to diminish. I also got raging vaginal infections every time I went back on the pill. That was probably the worst side affect—I have also read and been told by doctors that the pill can contribute to the things needed to get a vaginal infection, by creating a warmer, moister vagina with more discharge. Needless to say, I hate the birth control pill with a passion and think it's one of the most destructive devices ever developed for the female body."

"I think that women ought to withhold sex from any man (husband or lover or acquaintance) who is not willing to do something tangible to fight for their right to free legal abortion on demand. A woman puts herself in great danger by having intercourse, and contraceptives leave a great deal to be desired. I myself would like to feel that anyone who was close enough to me to be my lover would be fond enough of me to go to some trouble to see that I didn't need to worry about unwanted pregnancy. I feel that if I were sexually involved with a man who was threatened with some danger, I would exert some effort to help him. I would like a man to do this for me, too."

How important is sex?

Is sex necessary for health?

Finally, the sexual revolution also asserted that the sex "drive" must be regularly expressed to maintain "healthy functioning." Many women resented what turned into a commercialization and vulgarization of sex—a feeling that soon there would be "beds on the sidewalks and pills in the vending machines":

"We are taught that every little twinge is a big sex urge and we must attend to it or we'll be an old maid. I'm getting sick to death of sexuality—everywhere sex, sex, sex! So what? Sex is not the end all and be all of life. It's very nice but it's not everything!"

"I filled this questionnaire out because I wanted to think some about my sexuality. I found it helpful, though I felt uneasy sometimes. I felt divided: it seems progressive for women to affirm sexuality and their control of it but, on the other hand, I have long been oppressed by the overemphasis on sexuality. Also, for both men and women, sex in recent decades has been heavily associated with consumerism and with the ideological separation of public and private life. This overkill is politically bad and creates undue personal anxiety about sex for many people—myself included."

"I wish there wouldn't be as much of a 'hype' about sex as there is now. I hate the media's exploitation of sex and women. I would hope that women wouldn't be looked upon as things to look nice and to have sex with."

"For the most part, women are judged by their potential sexual worth. I would like sex to become more matter of fact, and more personal. In a way, I'd almost like to have back the hush-hush good old days when you just didn't talk about sex. It would not be hidden because it was dirty, but because it was a sweet, private thing."

The idea that sex is necessary for health became big business. Magazines, books, television ads using sex (or the happy couple) to sell their product, and some psychiatrists, counsellors, sex clinics, films, and massage parlours—all have a vested interest in the idea. We are constantly being reminded of sex in one way or another, and subtly coerced into doing it: "Why aren't you doing it? Everybody else is. Get on the bandwagon! You're missing all the fun if you don't!" (And you're probably neurotic and mentally unhealthy.) Many women commented on this, or felt defensive that they did not want to have sex more often:

"When I'm not seeing anyone in particular, I only feel interested in sex about once every two weeks. This makes me feel somewhat inadequate to say this. I feel it should be more frequent than this."

"If I go for long without sex, my desires drop ridiculously, which worries me. I start to wonder if something is 'wrong' with me, which makes me feel obligated to have sex. I usually think, 'Wow, it's been a long time since I've had it and I guess I ought to!'"

"Sex, but sex is something I do not have time for now, as building my career takes all of my energy. I guess I'm not as interested in sex as I should be."

To be told that we should have a regular "appetite" for intercourse does not coincide with how most women feel: periods of greater interest in sex with a partner, for most women, fluctuate according to attraction to a certain individual, quantity of work they are facing and (to a lesser extent), according to the menstrual cycle.*

*See Appendix 3.

Most women* emphasized that the appetite for sex with another person became really intense only in relation to desire for a specific person, although of course they could enjoy sex at any time. What causes the awakening of this intense desire or love for another, specific, person is very personal and mysterious.†

"Good sex involves a certain spark between two people. I once had a friend whom I had only to touch and the heat of his skin and his manner of being could arouse me. He had a very sexy way in my eyes, I don't know why. To this day I often think of him."

"Leaving out love and even commitment for the moment, good sex has to be more than anatomy or even 'psyching' yourself into it. It has to involve a certain amount of chemistry between two people. After a singularly disastrous experience trying to make a sexual relationship work when there was no attraction (just affection), I don't want to try to add sex to my friendships (unless I feel attraction too). I don't understand it in any way but 'chemistry,' but there certainly is such a thing as sexual attraction which can't be forced into existence."

"There is an irrational, mysterious element in sexual attraction and experience that I feel is left out here. It is real, but hard to discuss without ending up sounding like the cardboard fantasies of Hollywood movies and romance magazines—but it is real nevertheless."

"I've never been able to figure out what it is that draws me to a certain person; I don't think that it is any one basic trait. But although I can't define what the ingredient of attraction is, I usually know quite quickly

*This includes women who do orgasm with their partners as well as women who do not.
†All we really know about our sexuality is that we have a desire for orgasms, and that certain individuals and certain situations stimulate these desires in us more than others. Other primates like chimpanzees become genitally aroused from feelings of frustration or fear, anger, tension, joy, or exuberance, or from playful or affectionate body contact. Arousal, for humans also, is often brought on by tension or frustration, and not only by sexual feelings themselves.

after meeting someone when it is present; it is a combination of the physical and emotional make-up of that person. Occasionally, I will discover that I'm attracted to a person whom I've known for a long time—often I am surprised by this late attraction and wonder why I wasn't aware of it sooner."

"The thing I enjoy most is making love with people I have that 'special' feeling for—this is when it's most satisfying totally, even if it never gets down to real sex— it's still beautiful just holding them and feeling warmth and love with them."

Do you ever go for long periods without sex? Does it bother you? Do you feel you are missing something when you are not sleeping with a partner?

In fact, there is nothing unusual about spending various periods of one's life entirely without sex (with or without masturbating). Most of us went without sex until we were fifteen or twenty or twenty-five years old. Also, pregnancy, widowhood, old age, or being "single" are frequently celibate periods.

Many women had spent rather long periods of time in their lives without having sex with a partner— and sometimes without even masturbating—for many reasons.

"My husband and I go through very necessary times of emotional withdrawal from each other and at these times we don't have sex. We have been together for fourteen years and sometimes I am overwhelmed by a feeling of too much togetherness. We once went nearly two years without intercourse (although I did have orgasms by masturbation). It turned out not to be a serious deprivation, and of course, we were still very much in touch physically during this time."

"Having been single all my life, I have had long periods of celibacy in between lovers. I have presently been uninvolved for about six months, and I don't feel I'm missing anything in particular sexually. Once in a while I masturbate. Of course we were all celibate as children; in my case, I went twenty years until I was devirginized. If it didn't kill me then, I guess it won't kill me now."

"I have been divorced one and a half years and in that time I haven't had much sex. At this point in my life, it's just not really important, and I can't find many men that turn me on enough to want to have sexual relations with them anyway. Sex plays a very small part in my life, and I really don't seem to miss it."

"Military wives either endure or masturbate. I do both. I can't say I like a total diet of masturbation, however, because my best orgasms are through intercourse."

"Although reading both the book and the questionnaire make me extraordinarily defensive about this, having sex isn't very important to me for the most part. I lived with one man for most of seven and a half years; our sexual relationship was only active for about the first two and a half of those years. After that it dissolved almost completely—I don't think we fucked more than twice in the last year of it. During all that time I never had or actively desired an affair with another man (or woman), and the relationship with this one man was otherwise sufficiently satisfying and nourishing that I was able to imagine living with him for the rest of my life quite sexlessly. We were not unsensual—we did kiss and hug, and this physical contact was (I now understand) exceedingly important to me. I didn't relish the idea of no sex forever, but it seemed quite livable with, given the importance of the rest of the relationship to me."

"Since we broke up (eleven months ago), sex has become considerably more important to me, but what I think is operating is that having a relationship with a man is what is really important to me. After my first two sexual encounters after the break-up (both of which were one-nighters), I decided not to do it in the absence of at least the potential for a relationship. There are plenty of days when I feel very horny and very depressed and rather wish that I could take sex casually enough to just go ahead and do it with attractive men, but for the most part I feel okay about it, and would in the end rather spend time with women friends, or non-sexual time with men I like, or sit at home with a good book, or masturbate to relieve sexual tension, than go to bed with any but what someone in *Sexual Honesty* called 'quality men.'"

"I am single now, and my steady sex life is with myself, out of choice. As for sex with others, I seem to get hungry for it every couple of months. Which means I get to want contact with another body sexually enough so that my objections get minimized. Most of the time I feel I don't want to be that close to any man I know, or it's too complicated in terms of his or my feelings and expectations."

"I used to be very straight-laced about sex and did not engage in sexual intercourse until age thirty-four (this is true). I was very religious and thought surely I would marry, so I was waiting for marriage to begin my sex life. But I never found a man I wished to spend my entire life with, so when I reached my thirties and my sexual desires became even stronger, I compromised my religious beliefs. I felt some guilt at first, but quickly got over it because I had never known such lovely closeness and tenderness, or so much pleasure, before. And I realized that anything that made me feel so good could not be wrong. It was wonderful to be so physically and spiritually close to another human being. Now this man has been gone from my life for about three years, but

I've been quite happy without sex. I'm good at sublimating, I guess, and sometimes I masturbate. I still can't bring myself to have casual sex partners—I only want to have sex with someone I care about."

"I have had such a poor relationship with my husband for seven years that I no longer have sexual desires. I used to have desires for sex, but never reached the heights of passion I desired. A mental block formed somewhere during the last few years and I just gave up."

"I have been married for seventeen years. We no longer have sex. I don't have sex with anyone else, and don't think he does. We just don't feel that sexually involved, our sex life gradually trickled down to stopping altogether about four years ago, we talked about it and split up, thinking we should find others, but then we got back together again. I love him and he loves me. We want to be together. Is sex together so important? Why don't I get turned on to others, and why did he come back to me?"

"I was dismayed when a woman I started dating made comments like 'Rubbish' if I would try to call her 'Sweetie' or tell her how much I cared for her (heaven forbid I might say 'I love you'!). She made it clear that to her, all those soppy emotions are silly and not important. I tried to go along with it, but to me, I just can't get turned on or let myself go sexually without a little of the old romantic stuff, I just can't."

Sometimes celibacy could bring an increased sense of freedom and independence.

"Sometimes I get really high on being without any sexual activity. I think it's because I'm not dependent on anyone for anything."

"I haven't had intercourse for six months. At first, I fluctutated between depression and exuberance, but after a while I felt an increased sense of personal freedom and independence, and self-confidence. Now I like it, and I really enjoy having control over my desires."

"Not having any sexual relationships for a while (two years) gave me time to turn my life around—a beautiful and peaceful time."

"I have gone for long periods without sex (up to one and a half years), but not recently. During those periods, I felt a sense of spiritual growth and independence and increased self-confidence."

"I did it for nine months once. It was harder at first, then I got used to it and kind of got high off it, and energetic. I was only horny near my period. To know I can do it if I want is a real feeling of independence."

"I did it once for seven months, and was somehow glad of the time free from lovers to think things over. For a long time sex had been the most important thing in my life and I felt lost if I didn't have a steady lover. I learned to be more interested in me as a person, an individual—my relationships with friends, my career, *my* life. Now I don't feel as frantic about sex and proving my worth through it. It's still wonderful, but not all-consuming."

"About celibacy—I was celibate for about six months, the first six months I was at college. It was a conscious decision on my part not to deal with sex because I was having a lot of difficulty adjusting to being away from friends and lovers; I had had a very sexual year before that, with two lovers, and I didn't have the energy to get involved with anyone and didn't want to have any sex without emotional commitment. Celibacy was a really good thing; I became very content with myself, never thinking about finding someone to sleep with, never having to worry about whether or not I wanted to sleep with someone, being able to take all relationships for what they were on a purely platonic level. I learned a lot about myself, and how I relate to men. It's something I would recommend to anyone who wants time to sort out her feelings about sexuality, as not having sex for a while leaves you remarkably clear about what you really want, and from whom."

"I am currently celibate. I enjoy it but the society makes it hard to be partnerless sometimes. There are activities I avoid because they will be 'couply.' People often think there's something wrong with you if you're not part of a couple, but being independent is worth it."

"I love being single. I would never imagine myself being married. Celibacy is glorious. One reason I am glad I am celibate is that I am not as slavish as some of the women I see around me. 'You said you would call and you didn't.' 'Do you love me?' 'I love you so much.' 'Aren't you going to dance with me?' 'Where were you?' I feel I am in total control of my body and my life."

"Periods of celibacy can be useful for re-evaluating your life and rediscovering your sexuality—the fallow period before new things can grow. I did it for five years on and off once. By not having to please anyone else, I was able to get really deeply in touch with myself, and develop my understanding of the world—whereas before always having boyfriends had kept me so narrowly focused on them that I hadn't had time to think about my relationship to the larger scheme of things. I found that giving up physical sex was a small price to pay."

"As for celibacy, I think every woman should see it as an alternative. For years, I was so busy fulfilling male expectations I didn't know *what* I felt. I believe there are a lot of women who are going through what I went through. Now, I just have sex by myself—searching for I don't know what, just discovering myself sexually."

However, other women felt cut off and isolated during periods of celibacy, since sex is almost the only activity in which our society allows us to remain in close physical contact with another human being for an extended time—since all forms of physical contact are channelled into heterosexual intercourse.

"It doesn't seem to bother me physically, but emotionally I tense up. I miss body contact and find it extremely frustrating. There is a special kind of loneliness in being one in a culture that seems to think in terms of pairs."

"Without sex, I start to feel dead, ugly, and alienated—like life is passing me by. I begin to feel that I need to have sex as a psychological release."

"When I go without it, I become preoccupied with it. I especially long for the warmth and comfort it brings. When I was a child I never imagined there could be so little affection in the world."

"After about three weeks I get starved for affection and company, and life feels drastically incomplete. I miss the general physical contact, especially going to sleep and waking up with someone, to be at those moments of partial consciousness and feel that I am not alone."

"I miss feeling wanted and needed, and the body warmth when I wake up. I usually start feeling unattractive and undesirable too—mentally depressed, bored, low energy. I lose my sense of humour."

"I become withdrawn and feel inhibited and isolated and frightened. I have gone into deep depressions at such times, and had a feeling of disconnection from the human race."

"It really bothers me. I feel lonely and rejected without sex. Sex is great for breaking the shell of aloneness and fear that seems to come down like a curtain between me and the world when I have no one to love. I find sex to be a retreat to comfort, warmth and emotion in a cold world—rejuvenation. A sort of magic area of refuge."

Physical contact, "flesh to flesh, warm and tight," is tremendously important, and sex is almost the only way to get it in our culture—after we are "grown up." As one woman explained, "If I was deeply depressed, cold, lonely, even with a stranger sex could be regeneration to me. The closeness gives me a sense that I am not alone, and that life is not

all rough edges after all. It makes me feel loved and special."
Another woman said that what she liked best about sex was
"the feeling of crazy friendliness it gives, sometimes falsely.
And the reassurance, however momentary, of being held.
The closeness, intimacy, honesty—and after when you feel
alive and happy in a way you never do at any other time."

The idea that we should have a certain regular amount of a
kind of genital contact we call "sex" is a very mechanical
notion, to say the least. One woman put it very well:

> "There was a time when all across the country babies
> were fed at two, at six, and at ten o'clock. Then
> suddenly there was a revolution: the experts decided that
> babies must be fed 'on demand'— every ten minutes, if
> necessary. It took a long time before it became clear that
> these two methods weren't so different after all: both
> relied on the authority of experts. Now they tell us we
> should have sex 'regularly'—you should keep up a
> regular healthy sex life, but before you weren't supposed
> to do it except once in a while—shit. I don't need any
> experts to tell me when to have sex, how much or what
> kind. If I feel like it, I will—otherwise I won't. It's *my*
> life and *my* body, and I'll do what I want with it."

Conclusion

Finally, what was the ultimate significance of the "sexual
revolution" of the 1960s?

Although sexuality is very important, it is questionable
whether it is important in and of itself, apart from its meaning in life as a whole. The increasing emphasis on sex and
personal relations as the basic source of happiness and fulfilment could be a function of the lessening probability of
finding fulfilment through work. In the first place, most
people do not have the luxury of being able to choose work
that they would like to do; for most people it is a question
of finding some way to support themselves as best they can

from the very limited options available (unless you have some capital to begin with). Now, added to this, is the fact that since technology and the growth of large corporate business have taken over almost every aspect of life, most jobs have become very repetitive, impersonal, and boring. As one woman put it, "Sex* is clearly used as a universal panacea, to keep the masses quiet and stop them from realizing the emptiness, meaninglessness, and alienation of their working lives." It is interesting in this context to note that the sexual revolution came at a time when social and political unrest in the United States was a problem.

Sexuality and sexual relationships can be surrogates for (or obscure our need for) a more satisfying relationship with the larger world—for example, with work. In a way, as long as we accept this schizoid compartmentalization of public and private life, we are abrogating our moral obligation to take an active part in the direction of the larger world, and accepting an ethic of powerlessness. Meanwhile, the commercialization and pornographization of sex advances further into our lives, obscuring the deeper spiritual meaning for us. In fact, we haven't had a sexual revolution yet, but we need one.

---

*In the same way that woman's role has shifted from child-bearer to sex object since the decline in importance of child-bearing, just so the emphasis on personal fulfilment has shifted from family (as a larger group of people) to sexual and romantic love (whether in marriage or not).

8 Mid-life and older women

The sexual revolution did not include older women* as among those who could now enjoy sex—although this denial is nothing really new. For centuries it has been a hideous cliché in our culture that older women are not sexual women. I wonder how many younger readers, when reading the descriptions of masturbation or orgasm, for example, were envisioning exclusively twenty- and thirty-year-olds as having written them? In this section we will see how wrong these ideas about older women are, in some very eloquent comments from some very interesting women.

How does age affect female sexuality?

With regard to how menopause (or hysterectomy) affects sexual feeling, Helen Kaplan has explained that:

> *While some women report a decrease in sexual desire, many women actually feel an increase in erotic appetite during the menopausal years. Again, the fate of libido seems to depend on a constellation of factors which occur during this period, including physiologic changes, sexual opportunity and diminution of inhibition. From a purely physiologic standpoint, libido should theoretically increase at menopause, because the action of the woman's androgens, which is not materially affected by menopause, is now unopposed by estrogen. Indeed, some women do seem to behave in this manner, especially if they are not depressed and can find interested and interesting partners.*[1]

Mary Jane Sherfey has also pointed out that female sexual capacity increases as women get older, because they develop a larger and more complex system of veins (varicosities) in

*How old is "older"? Obviously, there is no answer to this question. I can only agree with Ti-Grace Atkinson when she says "the older woman is all of us."

the genital area.

Once again, confusion between reproductive activity and sexual pleasure is playing havoc with our lives. It's true that the capacity to reproduce ends at menopause, and that vaginal lubrication *can* decrease, but women's sexual arousal or orgasm capacity actually increases. What happens at menopause is something that happens only to our reproductive organs: sexuality and the capacity to experience sexual pleasure are lifetime attributes. Childhood is another time when, although we are not capable of reproduction, we are certainly capable of sexual pleasure. We should picture our bodies as being sexual all our lives, from birth to death, but with the addition during certain years of the potential for reproduction.

One woman was probably speaking for all "younger" women looking ahead to old age when she said:

"I'm only twenty-eight, but I'm already dreading it and thinking of it a lot—I'm angry that society views women's ageing as more detrimental than the 'maturity' of men. I see no reason why a woman should feel loss of sexuality or attractiveness at menopause. It's simply another phase in the female cycle, and part of womanhood."

"How does age affect sex? Does desire for sex increase or decrease, or neither, with age? Enjoyment of sex?"

Most women who answered this question felt that their sexual pleasure had increased with age.

"I believe sexual desire increases with age. Enjoyment certainly increases—I can vouch for that."

"I didn't know getting older would make sex better! I'm fifty-one now and just getting started!"

"Sex definitely gets better as you get older. In the past two years, I have simply done as I damn well pleased when it came to sex. I live every day as if it were my last. It's great."

"I think that men are conned into believing that it decreases in age for them. I don't think it decreases drastically for anyone, *especially* for women. My best sexual experiences are coming out of maturity and self-confidence."

"I am enjoying sex more in my forties than I did in my thirties; I enjoyed it more in my thirties than in my twenties. There's a liberating combination of experience, self-knowledge, and confidence, and an absence of pregnancy fears."

"I am just as horny at fifty-five as I was at fifteen, but my man considers me too old to be sexy!"

"I thought that menopause was the leading factor in my dry and irritable vaginal tract. My doctors thought that it was lack of hormones . . . but with my new lover, I am reborn. Plenty of lubrication, no irritation!"

"Even though I've not been through menopause, I've had a partial hysterectomy. (I'm forty-seven.) For me it's great! Only one partner was adversely affected—he thought he might someday want children and I would not be suitable to his needs, so we parted."

"My roommate (she is in her early fifties) had a hysterectomy five years ago. From what I see of her sex life she changed drastically: more sex partners and sex more often."

"I enjoy sex more since I no longer fear pregnancy. (I'm post-menopausal.) Also it's more enjoyable since my children are no longer home—children can inhibit sexual activity. Because I enjoy it more, so does my husband. He finds it a pleasant surprise—in fact, I put the excitement in his life!"

"I am answering your questionnaire because I feel there are not enough statistics about women septuagenarians (I am seventy-eight), not enough understanding of the widow's situation. At my age and without responsibilities I do not want matrimony but I have a continuing sex drive which keeps me looking fifteen to twenty years younger than my chronological age. Also I had heart surgery two years ago, which has completely rejuvenated me. I want to live to the fullest extent of my capabilities."

"I am sixty-seven, and find that age does not change sex much. Circumstances determine it. I have had much more sexual pleasure, both with my husband and other mates in recent years. I love not having menstruation."

"Menopause makes everything better, easier, and less dependent on time. My partners enjoy my physical freedom, as do I. I went through it fairly easily."

"I am sixty-six and sexual desire has not diminished. The enjoyment is as great as ever. I think it might diminish if you couldn't have sex. But enjoying it has nothing to do with age."

"I think that sexual desire, attitudes, pleasure, etc., certainly change with age, but the change is qualitative rather than quantitative. It's a matter of growth and development, from a simplistic yes-or-no view of sex to much greater complexity, variety, subtlety, fluidity. I don't mean this so much in terms of increasing sophistication in 'technique,' though I suppose that's part of it. It's like the difference between a young shoot and a tree with many branches and a unique shape and structure and pattern of growth all its own. This is a natural growth process, but I believe that in our culture this process is often inhibited and retarded; we've all been told that all cats are grey in the dark, and many of us come rather late to the recognition and appreciation of her or his own unique and intricate sexual personality. I find it much easier now to know and accept and act on what I want and feel, instead of worrying about what I should want and feel."

However some women did feel that sex was not that important to them any more.

"I find age (or maybe it is state of mind?? the 'space my

head is in') has cut down considerably on my sexual needs—that is, I don't seem to turn new people on *at all,* sexually—nor am I being turned on by them—but also I am not 'turned on' by former love relationships. I'm just not interested."

"I am seventy-three—living alone—and I don't miss anything. Male companionship is a bore. I was married fifty years ago. I don't want to concentrate on this questionnaire, but I'd answer it if I were forty or so. Enclosed is two dollars. I wish it were more. Good luck."

Other women were interested in sex, but were having difficulty finding partners they liked.

"I am fifty-four years old, living in a new state and city (I just moved). As yet, I have met no one I am interested in sexually—either man or woman. I do not seem to give out sexual 'vibes' at this point. I miss it some, but my sexual appetite also seems very low—I have had an opportunity for sex when I visited some women friends on the way out, but I was not even a *bit* interested. I do masturbate and that seems satisfying enough for now; but recently I purchased a vibrator which does *nothing* for me! I was disappointed."

"I am now forty-four and have had some sensational love trips, but my increased age has made a difference in sex for me, because of the culmination of my choosiness and the world's present insistence on sex as a youth symbol. I had thought that if a person (woman) were terrific in her own right and togetherness, her sexual attractiveness would be maintained self-evident for her lifetime. What a bummer! I think the sexual revolution is great but I just can't wait till they include grandmothers in the race of sexually desirable beings! This is one reason why I've started a concerted project with myself on going into autoeroticism—as far as I can find to take it. With what I know I'm capable of, and with what's available to me on the 'sexual marketplace,' it looks like it's gonna be a long cold winter for us single over-forty ladies. *Damn! Damn! Damn!!*"

"Menopause does not feel like an 'experience' to me; I am still on birth control pills—for hormones. I am aware that my body is less vigorous, I have less energy— that I look *old*—which I guess I am. It's hard to realize however that I *am* fifty-four years old, but I do not make any effort to conceal my age or years or experience—I just *am*. It doesn't seem to turn men on— maybe more women (??) but I have some fear of loving a person who might have a long-term illness, senility, etc. I've coped with *that* enough."

"Menopause" is a word many women have tried to change, asserting that it is "not a pause", for one thing, and for another, the word sounds frightening and not positive in any way. Yet no one has quite come up with a good replacement for it, though hopefully someone soon will.

The terms "menopause" and "older women" are thrown around in popular writing in a way that seems to marginalize both "middle-aged women" and "older women" (how old is "older"?)—unless a newspaper or television programme is talking about "a medical prob-lem" and trying to earnestly "take the medical problems of older women and menopausal women seriously." What about the wonderfully positive experiences most middle-aged and older women are having? Where can we hear about them? In fact, in the research, most women over age fifty (to choose a random figure) are much more secure and confident in their lives and work than they have ever been, and this is reflected in their sexual lives, as well.

The stereotype of a woman "over fifty" is of an unhappy woman, or a woman with problems—yet images of men in our daily media show Power Men almost always over fifty, and other Interesting Men of all ages (generally younger men are not seen as so interesting and intelligent as middle-aged men). Women over fifty are almost invisible in media, except for "the problems" of this age group, yet women over fifty are a vibrant and interesting, energetic group.

Some "older women" had lovers.

First, one long answer:

"This is the first chance I have had to let anyone know what and how my life has changed in the last eight years. I have one very close female friend who knows of my lover but besides that it is untold, as it should be for the sake of his wife and my husband. I do not feel guilty about this because I feel that I have been more understanding of my husband and his needs since my coming of age.

"I am now fifty-one, and my first orgasm was at the age of forty-four during intercourse with my lover. At about seven I made a feeble attempt at masturbation, at which I was caught by my mother, who gave me a very long lecture on how this would cause me to become insane. This was my last attempt at masturbation until seven years ago.

"There are many men whom I think it would be enjoyable to have sex with, but so far I have only had sex with my husband and my lover. With my husband I have always just given as he demanded to keep him in a good mood. He has always been very quick in having an orgasm and then going to sleep—often leaving me in a state of tears (in my early years of marriage) and now just in a state of sexual excitement. With my lover it has always been a mutual need and he has never left me unfulfilled. With my husband there is never time for myself. It seems that my lover always thinks of me first. Maybe that is why I have continued this affair so long. Seven years. Taking the long slow time to be aroused is the thing that my lover seems to be glad to do. My husband only takes about five or six minutes.

"I think my husband was as uninformed as I was when we were married and has not bothered to learn anything more. My lover is the one who taught me how to be sexual and how I was a complete woman who was not frigid and unfeeling. Now I am able to ask him for anything that is stimulating and he responds, and he also asks me for things that he likes. We have become very free with each other, and I am not ashamed at all. In fact, I am proud."

"I'm forty-eight years old, and I have never been more optimistic and hopeful. I do not have the sexual satisfaction I need yet, but with three new lovers in the wings and two current ones, I should do well. My sex life has left much to be desired, but my *love life* has almost always been rich and full, and right now is no exception. I am married, second time, eleven years. I hate being married but I try not to let it affect my disposition. It has been non-sexual for five and a half years (my choice)—sexual incompatibility. I have had about ten affairs, ranging from one to five years in length. The effect on me has been to make me blissfully happy (especially the last seven years or so). With my marriage, infidelity has allowed it to endure, both for our child's sake and for convenience. Open marriage may be okay for some, but it would not work for us; it seems important to us to keep up appearances."

"I am, as I stated, fifty-one and have been married to one man for thirty-three years. We have four very lovely children, who are married, happily, and have nine grandchildren. I did not finish high school until after my fourth child was born; at that time I finished my last year of high school and went on to college, and since then I have become a teacher. I have for the last twenty years worked at a school for the physically handicapped. My husband has a high school education and has worked at many different things. He has been disabled for the last two years after having several strokes. Eight years ago I met and fell madly in love with a man who is ten years my junior. I kept my distance, for I felt that this was very foolish of me and I was sure that he would think of me as an old woman. He made the first approach and I made sure that he knew that I was married and how old I was. From there he became my teacher and lover and still is. He is also married and has four children. He is good to his wife and children and I would not want to at any time break up his marriage. I just revel in what I have learned from him, that sex is good and that I am attractive and sexual and wanted. If I never was able from this day on to have sex with anyone I would not mind too, for I have had seven years of sexual relationship that cannot be put aside, for through that relationship I have learned that I am a real woman. I was an only child brought up by a very strict mother who has during her lifetime been married four times. I never knew my father, only stepfathers. Her attitude towards sex was, I am sure, part of my problem and the fact that my husband was not too interested in my part in the sex act. There had been much petting before marriage but I had always held back because 'good girls' didn't go all the way. After marriage I wanted to let go but because he was so quick it was not long before I was just enduring sex because he demanded. It is difficult to tell you what my lover has done for me—I dress differently, I think differently, I see myself as a rather attractive person now where before I felt that I was just a middle-aged woman getting more so each day."

Others had begun to relate sexually to other women.*

"I have had many sexual experiences with men, and found them satisfying. However, eighteen years ago (I am sixty-six now) I met Sarah, for whom I had great admiration and respect. When she announced she loved me and proceeded to demonstrate it, there was no further need for men. I feel my sex life is as complete

---

*Statistics in *Woman and Love* (Hite, Knopf, 1987) showed that a higher percentage of women between 42 and 62 began lesbian relationships than the overall percentage of women engaged in lesbian relationships.

now as it ever was. I haven't had any sexual relationships with other women. For me at this point it would be impossible. I feel my life is more complete and happier than if I were formally married. Ours is no 'male-female' relationship but a sharing of everything with mutual respect."

This reply was *signed*—by a woman who obviously had very few fears about life.

Other women enjoyed sex with younger men.
"I think that sex is better in my forties than ever before. I feel in my prime and at my peak. I have never felt better or looked better. I feel good about myself—my body and mind. I have found a very satisfying relationship with a man twelve years my junior and we are compatible. There will be a time for it to end and I think we will know it, but I really feel that will be just the beginning of a new phase of my life. I wish all women could find what I have found."

"My marriage was the deepest relationship I ever had, I suppose, and the longest lasting (thirty-five years). We had a wonderful mental thing going, and a serviceable physical relationship that was rarely great. We fucked okay, but he never really made love to me—was very unaffectionate and unsensual. After a number of years, I began to have affairs outside the marriage and that was when my real sex life started. Now, since the marriage ended, I have had one big love affair with a much younger man, which was very high both physically and mentally. It was probably the best physical match I have had, in many ways—but that was because of psychological factors more than anything else. Probably the best sex I've had in the last four years has been with younger men, come to think of it."

"I had a wonderful experience two weeks after my divorce. I was asked by a man twenty years younger than me to meet him the next day for an assignation. We both knew it would probably be a one-time thing, as we might never see each other again, and we had practically nothing in common except that we were both very horny. I had time to think it over, so I wasn't rushed into anything, wasn't in love, had no obligation whatever, to him or anyone else—for the first time in my life I was free to make a decision concerning my sex life without worry about the consequence. We spent a wonderful afternoon doing all the things we both enjoyed, and both of us were completely satisfied and happy. He was wonderful to talk to, and was the first person I ever talked to about other women. That was the first time I knew that other women couldn't come without clitoral maulpulation, like me. I have had many other wonderful experiences, some much better sexually, due to the cumulative experience of several years, and the tenderness and love I feel for my partner, but that one stands out for many reasons. For one thing, to learn that age makes no real difference in sex, that I was attractive to him, was wonderful for my ego, especially so soon after my divorce. Another thing was the twenty-four hours of anticipation, knowing I could change my mind."

However, quite a few women after various sexual experiences, decided sex wasn't worth the investment of time and emotion.
The following two women explained at length:
"Sex isn't important to me. I am fifty-eight years old, married to the same man and faithful thirty-five years. Lots of rough years. We've raised two fine children, a dentist and a lawyer—have four darling grandchildren. About five years ago, my husband at about fifty-two started drinking every night—knocked me around. I've never heard a word of praise except while having intercourse, and I keep wondering how in hell I could enjoy that when I'm so poor in every other way!

"I only have orgasms occasionally in dreams—about

strangers. Kissing the back of my neck is most important to me to have an orgasm. I told him that for years but he never does it. I do not like oral or rectal sex but both have been forced on me. I can be feeling pretty mellow with vaginal intercourse and when he mentions oral or rectal, I go on with the act but the glow is gone; I hope he gets his fun just talking about it.

"I've tried masturbation and *get nothing* from it . . ."

"In the early years I initiated sex several *times* but it never got anywhere—it had to be his idea. Sex is bound to be good if you are 'friends' with your partner—guess you can tell I'm pretty bitter. I went to a marriage counsellor two years ago—I'm immature—any husband hates all women, starting with his mother—he sends me roses—buys me gifts and tells me how stupid I am."

"Yes, I fake orgasms—nearly every time—which is nearly every night, sometimes twice."

"Now I'm very upset because he wants to sell our house (thirty-two years) and move to a small town—he handed me this questionnaire and said it could tell me why I'm nervous. I'm definitely not 'with it'—I'd settle for a few kind words."

"My current sexual life is zero. It has been zero for twenty-one years. That is, I have been celibate for over twenty-one years. I am sixty-two, and have been married twenty-five years (in my present marriage). I am married to a typical male boor, selfish and insensitive, also alcoholic, but I stay here because I am ageing, I have no skills, and I have cardiac problems.

"Masturbation has been important to me because I cannot seek sex outside of marriage, rotten as it is. So, masturbation is a release, but I do not practise it intensely because of religious and parental taboos left over from childhood. I feel guilty. However, since the women's movement and succeeding literature I am trying to modify my views. I enjoy masturbating 'during,' but later feel guilty and then try to rationalize. It usually happens during sleep. I have a dream where I awaken sexually aroused. I spread my legs, then go ahead and manipulate my clitoris or caress my vaginal area until orgasm.

"With my husband, I only sometimes had orgasms. He was more interested in his own wants than mine. Also, nobody ever gave me any information about sex— with parents and teachers, my God, you never *dared* ask! The first time I had sex, I had no knowledge of what to expect, and my husband was a crass pig—he said, 'Go clean yourself up.' No sensitivity, no anything! I was an object, a convenience. But I married him to escape home, so I did the best I could. Anyway, romance is really a laugh, just a bill of goods sold us by parents, the media, and the makers of products. From pregnancy to the grave, we are brainwashed on Romance.

"Since I have been asexual for all these years now and will remain so, I have adjusted to it. It gives me a sense of freedom; I don't have to play stupid games or use sex for bargaining or manipulation as I did in the past. I am sorry I am not one of today's young women—they are their own persons, can be free to choose a career, their own life style, and be independent. Many older women like myself have only known marriage and family—their own life was submerged into service for others. They are losers. Ask them!

"My sexual feelings have been repressed simply because of the situation, not because of my age. If one had a loving partner, why should feelings decrease? Age would not enter into it, except if your partner was ill, etc. I had a radical hysterectomy and I still have sexual feelings. But since I have no actual contact with my partner, I can't say about the physical part of it. The hysterectomy threw me into a deep depression (five months ago) and I am now in therapy because of that problem—and of course the support at home is not so good, so I am glad for the therapy.

"I answered this because if in any way another woman can identify with my one little statistic and know she is not alone—fine! I am stuck in a small bigoted Southern town where women keep quiet and rarely rock the boat and men beat hell out of them. You never saw such ignorance, but we are (a handful of us) trying! Good luck to you."

"I am now fifty-six, mostly a housewife but I work off and on. I never worked when the children were small. Actually I never had worked and had no confidence in myself. My husband used to give me the impression that I couldn't do anything anyhow that anyone would pay for. I know now that we both had a king-sized, low sense of self-esteem. Mine is better now than it was but he won't even admit that there is such a thing! At various times I've boarded children, been a sales clerk, been a receptionist, a file clerk, done indexing, and lately I've been paid for interior decorating! I'm a high school graduate.

"I was a virgin when I married at twenty and was so hung up. I did what I thought I was supposed to; never looked at another man (I mean that I would avert my eyes)! I didn't know about orgasms. Also, now I know my husband never did know what he was doing. I just knew it mostly was disappointing. I loved the foreplay and (to be honest) the feeling of power over him that the whole schmeer gave me. I could turn him on like a light switch.

"I thought I was in love with my husband; now I think I just wanted to be, and it took me years and years to realize that he just wasn't the man I idealized him into. He was a good guy, kind to me (but wanted to control me completely), but now I know he's a bundle of nerves (he denies it) and has more hang-ups than I do! He denies all problems! Also he was a virgin. I naively thought all men had experience but he didn't. My husband and I went together for five years. He was seventeen and I was fifteen when we met, so after about a year we started heavy petting. We never went all the way but we did finger fucking and oral. He did, that is; I had never heard of it before but I loved it. We were really hot—all I had to do was talk to him and I got all wet. I loved sex so much it frightened me. I'm not sure about orgasm, though.

"To make a long story short, after thirty years or so of marriage we got bored, started talking about swinging, then, when we finally went through with it I became so *sick* over the fact that my husband, my lover, was much less than ideal! I wanted him to be a good lover and earn a good living, be a good father and so proud of our marriage that he wouldn't want another man to touch me! Ha ha. He was a terrible lover— earned a mediocre living, was never ambitious. He was a so-so father—alienated the oldest almost completely and was not a strong personality as a father and also I felt he had no real respect for me or our marriage so I thought, 'What the hell!' If he doesn't care I might as well pick my *own* man. Besides by then I was on the hormones, had lost fifty pounds, and had become very active of nights with community improvement group (lots of nice men). So I started meeting one guy two years older than my husband. We'd been flirting at parties, etc. for years. So I said casually, 'We could have fun without hurting anyone,' and he jumped at it. He was *great* and I found out what sex was all about. That's when I learned about the orgasms. He was a passionate, tender lover. I enjoyed him about fifteen or sixteen times. I wasn't in love with him but it was good."

But some women were finding new experiences.
"I have been thirty-six years with the same man. I have not had extramarital experiences. I do not approve of my partner or myself having extramarital experiences, because we are happily married and sex is no barrier with us. As far as I am concerned, age (I am fifty-eight) only improves sex under the right conditions, as I am blessed with at this time: my husband and I have retired from employment, as of June last year, and due to

freedom of mind, plenty of time and relaxation, find sex is 100 per cent better, because now we have no kids around the house, no relatives and time is our own. We fuck whenever we feel like it, many times during the day and night, any way we wish it; we walk around the house in the nude and take air baths and exercises—take 'golden baths'— all of which makes us appreciate each other's bodies. In other words 'sexual freedom'—free from the old barriers based on sexual taboos. I am fifty-eight years old, my husband is fifty-seven; we have had two male children during our thirty-six years of marriage. Now I always come first in any sexual activity and my mate orgasms later, as he believes passion originates in the female. Always, he loves me for hours and stimulates me first, him second. I thought Masters and Johnson were okay but my husband and I could have written the book; they are amateurs!"

"I was seventy-five this September. I am a singer. Though I had an excellent voice once, my career was spoiled through enormous emotional and other experiences. I was married three times but had relations with many, probably twenty, maybe more. I was easily sexually aroused, went high—but had no release, most of the time. It drove me up the wall. I hope to make a comeback as a singer. Vocally I am not deteriorated, hope that feminism will help me to develop my personality, which it still needs much.

"Yes, I have had orgasms but in my rather long life, too few. Now I suddenly enjoy sex again. That is, masturbating, which I do now almost every night. Sometimes during the day. Since I began masturbating voluntarily and very strongly, not just playing around a bit, I must say it makes me quite happy—yet I think I am most of the time happy. I feel it frees me—or liberates me more. I am generally frightfully shy, can become stiff and unpleasant. I am now more friendly and easygoing. Sex without orgasm made me extremely nervous and upset. I believed it was my fault. The harder I tried the less it worked. With my previous two husbands I had only vaginal intercourse. I liked it, was aroused, but that was all.

"Once I began to use a vibrator, which made me feel as if I was torn apart. Very strongly. The pain I felt was wonderful. I always thought dying must be like this. Like blasting into outer space. I had an extremely strong orgasm, feeling like flying over the highest mountain. Maybe two or three weeks ago I did not even like to think of masturbating. Now, since I began to understand feminism, I *love* to do it. Unfortunately I need too many hours—mostly from three to six hours—by hand.

"I was married three times but I have had no relations with men for maybe ten years now. I did not want anything more to do with sex with men. I wondered if I am or became a lesbian; I love warm-hearted, interesting women, but never felt sexually aroused. I live alone since my husband died. Found it wonderful, but now I'm aware this isolation went too far. I very seldom if ever had discussions about sex. Did not dare. Now I love and need it. As I come just out of isolation (mentioned above) I love my children again much, see friends once in a while, most of the time they bore me. Music was always a wonderful surrogate.

"In my life I just fell deeply in love for no reason. I was more than once in love. It seems to me I was emotionally immature, desiring to lose myself. I don't think I could feel the same now. I don't like to say I feel superior to man, I don't find a better word. Man's relationship with me was too one-sided—only material and mechanical. I was extremely happy when my children were babies. I wanted at least twelve, but stopped after six, which seemed to be necessary.

"Now I have deep relations with my music teacher. He helps me tremendously in my technique and expression. But he does not arouse me. No man did this for more than ten years. If a man would like to play and arouse me sexually till I have orgasm I might do it. Yet it does not seem to be possible nor would I ask for it.

"I like my vagina and genitals. Smell good. I like my body. When I am slim, my body still looks good, but through losing weight once too often, my skin is now too loose, which I don't like. Therefore I don't feel comfortable.

"I now like tremendously to talk about sex and to learn a lot more about it. I like these questions very much. Filling them out I got the desire to know you in person and continue our questions and answers, especially now where I begin to see all about sexuality from a new angle. I was always for many years and am convinced women have to play an enormous new role, not to destroy men but to improve this world. It seems to me feminism is a bottomless entity to discover incredible treasures that none of us may be aware of now. It is really for this task I am living and fighting."

This is the subject of ongoing research. Readers who wish to participate should contact the author care of the publisher or via e-mail at info@hite-research.com.

9 Towards a new female sexuality

Un-defining sex

Our definition of sex belongs to a world view that is past—
or passing. Sexuality, and sexual relations, are no longer seen
as the important property right they once were; children are
no longer central to the power either of the state or the
individual. Although most of our social institutions are still
totally based on hierarchical and patriarchal forms, patriarchy as a form is really dead, as is the sexuality that defined
it. We are currently in a period of transition, although it is
unclear as yet to what. The challenge for us now is to devise
a more humane society, one that will implement the best of
the old values, like kindness and understanding, cooperation, equality, and justice throughout *every* layer of public
and private life—a metamorphosis to a more personal and
humanized society.

Specifically, in sexual relations—which we should perhaps begin calling simply physical relations—we can again
reopen many options. All the kinds of physical intimacy
that were channelled into our one mechanical definition of
sex can now be reallowed, and rediffused throughout our
lives, including simple forms of touching and warm body
contact. There need not be a sharp distinction between sexual touching and friendship. Just as women described
"arousal" as one of the best parts of sex, and just as they
described closeness as the most pleasurable aspect of intercourse, so intense physical intimacy can be one of the most
satisfying activities possible—in and of itself.

Although we tend to think of "sex" as one set pattern,
one group of activities (in essence, reproductive activity),
there is no need to limit ourselves in this way.

There is no reason why physical intimacy with men, for
example, should always consist of "foreplay" followed by
intercourse and male orgasm;* and there is no reason why

---

*This will be discussed from men's point of view in the analysis of the replies
received to the questionnaire for men, to be published as *The Hite Report on
Male Sexuality.*

intercourse must always be a part of heterosexual sex. Sex is intimate physical contact for pleasure, to share pleasure with another person (or just alone). You can have sex to orgasm, or not to orgasm, genital sex, or just physical intimacy—whatever seems right to you. There is never any reason to think the "goal" must be intercourse, and to try to make what you feel fit into that context. There is no standard of sexual performance "out there," against which you must measure yourself; you aren't ruled by "hormones" or "biology." You are free to explore and discover your own sexuality, to learn or unlearn anything you want, and to make physical relations with other people, of either sex, anything you like.

The future of intercourse

Sex as usual?

It must have been clear throughout this book how tired women are of the old mechanical pattern of sexual relations, which revolves around male erection, male penetration, and male orgasm. As one woman said, "Cutting an orgasm short doesn't leave me frustrated if I'm masturbating, but I am becoming more and more short-tempered about cutting sex with my husband short just because he is satisfied. Continuing along the same unsatisfying sexual patterns expresses to me a lack of care and concern for me that I am finding unacceptable. It isn't so much cutting an orgasm short and the biological tension that results that hurts—it is an emotional hurt that frustrates me."

In answers to many different questions women mentioned their frustration and annoyance with this pattern, and many wished for something different.

"What would you like to do more often? How would you like to see the usual 'bedroom scene' changed?"

The following types of answers came up over and over again.
"I wish men would be more sensitive rather than acting like a big penis, having an orgasm and that's all. I would say that 75 per cent of the men I have known knew nothing about a woman except that they had an

orgasm and that should be a big treat to me."

"I'd like to change the whole kiss—feel—eat—eat me—fuck routine."

"I would like more love and gentleness instead of bare sexual stimulation—more emotion and communication, rather than sex along the lines of expectation and demand and then routine follow-up."

"I wish it were easier to start sex play and see where it goes, rather than knowing this kiss will lead to touching each other's genitals, and then intercourse."

"I'm sick of focusing on cocks and cunts. I hate the feeling that I can't hug my partner without 'taking him all the way'—that means I must hold back lots of good feelings just because I'm not in the mood for intercourse. I also like getting into the sexual experience as much as possible and feel terribly frustrated when we don't because he has an orgasm and falls asleep. I would like to have an orgasm, yes, but then continue love-making and not make that the end!"

"More kisses, more time, more tenderness. Why don't men like to be touched in other parts of their bodies? I do. I would like to see more men with more imagination."

"I'd like to kiss mouth to mouth more often. I'd like my husband to act less controlled, less in control. I would like to be aroused to the point of complete abandonment. This I have never known."

"Men should stay awake longer afterwards. They should *never* get out of bed right after sex, or clean themselves off!!!"

"I would like to be able to sustain sexual activity indefinitely. I find a man's exhaustion after orgasm disappointing."

"I've never been able to say, 'Yes, that's all I could have asked for, there's nothing more I want.' I've always felt that my sexual encounters have been only beginnings; they've never been even nearly carried as far as I would like them to be."

'To me, sexuality should not be contrived, expected, or routinized. I feel sex should be an exciting, spontaneous thing—not a package you 'buy' with a marriage certificate. Since sex has not yet happened to me 'spontaneously,' I do not feel that I ever truly felt sex as I feel it should be."

"I'd like to see spontaneous *passion*. No contrived situations, like the lights *have* to be off, we *have* to be in bed, we have to wipe away the sperm, we have to be polite, modest—shit."

"More passion. Often he is in too much of a hurry and he pays too much attention to my vagina and not enough or *any* to my sensitive area near my clitoris. I would like petting-type genital manipulation, with clothes on, pushing up dress, pushing aside underpants, that sort of sexy thing. I would eventually like to be free enough to do anything and everything without embarrassment, with complete abandon."

Many women were also tired of men's preoccupation with mechanical perfection in performance, and lack of interest in general body feelings.

"Many men are not as free to be sensual overall or give as much to the partner as women are. They are almost always genitally focused."

"Men seem to be inhibited, in a way, and even show fear of my body and any 'surprise reactions' it might have—and they are especially preoccupied with their own pricks."

"Many men think sex is just fucking, or something to do with hands, mouth, and cock but not the rest of the body. Men don't feel that their whole bodies are beautiful or that the touch of thigh and thigh is a caress as much as a touch with the hand."

"I would like to have leisurely sex with a man more often, talking and fooling around and entertaining each other. Feeling relaxed. My doctor tells me men don't like this."

"No matter what I do or say, most men simply won't believe that having my ears and the back of my neck kissed is really important. I like playing with their bodies, but it seems that, except for fellatio and fondling of their penis, they don't get much enjoyment out of it. I remain confused as to whether they really have so few erogenous zones or whether they are afraid to feel sexy in 'non-sexual' parts of their bodies."

"Until I lived with gay men I never realized that a man could actually get intense pleasure out of sex; in my experience women and gay men let themselves be responsive whereas heterosexual men have to sort of grit their teeth and concentrate really hard on keeping it up long enough to come; I have kind of an image of straight guys ardently pursuing it but not really enjoying it once they get it; I always felt rather badly for my lover because it seemed that for him it was like scratching an itch—relieving himself of something negative— whereas for me it was absolute bliss."

"If only people would let down their fake fronts and be honest. Men are totally dishonest. Nobody will ever admit to his own inner feelings—they all act the way Hugh Hefner tells them to. There's more to sex than crawling on and off."

"Do you feel most men get more pleasure from intercourse than from sexual play?"

Yes	388
No	115
Not my partner	6
Not necessarily	47
Total	556

"Yes, men think of the preliminaries as an unnecessary delay. I feel during foreplay like I'm being condescended to, dealt with, like he's going through a necessary inconvenience for a long-run benefit."

"The foremost and principal male interest is ejaculation—unhappily the sooner the better. I learned long ago the essentiality of holding off their gratification until I'm ready."

"Yes, most men just want to have an orgasm, and sex play is their 'contribution' to my enjoyment."

"I think my present partner feels that any lingering by the way, or anything besides quick hit-and-run genital sex is unmanly. Macho shit—too bad!"

"He thinks foreplay is a favour, like opening a door."

"It's a big bore for most of them, just a necessity for the Big Entry."

"Yes, they like intercourse best, but fellatio is a close second."

"Yes, but even *they* like sex play if they're the centre of attention!!"

"He enjoys a quickie more than I do—but he also seems to enjoy *his* orgasm more if I play with him a long time before intercourse."

"They like sex play about as much, as long as *they* are the ones being played with."

Many women felt that this mechanical approach on the part of most men reflected not only a general lack of feeling for them, but also a lack of development of the man's own sensuality and ability to enjoy his own body.

"Yes, they enjoy intercourse more, but I think that's conditioning, because men feel that sex play is undignified and revealing. Actually, they can enjoy it as much as we do."

"If a man feels that way, I think of him as childish and undeveloped—he doesn't appreciate the subtleties of sex."

"Yes, men often don't know how to get into play, or just touching, and get hung up on orgasm. But they can learn."

"Yes, they don't know how to enjoy it. Many men have a completely genital approach to sex. Sex play is not play to them, but a series of mechanical manoeuvres needed to get the woman ready for what they really want. I try to teach them otherwise."

"Yes. They're so hopelessly confused it's not worth bothering with them. Men who do not like to 'neck' are usually bad lovers. Pacing is important in bed, and if a man is too impatient to get there he will probably be too impatient once he is there. He won't know how to enjoy it."

"No, not if he is sexually mature—a sensitive, alive person. My husband says it's a male myth that men enjoy intercourse more."

One woman explained in a long answer how disappointed she was in her husband's lack of interest in anything but intercourse.

"I have viewed married love as a growing together in the ability to express love and pleasure, but I haven't seen this growth in my marriage. My husband really doesn't seem to enjoy anything besides intercourse, and that very briefly, and I don't know what to do to change him. I've tried hard.

"Masturbation is very important for me and I am really sorry I didn't know about it a lot sooner. (I started doing it less than a year ago, at the age of twenty-seven.) I was interested in my sexuality, but my husband wasn't, so I decided to do something about it. Three years ago I came across the idea of masturbation for adult women in *The Sensuous Woman*. I cried and cried and cried because I had this romantic idea of having my husband care about and develop my sexuality—a feat for which I would be forever grateful and therefore endeared and close to him. (I had never had sex until marriage.) This was really important to me, so for the next two years I hinted and openly expressed my desire to have good sex and to develop my sensuality. Nothing much happened. So I finally said, well, if you don't care about my sexuality, I do! Then I asked him what he thought about masturbation. I found, to my surprise, that he did it! And that he thought it would be great if I did it! It relieves him of that responsibility(?) of having to touch, caress, and learn about my genitals(?). Now, I have learned to masturbate, and I do enjoy masturbating, but I feel sad that I can't develop my sexuality with my husband. For many women, sex is a union with another person and the cosmic universe. It is a leaving of the body and a dissolution of the self—so that isolation can end. Somehow I can't help but feel that my aloneness is intensified by the fact that my sexual partner hasn't shown any care of my sexuality. In that sense I really wish that I had learned about my own sexuality on my own a lot—being a teenager and learning about your body is different from being a married adult woman who is learning about her body because her mate isn't interested.

"I have accepted monogamy for seven years because I have felt a deep commitment to and a love for my husband. This is the only sexual relationship I have ever had. I do not think I am the kind of person who could jump in bed with just anyone—yet I have a certain admiration and envy of the woman who can jump into bed with anyone and have a great time. But I love my husband very much. I am very much attracted to him, and I care about him. I want to be close to him. I think that he is a wonderful person in so many ways. But I am also terribly disappointed in and hurt by our sex life. I haven't seen any growth in our ability to love each other well.

"I have been thinking about this questionnaire a lot, and through my responses I am seeing my husband as something of a prude and perhaps threatened or scared of my sexuality. All he ever wants is intercourse. I have been hurt by his refusals and by his lack of reciprocation. I don't feel my husband is emotionally involved during sex. I don't feel he finds me delicious—as it is, he doesn't caress me much. When he does, it is awkward, for the most part. I do most of the caressing. When I am caressed, I feel like it's stilted, not enraptured. Thus, instead of getting involved in the good feelings, I feel like I am an exhibit. Now I try to be aggressive and experimental, but the times when I only follow my husband's lead it is dull, insipid, uninspired! We end up just going to sleep after his orgasm and a brief intercourse. Perhaps this lack of excitement and involvement partially explain why I'm non-orgasmic with him.

"He forgets half the things I tell him that turn me on or off. At first telling him things like that was embarrassing because I would have preferred that he would have asked me if and what I liked. He didn't, so I began to volunteer information—at first very delicately, later more blatantly. I easily accepted his ignorance at first. No problem. We had a chance to grow together sexually. But after six years of marriage, I see his ignorance as evidence of not caring, and it really hurts.

"He still sees my clitoris as something that is secretive, hidden by hair (the first time he came down on me he came up spitting out hair. Now, when he goes down on me, he very meticulously pulls the hair aside). It is inconvenient to him. But his penis he sees as very convenient and available—although he feels compelled to jump up and wash it right after intercourse. I am coming to the conclusion that what I need is a more experimental, spontaneous, and uninhibited partner, who has a real sense of joy in sex and love-making."

Do women always want intercourse?

Not only were women tired of the old mechanical pattern of "foreplay," penetration, intercourse, and ejaculation, but many also found that *always* having to have intercourse, *knowing* you will have intercourse as a foregone conclusion, is mechanical and boring. If you know in advance that intercourse has to be a part of every heterosexual sexual encounter, there is almost no way the old mechanical pattern of sexual relations can be avoided, since intercourse usually leads to male orgasm, which usually signals the end of "sex." (It would be very interesting to explore whether this needs to be so.) If heterosexual relations are to be deinstitutionalized, intercourse must not be a foregone conclusion, or male orgasm during intercourse as the conclusion of "sex" must not be a foregone conclusion. Women must claim the right *not* to have intercourse, *unless they want it,* even when having physical relations with a man. After all, why is it "natural" for a man to expect intercourse to orgasm with or without clitoral stimulation, but treasonable for a woman to expect clitoral stimulation to orgasm without intercourse?

In addition, the kind of change we are talking about in this book is much deeper than just the idea that "a woman needs an orgasm too." It is not a question of the woman having an orgasm, and then the man having his, or vice versa. Fixing on orgasm as a goal also keeps physical relations focused on a mechanical pattern. In fact, sex need not always be directed at orgasm, or even at genital stimulation. There are many other ways to relate physically to another person. Male sexuality too must be expanded to include many more options, without the almost hysterical emotional fixation on intercourse and orgasm currently prevalent. What is really needed is a total redefinition, or that is, an *un*-definition, of sexuality, and an expansion of our idea of physical relations to another level of awareness.

Would women still want to have intercourse at all, since it does not usually bring them to orgasm, if they were not pressured to have it?

When asked "If you had to choose between intercourse and clitoral stimulation, which would you choose?" most women perceived their choice as being between intercourse and masturbation—not even considering clitoral stimulation by a partner as a possibility!

In their answers, most women showed mixed feelings.

"Which would I choose? I don't know—on the one hand, I wouldn't like intercourse at all probably if I didn't love him. By itself, intercourse is really nothing, but with him on the other end, it's dynamite. However, I only have orgasms through masturbation. I have never had an orgasm with my lover, although God knows we've tried. And having orgasms is extremely important to me. When my lover has one and I am left to fall asleep wishing I could have one, I could cry (and I often have cried myself to sleep). Still, I enjoy sex—obviously, or else I wouldn't be sleeping with him. But it would be much better if I had orgasms. (Maybe part of the problem is that I happen to masturbate in a very unusual way; I have to be leaning against something, like a chair, and rotating.) I guess if I didn't love him, I might not want intercourse so often, but I'm not quite sure what I would want."

"If I had to choose between having either intercourse or clitoral stimulation, I'd pick clitoral stimulation. I've thought about it more and I don't know. I imagine good sex to be an experience where both people sincerely want the other person to feel good, be satisfied, be pleasured as intensely as possible—not just a deal where your partner's satisfaction is the coin you use to buy your own satisfaction. I was going to blithely choose clitoral stimulation because I enjoy this and would be getting what I want, but perhaps that's unrealistic—search for balance."

"I used to like penetration a lot, but lately I wouldn't miss it if we left it out. Physically, it doesn't really stimulate me (except for deep, deep penetration). Psychologically, I love the feeling of closeness, but it still isn't all that important to me. However, it is for my lover. Since he is concerned about my satisfaction, I am equally concerned about his. Therefore, I would not be able to choose either without the other."

"Intercourse is something in itself which will never make me come, however exciting and treasured an experience it *can* be for other reasons. When the contractions seem about to begin and the final drive to orgasm is on, they seem to be stopped by the resistance of the penis itself. It seems to be a 'no win' situation—at least by the terms of conventional intercourse success. I would solve it by making my orgasm a non-intercourse matter. Then I could entirely let myself go and enjoy bodily and spiritually the trance-like state and the special male–female chemistry characteristic of good intercourse."

"I guess it wouldn't be necessary to choose if I could masturbate while intercourse is going on, although men resent this. But strangely my clitoris sort of blanks out as the movement of intercourse continues. Although it is exciting in itself, I can't come during intercourse and even if I masturbate after intercourse (I have only done it secretly), I have a hard time getting the clitoral feeling back again. Perhaps good intercourse in relationships has not occurred a sufficient number of times for me to learn how to deal with it. Maybe if I persuade men (and myself psychologically) to let me stimulate my clitoris during or after intercourse, and just me enjoy intercourse undisturbed, we can have both without choosing."

"I have always felt that accepting a penis in my vagina was an act of pleasing the man. At first I super got off on my new ability to please and give pleasure. It made me really happy. I liked it a whole lot; it felt really good to be able to please someone I loved so much so directly, so specially. And I liked it because he loved me and was trying to please me too, and I liked being petted and touched and getting a lot of attention and earning my man's love in a deeper way. I was eighteen and I wanted to be a woman, and in my mind I needed to have a man to be a woman and all in all it seemed like a real good deal—I was getting a lot of things I wanted: love, physical affection, attention, protection, and a role to play to make me seem real, grown up, realized. But as we lived together longer, grew out of our Acute Romantic Phase, we were no longer the total energy centre for the other—life went on—my lover was very busy, working long hours, going to meetings at night, teaching on weekends, etc. He began to do the wham, bang, thank you ma'am routine and I felt cheated, used, and rejected. I tried to forget about it. The good woman's role is not to question her man. By the time I brought myself to speak with him about it I had a lot of anger. I'd begun to question what I do want and what makes *me* feel good. It's never since been joy enough just to please my man. This began a time of painful and good search and questioning which has lasted four years (with the same man—I like him) and isn't ended yet—with long cop-out periods of copping out, wanting so bad to return to our first blissful months together, when I could follow his lead, think only of him and feel very, very happy and good. Now I'd have to have something more than intercourse, but I still would enjoy intercourse sometimes."

"I like intercourse in some ways. I like the feeling of having the man's penis inside me. What I don't like is the psychological feeling of pressure to 'come,' to perform. If the man comes too fast it feels like I haven't been part of it at all, and if it takes him a long time, I feel inadequate, like I'm doing something wrong, or not doing something that I should be doing. I like just lying together with the man's penis inside me, and being close, but when the man starts thrusting, I often feel detached, passive, like an object with no real part in what is happening. It doesn't feel like we're together."

A few women did choose clitoral stimulation.
"When I was freshly in love with my husband, I wanted

to be fucked by him all day and all night. This lasted a long time, but gradually grew into the need for less fucking. Now I wouldn't like to choose, but if I had to, I'd pick clitoral stimulation."

"Vaginal penetration is more psychologically than physically satisfying to me. Sometimes I find it boring and would like to leave it out entirely. I don't like the idea of feeling determined for intercourse after foreplay, like something inevitable. I'd like it to be more flexible and optional instead of it being the regular or main course of action. There is a certain form of unity in intercourse which is beautiful, but during other forms of sex, when we do things to please each other, there is still a distinct sense of unity there also. I would definitely choose clitoral stimulation. I find it much more exciting, delicate, loving, and fulfilling."

And some women chose intercourse.

"I would choose intercourse. I feel very close and content then, and it makes my partner very happy."

"Although I feel very physically satisfied after masturbation, I miss the sharing I feel during love-making. Sometimes I also feel puzzled, or even guilty at the thought that I am often more satisfied after masturbation than I am after intercourse. I love my husband and the union of our bodies is a beautiful experience to me. However, I feel more fulfilled when I have an orgasm, and that only happens during masturbation. There are times with my husband when I just don't seem to get excited, and I have to psych myself up for intercourse. But over all I like it best when my husband is just so sexy that I can't resist him and I just let myself move to his movements and let myself go. That is the best for me, and also I would not choose to do without sharing his orgasm."

"I would always want to have intercourse because it makes me feel good to cause so much exultation in my husband."

"It is easier to orgasm by clitoral stimulation without intercourse, but I would prefer intercourse because it is a fuller, more total experience and I feel as though *sharing* penetration is a much happier experience.

"I think I may put too high a value on penetration, tending to discount other kinds of sex as not 'really' being sex. But I really do like the feeling of a man's penis inside of me, and those moments seem much less detached, less controlled, much less contrived, less like people 'operating on' each other than the others. I would choose intercourse, but maybe I can only say that because penetration really does bring me to orgasm."

Quite a few women mentioned having had stronger sexual feelings as a teenager during "necking" or "making out," before sex had always included having intercourse.

"My best experiences were some sexual encounters (not intercourse) when I was a teenager. In those days, sex seemed like a powerful force that could overcome all kinds of conventions and inhibitions. Whereas today, as a woman of thirty, it seems that it is a much more mechanical routine which actually works as a barrier to keep me and the man from actually experiencing each other. But in those days, it was like some powerful force would just drive us together and we would find ourselves making out."

"My best sexual experiences were all the heavy petting I did before I had intercourse at about nineteen. I used to do that for hours on end and fantasize afterwards for hours. It was the most beautiful, pleasureful thing in my life—especially with one guy I loved and went with for two years."

"My body responses are the same now except I think I was more easily stimulated when I was a virgin and always reached orgasm even with my clothes on. Maybe it was just the excitement of knowing I wouldn't have intercourse."

"I worry about the loss of sexual feeling from what I

had back in college before I was introduced to orgasms and intercourse. I feel my responses have become dulled since then in all areas."

"I was in those back seats in the late '50s, caught in the double bind of having to put out something in order to get dates, but not allowed to fuck. I had innumerable orgasms without penetration. When penetration came along, it wasn't as good."

"I had been masturbating since I was twelve years old on a regular basis (reaching climaxes), but somehow the penis penetration of my first intercourse did not arouse the same feelings in me at all. I vaguely thought (from his urgings) that I had reached a climax when we made love, but it was completely different from masturbation and in my vague innocence I didn't connect the two. The next person I made love with I went with for two years and lived with for one. We petted for three months before I broke down and went on the pill. Our petting was ecstasy and I felt higher on sex than ever before in my life. Then when I was safe on the pill, we made love at a crowded parking place under the steering wheel. He came instantly (shocking after the hours of our petting, when I wasn't safe). It was very disappointing for both of us and our sex life was very poor for the next two years. Foreplay was very poor (I could never get used to that after the hours of passionate petting earlier) and sometimes he took forever to come and just couldn't. It was then I started realizing that Steve was never touching my clitoris and I was very aware of the intense feelings touching it could give me (reinforced by my own masturbation). I tried to show him gently and he got furious, saying wasn't he a good enough lover for me, etc. I was crushed and after a few more half-hearted attempts to show him, I gave up."

"I would like more kissing, more stroking, more slow sensuality to love-making. Perhaps, then, I would get that marvellous feeling back of 'butterflies in the stomach' that I would feel for *hours* when I was fifteen and endlessly petting and having neither intercourse nor orgasm."

"What my generation called 'petting' was very exciting. We were 'demi-virgins,' which meant *anything* as long as the hymen remained intact. Although actual genital sex is enjoyable, it never reaches the heights of virginal necking."

And one teenaged woman said:

"It is strange, but being tickled on my back gives me a great deal of pleasure, and I don't insist on it, though often I indicate that I really like it and would enjoy having it done. As things stand, I much prefer having my back tickled to having intercourse, but so far I haven't said this to a man. But I think I will pretty soon just to see what will happen. I am tired of being so secretive, and I would rather be called weird and 'not a real woman' to having all these withholds and secrets."

But some women thought intercourse felt good even though it did not culminate in having an orgasm.

"The feeling of penetration, especially if the penis is large enough, is fantastic to me. I sometimes just like to hold it inside me—not moving at all. I love the feelings of different positions, each one seems like a whole new sensation. I like deep, hard thrusting, although most men don't seem to be able to do deep or hard enough (some have been able to, so I know what I like). I also love the feeling of it sliding in and out and love to be teased by taking it all the way out and begging for him to put it back in. It never leads to orgasm for me."

"To be filled is a great body pleasure. There are nights when I want just *everything* in me—including in my mouth, my ears, my vagina, and my rectum—wow."

"Sometimes, if my lover slowly penetrates very, very deeply—and then doesn't move, I get these ecstatic flows and ripples all through my lower abdomen, inside and out. It's not exactly a climax—I'm not exactly sure what to label it—but when my lover lets me fully enjoy his penis, with no direct motion on his part, the feeling is glorious."

And, finally, as observed earlier in the book, many women liked to give a man they loved pleasure, and to feel his body experiencing it.

"Intercourse doesn't give me an intense clitoral kind of orgasm but I still get very carried away. Most of the excitement is about holding and being held, and especially having him come, which both of us can feel intensely—which is very satisfying to me."

Finally, to answer the question of whether women would still want intercourse if they didn't feel obligated to have it, the point is not whether women in *general* would still want to have intercourse, but that it would become a choice, an option, for each *individual* woman. Whether she wanted to have intercourse or not would become her own *choice,* not something she had to do to have physical relations with a man.

Intercourse, as a pleasurable form of physical contact, will always be one of the ways people choose to relate. However, it will not continue to be the *only* way. It will become de-emphasized, one of many alternative possibilities in a whole spectrum of possible physical relations. Heterosexual intercourse is too narrow a definition to remain the only definition of sex for most people most of the time.

Of course, it can only be surmised at this time how much of what we feel now during intercourse is real physical pleasure and how much is a product of the glorification of intercourse. Most women would probably still want intercourse sometimes—especially with men for whom they had strong feelings. Some women might like intercourse almost always, while others would almost never want it. Perhaps it could be said that many women might be rather indifferent to intercourse if it were not for feelings towards a particular man.

Three women had stopped having intercourse, but continued sleeping with their partners, with varied reasons and results.

"I used to like intercourse but my lovers' insistence on the pattern foreplay/fuck/sleep turned me off intercourse. I always felt/feel pressured to fuck (are you ready yet?). I started to resent it and now I don't like fucking and I've fucked only once or twice in the past year. I like putting my foot down and trying new ways to get what I want from my lover, but it's created another block, because I've had to stop fucking out of stubbornness and not anything cooperative and mutual, and it seems like communication around this is hard for both of us. However, since I've stopped letting myself be fucked, it's been hard for my lover to ignore my sexual dissatisfaction—which was real easy for him to ignore as long as he was happy. At least now he's started to look for solutions too."

"With my boyfriend of four years, we pretty much stopped fucking, because it just wasn't worth it for me, and he doesn't want me to do it if I don't like it. What with the problems of contraception and no orgasms, it's a waste. We fucked about twice in the past four months. I feel a little guilty about not fucking my boyfriend, but I know I'm right. He still comes, and I do too, and I don't have to worry about pregnancy. It's good this way. I get mad if we fuck and I don't come (and I never have)—I feel 'frigid' and 'out of it' when my partner is ecstatic. I feel silly. I feel like a punching bag."

"I've just come home from vacation all geared up and enthusiastic about being sexually honest, and I ran into a difficulty with my boyfriend. He's been pressing me to go and get a diaphragm, and I have some kind of hang-up about it. I thought it over and decided that I didn't want to make an 'official' promotion of sexual intercourse by getting something to make it always possible because I really don't *like* sexual intercourse. I told this to my boyfriend and he felt very highly insulted and made a scene and told me we'd discuss it later. We haven't discussed it yet (two days later) but I have the feeling that in order to continue seeing him there is a prerequisite that I have to have intercourse with him. This is terribly upsetting to me."

Towards a new kind of intercourse

Not only are intercourse and male orgasm not necessary in every heterosexual contact, but, in addition, the manner in which intercourse is practised can change to become more mutual and more varied. It is not necessary for intercourse to be a "male dominant" activity. Intercourse can become a varied and individual practice, which can be done in any way you might create. For example, there are many ways of joining and having intercourse besides male "penetration" and "thrusting." Remember the answers women gave in the intercourse chapter, explaining how they had orgasms during intercourse? Much of this intercourse did not involve any in and out movement, but more a kind of pressing together (with the penis inside) so the clitoris could get the kind of continuous stimulation necessary for orgasm.* Intercourse need not be as gymnastic as we have usually thought, and it is probable that what we think of as the "natural," physical, movements of intercourse are nothing more than "learned" responses. Isn't it possible that men have been told that "mounting and thrusting" is the "right" thing to do, but that they too, if allowed to experiment, would find many other ways they liked to have intercourse?

Although the most common position used for intercourse is the man-above-woman position, there is no physical reason why it should be better for men. As a matter of

---

*Whereas male stimulation for orgasm can be discontinuous, female stimulation, due to differences in anatomy, must be *continuous* for orgasm to occur.

fact, Masters and Johnson have pointed out that if a man is on the bottom, he can receive more orgasmic pleasure, since he is not at the same time involved in physically supporting his body, etc. Furthermore, to call male "mounting and thrusting" natural and "instinctive" is highly questionable. After all, most men masturbate *not* by thrusting but by moving their hands on their penises; women with Type III masturbation always thrust. What is natural?

In fact, a few women felt the man-on-top position was more political than natural, as evidenced by their replies to, "Do you feel that having sex is in any way political?"

"Yes! who gets the top?!!! Everyone knows that a woman is more likely to have an orgasm on top, since you have more control. On the bottom, you must more or less just cooperate with the one on top—sort of like having a man 'take care of you,' like you're a baby almost."

"Yes, it is political in every way. Men are demanding, women are meant to please. Men are on top in a traditional sense—in society and in conventional intercourse. Men do the action, women are meant as the orifice to be used. I'm *tired* of being on the receiving end!"

However, once again, the point is not to "reverse" the situation but to expand our ideas of what physical relations can be; there is no reason to believe that being on the top is always better than being on the bottom for all women. Many women did enjoy the bottom position sometimes, mainly because it is good to just lie with another person's body and the bed completely surrounding and enfolding you.

"I like being on the bottom. I feel closer and more connected then."

"I like the bottom. I am shy about being on top, and I miss being held in that position."

"Being on top is most stimulating when I feel there might be a chance of orgasm. On the bottom is most comfortable, cosy, and loving in terms of being freer to embrace."

In the same way, a passionate desire to be "taken" or "possessed" by someone during sex is not automatically a sign of victimization, as long as it is not the only feeling you ever have. The desires to be "taken" or to "possess" someone, to "take" *them,* are merely part of the natural spectrum of feelings that can be experienced by either men or women at times of great intensity.

Intercourse can also become more androgynous.
    "I'm inclined, at this point, to try and describe the situation with my current lover. T is ten years younger than I, and was a virgin when we became lovers. Although I had had a good deal of previous sexual experiences, I can hardly say I taught him all he knew: his openness and wonderful curiosity have taken me into explorations I'd hardly dreamed of, in a forthright and fearless fashion. We've also struggled a lot with the differences between our sexualities, especially men's limited ability to have orgasms. We have evolved a way of making love that accommodates both our needs, or tries to: usually starting with long slow kisses and caresses, then mutual manual and sometimes oral stimulation. As I get more aroused I have a hard time paying attention to what I'm doing to him and eventually stop, letting him work me into several orgasms. Then he enters me—positions vary—and continues to stimulate me for as long as he can. I usually climax several times, sometimes with a frightening emotional intensity. Just before he's going to ejaculate, we switch positions so that he can lie down and I sit on him, penis inside me. I move up and down, my vagina tight around him, and usually insert a finger in his anus and play with his nipples. He gets to be passive, just lies there and *feels* the full intensity of his coming. Yes, it does give me a sense of power, and also a lot of joy in being able to return the pleasure he gives me fullfold. The feelings are very strong and loving. I get a little of the same feeling sticking a finger in his anus—it feels

very good to him and I like being able to penetrate him, not having it only go the other way."

"I reached the point several times with both men and women of being very excited when on top, feeling I had, or wanted to have, a penis and penetrate them. Other times I have thought it would be fun to trade bodies and find out what it feels like for a man to make love. To identify with his penis, and his whole body, and the emotions behind his desire . . . "

Suppose men won't cooperate in redefining intercourse, or in leaving it out sometimes? What if they still try to follow the same old mechanical pattern of sexual relations? There is no reason why women must help men during intercourse. The fact is, we usually cooperate quite extensively during intercourse in order for the man to be able to orgasm. We move along with his rhythm, keep our legs apart and our bodies in positions that make penetration and thrusting possible, and almost never stop intercourse in midstream unless the man has had his orgasm. We do not *have* to cooperate in these ways with a man if he will not cooperate with us.

Although we do not *have* to, we are taught that if we are anything but helpful (or at least non-interfering) during intercourse, it is tantamount to castrating the man. This is nonsense. Our non-cooperation with men in sex is no worse than their non-cooperation with us—for example, their using clitoral stimulation as a "foreplay" technique, and withdrawing the stimulation just before orgasm. It is perfectly all right for us to follow the example of one woman who said, "I feel quite confident about ending sexual activity in midstream if it is not working out, or if I begin to drift or feel disinterested." As another woman advised, "Try to get what *you* want and do what *you* feel. (Don't be afraid to act on your most basic, secret, and ultra-secret desires.) If you are not enjoying it in the midst of sex, *say* so. Ladies, you don't have to do anything you don't feel like doing!"

And another woman: "I spent most of my adult life doing what I 'ought'—and having an awful time. It was only when I broke out of that, fairly recently, that sex began to mean anything to me, or feel like anything. And I got no help from the popular culture, or from psychoanalysis, or indeed from anything except something a friend chanced to say, and the women's movement. I would advise women to look to their *own* hearts and bodies, and follow them wherever they lead."

Do men need intercourse?

Before we automatically react to the previous section with: "Well, what about men? Don't they *need* intercourse? Won't less intercourse mean less pleasure for men?"—let's re-examine briefly what little we know about male sexuality. There is no basis for saying that men are getting the greatest pleasure they can get from our current model of physical relations, although they are at least having orgasm. Isn't it possible that male sexuality is capable of more, and more in the way of individual variety, than men's sex magazines would have us believe? Are we sure we know what male sexuality is? Books and articles by men have started to appear that question these old stereotypes, and many men—though far too few at present—are beginning to take a fresh look at what they are getting out of their sexual relationships.

Rollo May and Marc Feigen Fasteau, among others, have written that they feel men, by concentrating on achieving orgasm and the *satisfaction* of desire, are in a way missing the whole point of sexual pleasure—which is to *prolong* the pleasure and the feeling of desire, to build it higher and higher. This is what women were talking about in the chapter on orgasm when they described the heightened feelings of arousal they felt before orgasm. Rollo May:

> The pleasure in sex is described by Freud and others as the
> reduction of tension; in eros, on the contrary, we wish not to

be released from the excitement but rather to hang onto it,
to bask in it, and even to increase it.[1]

If the importance of female orgasm has been under-empha-
sized, to say the very least the importance of male orgasm
has been greatly over-exaggerated. Although orgasm is wonderful, a very large part of the pleasure is building up to the
orgasm, as Fasteau wrote:

> *What the masculine disdain for feeling makes it hard for*
> *men to grasp is that the state of desire . . . is one of the best,*
> *perhaps the best, part of the experience of love.*[2]

A woman in this study said something similar to this:
"My sexuality has more to do with the desire than with satisfaction. I am not interested in 'satisfaction.' I don't know
what it is or why it is considered valuable. I like to be hungry for a person, to desire intimacy and understanding, to
be inspired to be loving and to find reciprocation." The real
pleasure of sexual relations, in this sense, then, is the prolonging and increasing of desire, not ending it or getting
released from it as quickly as possible.

It was recommended in ancient Sanskrit and Hindu literature (and was actually practised in the New York Oneida
Colony, in the nineteenth century) that men could achieve
the greatest pleasure by the continual maintenance of high
levels of arousal, by refraining from orgasm for long periods
of time:

> *In this technique it is common for the individual to*
> *experience as many as a dozen or twenty peaks of response*
> *which, while closely approaching the sexual climax,*
> *deliberately avoid what we should interpret as actual*
> *orgasm. Persons who practice such techniques commonly*
> *insist that they experience orgasm at each and every peak*
> *even though each is held to something below full response*
> *and . . . ejaculation is avoided.*[3]

This concept is again being tried at present by some groups of men living in various experimental communes.

There is no reason why the reintegration of intercourse into the whole spectrum of physical relations should threaten men. Men too can profit by opening up and re-examining their conception of what sexuality is.

The association of intercourse with masculinity is at least as much cultural as it is physical, and it is to be hoped male sexuality will also undergo an individualizing and expansive process. Men who would like to contribute their information and feelings by answering the questionnaire for men can write to me c/o the publisher or e-mail info@hite-research.com.

Touching is sex too

Feelings about physical closeness

Besides changing the inevitability and manner of intercourse, what other changes did women emphasize they would like to see in physical relations? One of the most basic changes involves valuing, touching and closeness just for their own sakes—rather than only as a prelude to intercourse or orgasm.

"In the best of all possible worlds, sex would be a way of being close, of communicating with another person. This would not necessarily mean that we would all have sexual experiences with more people or that I, for example, would be running around bedding down with all our male acquaintances. It might even make it possible for me to have the closeness and affection I need *without* having it lead, inevitably, to sexual intercourse. Perhaps if we all had more people we related to with physical affection and touching, we'd have a generally more loving atmosphere in which to dwell; we wouldn't necessarily feel that every contact points in the direction of intercourse . . . a warning and yet somehow commanding finger . . . so that you don't feel free to take Step A unless you are willing to take Step B, C, D, etc."

Does having good sex have anything to do with having orgasms?"

Women often said, in answer to this and to many other questions, how much more important body contact and closeness were to them than orgasms *per se* in sex with a partner. This *could* be accepted purely at face value; however, since women do masturbate for orgasms it is clear that orgasms are also very important to women. The truth is that both orgasms *and* close body contact or touching are extremely important to women,* but they have often been forced to get them in separate ways. The important point to realize in reading the answers below is how important touching and body contact are and how undervalued they have been in our model of physical relations.

"Orgasms are important but being close and loving is *as* important. My husband, knowing I have multiple orgasms, feels the more I have that the better sex is. That is not true—my orgasms are purely physical and can be arrived at without much foreplay. I do not feel it is 'making love' just because you have an orgasm. It can still be just a quick 'screw.'"

"I have intense orgasms during masturbation, but intercourse involves a sort of emotional as well as physical satisfaction being with the man I love. Just from the point of view of having an orgasm, masturbation can be just as satisfying, but the rest of my body isn't always satisfied. I still want the rest of my body to be touched and kissed and to feel a warm man next to me."

"Closeness with another person is more important to me than orgasm (which I can have by myself, if necessary). If I had to *choose* between the two, I'd choose touching. I really dig kissing, hugging, fondling, looking at, and feeling the other person. I feel like I'm sharing

---

* See Appendix 3 for statistical breakdown. Many other answers to this question did reflect a militancy about getting orgasm, not represented in these quotes. For example:

"If I could not orgasm with a partner, I would look for another. If a woman has *never* had an orgasm, she might think she's having good sex without them, but I never could. You're not really experiencing sex without orgasms."

"Having fabulously outrageous sex has to do with having orgasms for me. I *can* have a wonderful sexual experience without orgasm if I am very high emotionally. But sooner or later I feel that I am missing out unless my partner learns to bring me to orgasm."

more if we don't get into genital stimulation, especially when first getting to know each other, because sexual arousal and orgasm takes a sort of concentration on myself, so I feel more alone when I'm into that—although it can be shared, too."

"Good sex, for me, is much more than genital. It involves two whole bodies and two whole souls, exploring each other, sensitizing and being sensitive to each other, holding, caring for, being gentle with each other, being very aware of each other and working into a oneness that is neither and both persons. Orgasm can be the peak of that process, but it's only one (and not necessarily the best) point in a complex process."

"Too much pressure to have orgasm makes sex goal-and-success-oriented and misses the whole point. Trying to make women have 'just as good orgasms as men' is male-oriented and not the right direction at all. Sex should be sheer luxuriating in pleasure, being close to the other person, enveloped in warmth and touching all over—not a race for orgasm."

"I think the emphasis on orgasm, the separation of orgasm from general sensuality, from warmth and openness and love, is unfortunate. I have the feeling that women's sexuality is emulating the orgasm-oriented, mechanistic male style in this. Good sex, for me at least, has much more to do with a sense of real communication and closeness, and a kind of passionate nuzzling."

"I do think you emphasize orgasm excessively. There is, it seems to me, an erotic continuum, of which orgasm is merely one point, one period, more intense, but qualitatively not different from the experience preceding and following. I often wonder if questionnaires like this and all the how-to-do-it books aren't a bit like the college co-eds who keep their orgasm average. Since it's been proven scientifically that women have orgasms, therefore if you don't have them every minute there's something wrong with you. The kissing, touching, talk, and tenderness that happens when two people like and enjoy each other is much more important than orgasm. The understanding of each other's sensuality and the appreciation of physical togetherness is what sex is. It is a kind of intensified aesthetic experience—experiencing with all of one's senses the complete beauty of another person."

"Do you enjoy touching?"

"Touching is the most important part of sex, part of a natural eroticism, being in physical touch with my body and others' bodies."

"Long, gentle passionate encounters, with much touching and enthusiasm, give me a feeling of being loved all over and are all I need most of the time."

"I love making out fully clothed—just kissing and *very* lightly petting—all clothes on and all buttons buttoned, touching and talking. I would rather make out than screw. And it's not the same if it's just a prelude to screwing. A lot of times I screw when I'd rather just make out. I guess I don't think of it as a choice I have."

"General body touching is more important to me than orgasms. A good kiss, to touch each other in the middle of the night, to listen to breathing and heartbeats, smiles, eyes (for sure eyes), the open talks that occur in bed after making love, all of these make sex extra, extra special and cannot be filled by masturbation or orgasm. A good hug—and I love-you-and-always-will-and-care-so-much-for-you-and-here-is-my-heart-and-soul-and-I-am-taking-you hug is worth the world. It is so much more than words. A really good hug will take over an orgasm any day."

"You can't love sex without loving to touch and be touched. It's the very physical closeness of sex that is the main pleasure. With my present lover we spend anywhere from two to six hours caressing, touching, cuddling and hugging, kissing, and just resting against one another. It feels marvellous!"

"I am a snuggler and a toucher. Now that I am single, this has had to be suppressed. I had been in the habit of sitting close, sleeping snuggled up, holding hands. The death of my husband ended that abruptly. But now I try to continue this 'touching pattern' when I get a chance with my lovers."

"Hugging is really important to me. I also like kissing and caressing all parts of the body. I like a lot of eye contact, and I like to be touched on my face and head. It depends on my partner and my mood whether talking is important. I enjoy these activities as much, if not more, than regular genital sex, because it is very communicative, and very personal. I like a man to say my name. I really enjoy just holding each other."

"Best are the long tender hours of stimulating each other and relaxing before orgasm, then starting again, talking, petting. It is extremely important to me to have this much body contact, and I also like sensual touch games—wrestling is great, and dancing nude and sexy, and also just immature cuddling. A previous lover told me I'd taught him love-making was 75 per cent touching and 25 per cent intercourse."

"I like to neck on the floor, fully clothed, to music— and play silly games pretending this and that, feeling utterly abandoned!"

"There's something very warm and intimate and very beautiful about lying in the dark with someone, holding them close and talking softly. Frankly, I enjoy it more right now than genital sex, but that could be due to my rather limited experience."

"Sex itself is not terribly important to me, but physical contact in the form of touching, hugs, embraces, caresses, etc. is most important. I am more interested in having that kind of physical contact than I am in having sex. Sex doesn't play that big a part in my life. If I have the above-mentioned physical contact with the person and I really like it and the person doing it, then I may have sex—not always, though."

"I like the intimateness of love-making almost as much as the sex itself. Hugging and kissing and caressing someone is more loving than sex, and is very important. I also love the way people talk and smile and giggle when they make love. People after sex tend to become very silly, and sharing that is really important to feel loved. If you want a good orgasm, you can masturbate. The whole reason you make love with someone is to share the closeness and warmth of making love, of giving pleasure, of appreciating each other's bodies, of saying things you would never say elsewhere, of being very loving without feeling silly or foolish—anything is okay to say in bed."

"I *do* feel very strongly that keeping in physical, real physical *touch,* flesh to flesh, with another, or with other human beings, is absolutely necessary to keeping healthy: sane. I *know* that for me it is. That's why I do feel that 'there's more to sex than that,' only nobody's found ways (no biological stain, or recording device) yet to *see* what the effects are of sex, mating, fucking, touching, all that physical stuff—on the people who do it together. I feel that there may be subtle neural and chemical interactions set in motion in each partner's body by direct physical contact with the other partner."

The overwhelming number of answers received to this question were just like these; desire for more touching and body contact was more or less universal.

Sometimes it has been implied that petting is "immature"—something people do only when they aren't able to "go all the way." This is not true. Petting has been a major form of sexuality from time immemorial, but, once again, it was condemned in the Judaeo-Christian codes unless it was an adjunct to intercourse, and continues in this status up to the present.

Other mammals also engage in a lot of petting and "making out," as Kinsey pointed out:

Among most species of mammals there is, in actuality, a great deal of sex play which never leads to coitus. Most mammals, when sexually aroused, crowd together and nuzzle and explore with their noses, mouths, and feet over each other's bodies. They make lip-to-lip contacts and tongue-to-tongue contacts, and use their mouths to manipulate every part of the companion's body, including the genitalia . . . The student of mammalian mating behavior, interested in observing coitus in his animal stocks, sometimes may have to wait through hours and days of sex play before he has an opportunity to observe actual coitus, if, indeed, the animals do not finally separate without ever attempting a genital union.[4]

There is no reason why we should not create as many different degrees and kinds of sex as we want—whether or not they lead to orgasm, and whether or not they are genital. If the definition of sexual pleasure is sustaining desire and building arousal higher and higher—not ending it—many possibilities for physical pleasure and for exciting another person open up. The truth is that "sex" is bigger than orgasm, and involves any kind of deep physical intimacy one shares with another person. Intense physical contact is one of the most satisfying activities possible—in and of itself.

However, in reply to questions about their desire for physical affection and touching, many women said that men usually did not like to touch except during sex.

"Touching is very important, but I don't do it as much at all as I would like. Men never want to touch and kiss without fucking."

"Touching is very important and meaningful, but doesn't happen often because men most generally have but one end in mind when they touch you. Although I have discussed this with my husband, he ignores me. And he insists he knows I *really* want 'it.'"

"I really enjoy it, but I find that some men do not

understand this and so become aroused and want to have sex. Yet I just wanted closeness and affection. So at times, in order to get this, I have ended up having sex, which is not what I started off wanting."

"I have had sex just to be close and touch a man, but not often any more because I get the orgasm off by myself and the hugging satisfied to a large extent from my daughter."

"Very important. I only wish men could do this without it always and only being a lead-in to sex. I don't think I would feel as used and frustrated all the time if there were any playing around, or signs of affection without it being in bed."

"After sex it is very depressing for me if there is no hugging and kissing. I feel like a discarded shoe. But most men don't like to do this."

"I feel affection is very important. How nice it is to know someone is hugging you, because they really care about you as a person, instead of a cunt. If a partner is not very physically affectionate at times when sex is not involved, I resent being touched later just to prime me for sex. Too many men act this way."

"Extremely important. I love touching, physical demonstrations of affection and all that. Right now I am able to do as much as I like and receive as much too, due to relating exclusively to women. It was difficult to get enough and give enough with men."

"I feel physical affection and touching are much more important than all sex and orgasms, but I am somewhat deprived because my boyfriend feels that a need for such contact involves neurotic insecurity."

"I have become very much aware (since my divorce and subsequent cut-off from easy contact with another person) of the importance to me of touching others. I long to embrace and be embraced; just to stretch out next to a man and feel the contours of his body. I certainly do not do as much of this as I would like to, because it would only be accepted as part of sex and I really am not ready for that yet."

"I crave physical affection. I don't get it at home, and have gone out and taken a lover because he will hug me. I require hugs and in exchange give sex. This is all right with me because I enjoy sex; however, I want to stress that often all I really am seeking is for a man to touch me."

"Touching is as important or more, to me, than having sex, and is my main motivation for sex, with intercourse itself sometimes an unwanted intrusion."

"I used to be starved of physical affection and so got into sexual relationships with men looking not for sexual satisfaction (I could please myself more easily) but for physical contact and tenderness, which is what I want most out of love-making. Now I get a great deal of it from my husband, but formerly that was probably about the only reason I went to bed with anyone."

"With my husband, physical touching always leads to sex, which inhibits me from being affectionate when I just feel like cuddling and not making love."

"Physical affection is tremendously important to me. Often I resent the fact that my husband limits most of his kissing to sex-resulting situations. I like being held and kissed spontaneously, and playing around—but he doesn't."

"Physical affection and touching for its own sake is so devalued and devoid in my life I could cry. I don't dare do it without really thinking first, but sometimes I sacrifice myself to a man just to get it."

"Physical affection and touching are extremely important to me, and a large part of the pleasure of sex, as far as I'm concerned. However, this is a part of my marital relationship that is lacking. A caress or a kiss can feel great, but not the dead fish type of kiss that seems to come about after a few years of marriage."

"I have learned within the last few years to be unafraid of open expressions of feelings, including hugging and kissing people of all ages and sexes, whom I feel good with. One of the problems I had when I was married (1938–48) was that touching was only a prelude to sex, and I resented it tremendously."

"*Very.* But touching and holding like I want makes men tire of me. I can never hug or hold on to a man like I want. Sometimes I feel cheap."

"Essential. In the background of my alienation from my husband is his dislike for touching and demonstrativeness in general. He is not able to give affection and touching freely and easily to anyone at all (it isn't just me)."

"I love physical affection and touching but find that this inevitably leads to sexual desire on the part of men. Therefore I refrain from physical affection even with men I like unless I am willing to have intercourse with them."

"I've learned that unless a female wants sex, it is wise not to touch a man *too* much. Most men interpret my caress as sex-inspiring when all I was doing was trying to relax. It pisses me off because most men can't accept it and make me feel like I'm 'leading them on' unless I sleep with them. Phooey."

"I usually don't touch as much as I'd like because girls think I'm queer and guys think I want to be raped. Once I was touching this guy, just to make us both feel good, and he said, 'Why are you making me hot?' and I said, 'Am I?'"

"I like touching very much, but with my husband a touch is all he needs to think it's time to hop into bed. *All* of our marriage (two years) he touches me *all* the time and never gives me a chance to touch him—and then he claims I'm not affectionate. But *his* affectionate moves drown mine! It's all a vicious circle."

"Hugging and kissing are *so* important. Odour is great too. I love to stop and just smell each other. I don't get enough of hugging and kissing though. My lover is a fantastic person, but his level of affection can be very low. He has sometimes rolled over and gone to sleep after we've had sex. I can't blame him, I guess—he's not much good when he's dead tired. I just wish he could hold me while we fell asleep. He will if I ask him, but it won't last for long. Once he's asleep he's untouchable and needs a lot of room. I have very mixed feelings about this. I *need* a lot of hugging and kissing. One time we had sex without kissing each other at all and I felt really terrible."

Lesbian sexuality, as seen in chapter 5, is quite different and does often involve this kind of extended intimate physical contact. Since one orgasm does not automatically mean the end of sex for most women, whether or not the focus of sex is orgasm, touching and kissing can be continued almost indefinitely.

There were a few exceptional men.
"My long relationship with John had a lot of touching and petting. It was such a super relaxer after my awful job—it connected me with him and humanity again. He would pet me into a blissful haze on many a night. What a doll."

"I've just met a man who loves all kinds of touching—we shower or bathe together, we often sit and simply snuggle, we go to sleep entwined. At odd moments he simply reaches out to take my hand. Sometimes the closeness becomes blissfully erotic and sometimes it's calming beyond belief. His delight in it all tells me volumes about his generous look on life."

In reality, it is likely that men do like physical intimacy and affectionate contact as much as women do, but are afraid to express these feelings.

Not only is touching men outside of sex generally impossible, but touching other women in friendship is not generally acceptable either.
"Sometimes I get so angry at this society for being so cold. There are so many times I would like to kiss a girl friend or hug her or even put my arm around her but I can't because she would be horrified, and think I was a

lesbian. Damn, that makes me angry."

"I would like to touch some people, but hesitate because they are aware of my 'sexual preference,' and this makes me and them uncomfortable. It's awfully hard to explain to an old friend that I only want to hug her because she is an old friend and not a potential bed partner."

"I enjoy touching other women, but most of the times you are allowed to do this, like with hellos and goodbyes, the hugs lose most of their sexuality and become just reassuring routines, and as far as I'm concerned don't serve any purpose at all."

"There are occasions I'll look at a friend—someone I've been close to for years—and see them as very beautiful, and I'll wish we could be very close. I've always been too frozen in the safe patterns of friendship to reach out to a friend when I feel sensually and sexually attracted to them. I would like to be able to do this, to see what happens, and take these feelings out of the realm of my mind even if it's only to say to the man or woman, 'You're looking really *good* to me right now!'"

Aside from touching one's partner during sex, it only seems possible to touch children and animals.

"Right now touching is mostly reserved either for parent–baby relationships or sexual relationships. Outside of this it is often construed as sexual even when it isn't. I touch my friends, my dogs, my cats, soft things, myself, and children. Actually, my daughter is about my favourite person to touch."

"Until recently, I satisfied most of my need for touching and physical affection with my young children, including breast-feeding."

"I am in conservation service in wildlife and it is amazing how much a *homo sapiens* can relate to other species (all wild) through touch and speech. It means a great deal to me."

"In regards to touching and kissing—I enjoy kissing a cat. It is a pleasant sensation for me to put my lips against a cat's soft warm body. Also, I love to feel the vibrations produced by a cat's purring. Needless to say, this is not sexual—certainly not!"

"I only touched my beloved kittens and cats when I was growing up. People have never measured up since. I love touching children and men I love, and I would doubtless love much more general touching if it were allowed and cultivated."

But even parent–child touching is curtailed, lest there be the slightest "sexual" (genital) overtones!

"My mother and I used to hug a lot when I was young. But as I got older she sort of weaned me away from that, fearing I might turn into a lesbian. As a result, it's just in the last couple of years I am beginning to feel comfortable in kissing or touching relations."

"I sometimes felt that my son derived sexual pleasure from my touching him (say, while giving him a bath). He was about four or five then. It was very confusing and embarrassing to me; I also felt guilty—clearly if I'd been a better mother this wouldn't have happened. I knew that guilt and evasiveness made everything worse, but I simply didn't know how to deal with it."

"Sometimes I feel turned on embracing my little sister, who I'm fond of. Yet I cannot imagine actually 'doing anything' with her—the thought horrifies me. I've heard that one often feels warmth and contentment in a seemingly sexual way because emotion does register in the genital area, as well as actual excitement. But I don't embrace her as often as I would like, since I am afraid it might look funny."

"I touch my children a lot hoping they will grow up more attuned to it. I was raised in the 'cry it out' school of child psychology by a very well-meaning but frustrated mother. Now she touches my kids a lot too."

"Both my sons wanted to sleep with me when they were little, but I never permitted it or had sexual desires towards them. I told them that big boys didn't sleep

with their mothers; they had their own beds—but that I
was very near and if they needed me for anything, they
could call me and I'd come."

"Once in a while I look at my big six-foot fifteen-
year-old son, nude—and think—wouldn't it be nice if
part of 'parenting' was to teach one's children (male or
female) loving sex techniques; instead I bought him *The
Joy of Sex,* which he seems to peruse occasionally, as well
as *Playboy,* I regret to say. I also used to have sexually
stimulated feelings when nursing *him* and I liked it."

"There was a time (around age nine, I'd say) when I
liked to play a game with my mother: I was the princess
and she was the prince. I would wear a long nightgown,
and I wanted my mother to take off her dress—her
stockings and garters made her look more 'like a prince'
to me. She didn't like the game at all, and would only
play it reluctantly, usually not in the 'costume' I wanted."

However, one woman said:

"I think perhaps I have had sexual feelings towards
family members but they are hard to acknowledge
usually. Like last night when my daughter was cutting
my hair and her breasts and body were close to mine—
it was a nice feeling—and after she was through with the
haircut she bent down and kissed me—this doesn't
mean we want to jump into bed together—but I think
it is sexual and good and not to be feared."

**Most women felt they would like to be much freer to
touch others.**

"I would just like it to be normal to touch the body, not
necessarily to further sexual contact, of anyone I felt
close to. Especially I wish I could be more comfortable
in touching my friends."

"There are so many people I would like to touch,
but being a part of a 'no touch' society, it is either
misinterpreted or taboo to touch anyone else in a
friendly gesture or even one of deeper commitment. I

hate it when people pull away from my touch."

"Physical affection and touching are so important it's beyond belief. So many people (including me) are suffering from lack of it that if we could get rid of our social hang-up about it, half the psychiatrists in this country would be out of business. But people tend to shy away from you if you touch them anywhere on their body. I think we are becoming a country of 'touch me nots,' lest they feel an emotion arousing in them."

"I think all people of both sexes could use more physical touching and massaging for the sense of real human contact and relaxation that it gives. None of us ever get as much of that as we can use. I don't do as much as I would like because I feel inhibited socially and hold back touching friends, because I do not think they would be accepting. I guess we have all had sex just to be close to someone and be touched when all we ever wanted was to be loved."

"My sexual life is very separate from the rest of my life. I wish I could be more open, loving, and physical with children. Perhaps I wouldn't feel such a strain in my relationship with my husband if I also had some other outlets for the love, openness, joy, and affection I feel and want so much to express."

"Touch brings feelings of warmth, security, comfort, and tenderness. It makes me feel more human, and gives me a sense of kinship, belonging, and acceptance. Besides, it feels good! But where are all these people that let you touch them like that?!!"

"In the best of all possible worlds, what would sexuality be like?"

"Sexuality would become just a simple joy and recognition of one's sexual feelings and from there letting all humans define their sexuality as what is most comfortable for them at any given time, in any given situation. 'Sexuality' would become an integral part of being, greatly varied and personalized, part of life as a *whole.*"

"Sex would be more nourishing. Self to self, self to others—lots of warmth and involvement and love and touching on all possible levels as a natural expression of body and emotions. Babies, children, pets, old, young, everyone would be cuddled and fondled, touched and encouraged to do so, to and for each other and themselves. There would be public rejoicing in the pleasure of affection and the human body."

What kinds of touching do women like?

Sleeping together.
"My lover and I are very physical with each other although we don't have sex very often. We sleep naked and intertwined together every night, we shower together and kiss and hug, pat and touch, bite, etc. all the time."

"I really like touching, sleeping next to, and waking up the next morning with the person still there. Holding them. I have slept with two of my close friends like this, and it was wonderful."

"Touching is very important. I sleep cuddled up with my best friend and have for six years, although we do not participate in sexual behaviour. (That is her decision, not mine.)"

"I love to embrace and touch completely. I love to curl up back to front together in bed. I intensely enjoy sleeping with my little girl, cuddling with her, stroking her back or her mine."

Pressing together.
"Lying pressed together is a wonderful feeling—a kind of body to body embrace. I like to lie in this position, bodies touching all around, kind of mushing."

"My favourite: deep kissing and pressing of bodies

together full length with arms holding tight. Opening my whole mouth to the other person and vice versa."

"I get this kind of swelling feeling in my chest, a feeling like I will burst with emotion and feeling—and a desire to press them to me and myself to them so tightly—"

"I love it when my husband presses me up against him *real tight,* squeezing me all against him. I like to wrap him up in my body, bury my nose in him, wrestle, kiss, and fuck."

"Until a few years ago, I experienced desire separate from sexual desire: it was an intolerable burning sensation in my chest rather than in my genitals."

"What is most stimulating to me is the closeness of the entire other person. If I can feel any separateness or separation of us, it reduces the excitement. Pressure is the single most important arousal element—generalized, dull (i.e., not sharp), rhythmic pressure. This gets me really excited, and my nipples, clitoris, and genital area go crazy for it. If it keeps up like that, I will have an orgasm."

"Merely lying on top of a desired person will bring me extremely close to orgasm. The only thing required is body movement."

"I like the total immersion of body and mind—if it were possible for the entire surface of my body to be simultaneously very lightly stroked, slow probing kisses all over, tender yet firm—hugging our bodies together and rubbing."

"I like to get in bed and hold each other, flesh to flesh, warm and tight."

"The embrace, which involves the whole body, is important to me. Having my naked body lying against the naked body of my partner—especially my full front touching my partner's full front."

'Two naked bodies together just feels good— complete head to toe contact!"

"My best sexual experience was a long embrace with

a boy my age (age sixteen)—full of warmth. It was not so much sexual as something from a sense of happiness."

"I often feel this urge to squeeze people very hard."

"I'd like to examine another body closely, press it to me maybe, or press myself against it!"

"I think of myself as flat (stretched out) to their flat—front—arms stretched out, spread, pressed flat and symmetrically together—close and kissing."

"I would like to be naked and have my girlfriend naked too. We would face each other and press ourselves against each other."

"Pleasure for me is wanting to give and being hungry to take—kissing, embracing with all of the body, lying on top of, being lain on—occasionally intercourse and cunnilingus. Rejoicing in desire for the other person."

Kissing.

"Tons of kissing is what I relish."

"A lot of kissing and eye-to-eye, face-to-face contact. A lot of stroking, caressing all over—sides, back, stomach, legs, vulva, vagina, and clitoris. Verbal communication."

"Kissing is *very* important to me. I can sometimes almost orgasm from kissing."

"Gentle and passionate kissing especially on my neck—ahhhh . . ."

"I could kiss with a good kisser for hours!"

"I love an excellent kisser. It is also important to enjoy it without always having to have intercourse after."

"When my lover hungrily kisses my mouth and eyes and whole body—wow!!"

"I love kissing, especially when some of the fleshy, inside parts of the lips touch."

"We used to walk in the woods together, talk, take off our clothes, and just look at each other. Sometimes we would walk around completely or partly nude. And we would talk and kiss and touch, usually kissing with me kneeling over him and him lying on his back. I loved to watch his mouth, the way it would quiver after each kiss. It almost made me feel dizzy, the feeling was so intense. We used to stay that way and look into one another's eyes for a long time."

"Once my lover said he wanted to spend a whole day doing everything for me that I would normally do for myself—from the minute I got up until the time I went to bed. He started with brushing my teeth and washing my face, then brushing my hair and dressing me. It was so wonderful, I'll never forget it my whole life long. It was the most intimate I've ever been with anybody, and we're still together. We put our fingers and tongues inside every place of the other one's body, and try to be as totally close physically as possible. He is beautiful."

"My best life experiences were sexual, I suppose, erotic experiences; but not genital—most of them an instant of exchanged glances, secret, instant, 'cosmic' understanding, with the few people I have loved . . . "

Postscript 2000: A new sexuality for women?

UK, Australian and New Zealand women

Analysis and comments on statistical findings, 1994–2000

There are significant differences between what women now living in the UK, Australia and New Zealand say in my research here, and what I discovered about women living in the US in the 1970s (1972–76). While no one can be certain how much these variations are due to their differing cultures or to the years that have elapsed, these differences should be noted.

The female orgasm

Physiologically, of course, the human body is the human body; there are few significant differences in sexual anatomy or need for stimulation to orgasm. The number of women able to orgasm with self-stimulation (masturbation) remains at the same level in the UK/Australia/New Zealand studies as in the US study: over 90 per cent of women can masturbate easily to orgasm, and for almost everyone, masturbation is done using clitoral, pubic or exterior vulva stimulation; for only 5 per cent is vaginal penetration used, even as an adjunct during exterior masturbation. This does not, it may be important to repeat, mean that the conclusion to be drawn is that women "feel nothing during penetration," but rather that, as women in this research state, they like penetration (especially with a specific person), since this is 1) a culturally reinforced symbolic activity, rich with meaningful connotations, and 2) a physical pleasure, one of its complex characteristics being the brink-of-orgasm feeling that it can create, i.e., it brings some women to a high state of arousal that is deeply pleasurable, and gives others an intensely charged sexual feeling.

These findings also have significance for the theory of the "g-spot," as noted in the Introduction. Clinical researchers in the 1980s published their theory that one of the interior walls of the vagina contains a spot or interior point that, when contacted, stimulates female orgasm. Though there has been much talk in the media about this g-spot, so that therefore people have had ample time to try to locate this "point" in order to produce orgasm during intercourse, research has not shown a significant increase in the rate of orgasm during intercourse without the use of stimulation of the mons–clitoral area. Additionally, common knowledge for at least a century has been that women have "difficulty" reaching orgasm during simple coitus ("the act"); why would this have been true if an interior spot was capable of causing orgasm in women? If there has been a physiological g-spot, it would have proved effective for female orgasm all along.

This research (UK, Australia, New Zealand and US) clarifies that for almost every woman, masturbation (the stimulation chosen by women themselves to use in private as the most effective means to orgasm) is clitoral/exterior. Women (not having been taught by society how to masturbate, and thus simply discovering their bodies' feelings and needs) indicate with their choice of stimulation during masturbation how they most easily orgasm. If the g-spot were an important reality for most women, at least some women would masturbate by contacting it, not by exterior stimulation, or would at least use this internal stimulation (touching or stroking this part of their vagina with their finger or an object) to enhance stimulation during clitoral masturbation. Yet neither is commonly the case.

These samples confirm that it is the c-spot and not the g-spot that counts, insofar as orgasm is concerned.

Once again this does not mean that women do not enjoy or seek "vaginal penetration" (or "penile covering" . . .). One of the complexities of sexual desire is that for many women, coitus or "vaginal penetration" is an extremely pleasurable part of foreplay, bringing them to a high pitch of arousal, though they like clitoral stimulation to orgasm to follow (or have preceded) this coital foreplay.

Another intriguing complexity related to orgasm, a mystery as yet unravelled, brought to light originally by this research several years ago, is that of the leg position women need in order to orgasm. The data on masturbation shows that individual women need varying leg positions in order to orgasm. These differences, unnoted by other researchers (one wonders why), are probably related to internal muscular and anatomical variations. Anatomical studies should be undertaken to investigate these, and how they affect women's ability to orgasm.*

Other unanswered questions include: Why do the contractions associated with orgasm push outwards rather than inwards? Is this because the female body is built for child-

---

*At issue here, also, is the correlation between whether a woman orgasms during sex with a partner, and whether she is expected to open her legs (for either coitus or cunnilingus). The leg position necessary for a woman to orgasm is an essential, if mechanical, matter. If, as is true for approximately two-fifths of the group studied, a woman finds it much easier to orgasm with her legs together (not only do many women hold their legs together while stimulating their clitoris-mons, but some women also masturbate by simply pressing their legs together, using the strong muscles of the inner thighs to press the tissues of the genitals together, causing rhythmic blood flow into the interior arteries or clitoral system), then it may be difficult for her to orgasm with her legs apart. Since it is usually necessary for the legs to be apart for entry of the penis into the vagina, except in some sideways or posterior copulating positions, then it will be likely that such a woman may enjoy vaginal stimulation with a partner, but orgasm only during activities in which she has her legs more closely together. This does not, of course, imply "if only she didn't need her legs together, orgasm would be easy"—since rate of orgasm during intercourse by women who do masturbate with their legs apart is similarly low. Of course, a closed leg position does not imply rejection of the partner in the woman's mind, or any symbolism to the contrary.

bearing and thus, for reasons of body economy or muscular practice, the contractions are designed to push outward? But, why aren't the contractions designed to pull the penis and/or the sperm inward, in order to enable impregnation? Both of these questions, of course, rely on the belief that orgasm in women is somehow connected to reproduction, as it is for men—but it may not be.

A note on the use of "orgasm" as a verb. Throughout this book the word orgasm, usually a noun, is used as an active verb, contrary to standard usage. The reason for this innovation grows out of this research. While the commonly used phrase is "to have an orgasm," that usage reflects the passive mentality that has been in place: sexual passion as something that visits the body from outside, descending, as it were, onto the person. One of the most striking points this research revealed is the need for action on women's part in order to orgasm, especially with a partner. Women generally have to take action (either in terms of motion, body position, using their own hand, etc.), though clichés have for years suggested that during coitus the man moves and the woman need only "lie back and think of England." (Even if the woman is on top and doing the motion, clichés do not include her rubbing her mons clitoris against the man.) Also, many women are brought up to be "ladylike" in sex (especially in sex)—and move very little, compared with what they are capable of; clichés lead women (and men) to believe that the man's thrusting penis should stimulate orgasm in women.

I propose that it is better to use "orgasm" as a verb in order to emphasize the active behaviour necessary to create this event in the body, i.e., one would say, "I'm going to orgasm," not "I'm going to have an orgasm." This change in language will help overcome the sluggish clichés still seen in both Hollywood films and porno videos. While it is true that in the "modern" sex video women do move and are "active," the way in which they are active is not authentic, but is more a mimicking of (some) men's idea of The New Active Woman. In other words, women are now encouraged to be "active" in "male copycat ways," such as performing actions that demonstrate intercourse is making them more and more excited (may or may not be true), "initiating" sexual activities long defined to be "sexual" by men, or actively "acting up" (counter to the ladies-don't like-sex, or Maria-is-pure-and-good stereotypes of women), etc. In reality, being active in sex has an entirely different meaning, a meaning that is only beginning to unfold.

One of the keys to female sexuality during the next hundred years, I am sure, will be that women will begin initiating a new type of sexuality—something that will cause a true revolution in sexuality, one that has as yet barely begun—despite all the courageous changes women have made in their sexual behaviour and private lives, and all the laughter at the sexual stereotyping of women. Women have hardly begun to show who they are sexually.

Sexual differences between women in the UK, Australia and New Zealand

Though the physiological aspects of orgasm and need for stimulation* described by women in the US in the 1970s remain essentially the same in the new UK/Australia/New Zealand report, confirming the findings that thousands of sex therapists around the world have endorsed during the last twenty years—that the stimulation best for female orgasm is exterior clitoral area stimulation, no matter how much any given woman may prefer vaginal intercourse with a partner, even without orgasm, and that women are the experts on their own needs for orgasm via masturbation—many other findings in this study have not remained the same.

*These comprise the largest part of the original findings.

The sexual revolution and the double standard

The major areas of difference between the US sample and the UK/Australia/New Zealand samples are visible in the ongoing debates over "sexual freedom" and the evolving meaning of "sexual rights" for women.

Culture and opinion surrounding sexual behaviour does differ, and this is particularly true of the question of how women feel about the "sexual revolution." In their opinions, women differ not only from culture to culture but also from individual to individual. "Sexual freedom"—how women would like to define it, how they feel about the social context in which it is promised as an option, whether it is helping or hurting women—is a multi-faceted debate in the countries concerned. Women in the US, Australia and New Zealand more often make ironic or barbed comments when asked their opinion of this freedom than their UK counterparts, whether Scottish, Irish, Welsh or English. UK women are most likely to point out the positive sides of the "new sexual freedom for women," indicating the successes of women's rights in birth control, abortion and self-expression. Those pointing out the negatives emphasize the exploitative nature of feeling expected to be "sexy" as a "modern woman," always appearing to remain under the age of forty (and not overweight), etc. Of course, in this research women of every age and size disprove the clichés as women of all ages and appearances marry, have lovers, enjoy their sexuality and prosper.

Some people, undoubtedly, would like to look at this study to discover "who is better": are women in the UK—whether London, Leeds, Manchester or Oxbridge—hipper or freer? Are UK women more sexually liberated than Australian women? Are New Zealand women "closer to nature"? However, even if the boilerplate adjective "sexually free" were not extremely objectionable, this question could not be answered as stated, as it involves a value judgement.

The question can better be answered in a more focused way, relating to the very precise research done here.

Women in all the countries noted heartily dislike the exploitation of the female body to sell magazines, newspapers and products, i.e., "Sometimes I think if I see one more ad for chocolates depicting a stacked woman putting a melting chocolate languorously into her well made-up mouth, I'll vomit . . ." Sometimes women even go so far as to credit—or blame, depending on point of view—the original *Hite Report* for giving the impetus to two decades of women's magazine covers featuring 'Sex! Sex! Sex!', e.g., "Women tell all" or "Sexual secrets revealed." In fact, this book's research involved a serious and careful investigation into female sexuality over a period of years, during which women's own voices were respectfully and laboriously recorded. (In fact, this was a revolution in research method that caused considerable confusion among reviewers. Was it self-help? Psychology? Sociology?) Indeed, many women's magazines, after noting the popularity of this work internationally, began to run their own sex questionnaires and articles about sex.

As with the sexual revolution in general, there was some good and some bad that came out of this media exploration (or exploitation) of the serious debate between women of all ages speaking out in my report. In the media mayhem, many of my conclusions, both statistical and theoretical, as well as new theories and future predictions, were either not heard, overlooked or ignored.

One of the most problematic aspects of the sexual revolution (an aspect addressed by other feminist writers, as well as myself) was the fact that, though women were told they were "sexually free now" (the birth control pill, no disapproval for sex without marriage), ironically they continued to experience judgemental attitudes, a double standard of morality that had always seen female sexual expression as "lewd" (Maria is pure, Eve is sinful; wives are good, mistresses are bad). UK and Australian single women, especially, say that the double standard is still wreaking havoc in relationships, though some of their Scottish and Irish counterparts would disagree. As one woman in London describes, "After we had finished sex, he began slagging me off, saying things like 'Oh you cheap little whore . . . and you could be better in bed, too! (Need some practice in the oral bit, don't ya?) But I'm crazy about you!' . . . then, imagining I should be happy hearing that, I think he expected me to smile and give him that puppy dog look, and tell him I love him."

The new power to control fertility, and put off having a child until it is economically viable—*in vitro* fertilization and freezing eggs, as well as other fertility treatments—are now widely used, especially by women in the UK and Australia. These women should be commended for taking part in such experiments by using their bodies, since none of the ongoing advances in understanding fertility and reproduction would be made otherwise.

The issue of "single mothers" is a hot political topic in many countries, perhaps especially in the UK:

"My father left my mother, my two sisters and myself seven years ago for a woman half his age, and I am getting heartily sick of posturing politicians like Peter Lilley and Michael Howard making cheap shots at single mothers to deflect blame for society's 'ills' from themselves.

"I became a feminist as I discovered more and more about my father—how my mother had found him in bed with someone else when I was eighteen months old, how he was always running around with different, younger women. How my mother couldn't leave because she had no job, no money and nowhere to go, seeing how she was ripped off by the divorce courts, and her incredible strength when faced with the terrible situation. It has taken me a long time to trust men again, I've resolved never to marry or have a joint bank account.

"Men are scared of the increasing independence of women. After all, if they lose their role as the major breadwinner and head of the family, what have they got?

There is a smell of desperation in men trying to grab back their dominance in all areas of life—except childcare. This is demonstrated in the furore over the Child Support Agency, with fathers who have either deserted or divorced, and are now with a second family, marching on Parliament to avoid paying for their first families. It seems as though they are trying to escape their responsibilities while women are struggling to bring up children on their own (and succeeding).

"As for single parents bringing up criminals, then I would just like to say that my thirteen-year-old sister endured nearly a year of being sent to Coventry by her school 'friends' (most of whom come from 'traditional' nuclear families) because she refused to indulge in smoking, drinking and shoplifting.

"It is absolutely true that single mothers should be praised for bringing up children and holding out against the continued knocks and prejudices dished out by the rest of society. For biting their tongues when asked, every time something goes wrong for their children at school—'Is everything alright at home?' (although women have been biting their tongues and turning the other cheek for too long, we need to shout back). My mother survived humiliation and near poverty to bring myself and my sisters up. I am now twenty and doing a degree in history and sociology. My eighteen-year-old sister has an interview at Oxford University next week and is nearing her goal of being an international swimmer, and my youngest sister is in the top few per cent at school."

Looking at UK and Australian/New Zealand women's answers during the last five years, it is striking that there is an increasing correlation between a woman's ability to orgasm during sex with a partner (during either coitus, manual clitoral stimulation or cunnilingus) and absence of the fear that she will be judged negatively by her partner. Many women still fear that if they let themselves "go for it" and behave truly as sexually as they want, make themselves orgasm several times, etc., a man may later not consider them as seriously as he would if a woman was not so "free," i.e., she is "cheap and vulgar, I can't introduce her to my friends, I must hide this part of my laddish, lustful nature."

Why is there a discrepancy between the ease with which a woman can orgasm via self-given clitoral stimulation and during clitoral area stimulation with a partner? It would appear that women, in some ways, are still fearful, or that many men are not yet well informed or do not fully accept women's sexuality.

Fellatio is a particular case in point. With the sexual revolution, women were expected, as part of being "sexually free," to now include fellatio in their regular sexual activities. The pressure to "be sexy" that began in the '60s and continues today suddenly *required* women to take part in a type of sexual activity that had been considered "degrading" and "unladylike," as well as "not fun for women," in the past. It is difficult for women to know whether they do or don't like fellatio since the implication of "you'll degrade yourself" persists.

When women in the UK, Australia and New Zealand were asked (in written form) how they felt about fellatio, the statistics showed that:*

39% offer fellatio (*not* to orgasm) during the majority of sex acts with a man
25% offer fellatio to orgasm during the majority of sex acts with a man
36% do not offer fellatio in any form

41% enjoy fellatio
59% do it to please the man, but do not especially enjoy it.

Whereas twenty-five years ago, it was perfectly acceptable for a woman not to like fellatio and not to do it, today it "must be part of every girl's repertoire." Some women in the UK

*In my original US research, women were not asked this directly, though men were asked in a later study how often women gave them oral sex, and whether it was to orgasm.

report they feel more pressured into man-pleasing than ever, though no longer in terms of baking cakes or "feeding him a hearty breakfast" but rather by being an exciting sex playmate, at what ever age.

In summary, underlying the complexity of our current sexual relationships and discussions of the meaning of "family"—along with the issues of rape, sexual harassment, AIDs, single mothers and gay rights—is the heritage of the "sexual revolution," that New World view that began in the 1960s, included the development of the birth control pill, and combined/clashed in the 1970s with the feminist movement. With the Pill, women achieved more control over their own reproduction, but also came under great pressure "to have sex at the drop of a hat." The feminist movement challenged this pressure, and tried to make a space in which women could have control over their bodies and sexuality, as later stipulated by the United Nations Declaration on the Rights of Women (Beijing, 1995).

The sexual revolution should not be confused with the feminist movement nor women's liberation, as was done by the BBC television programme *Panorama*, 26 January 2000, for example. The sexual revolution was linked to women's growing status in society: a 1920s' women's movement had meant that by the 1950s and 1960s, a large number of women went to colleges and universities and received degrees. This widespread college education began to mean economic independence for women, and gradually a new development took shape, a "second wave" movement in which women determined to redefine themselves and the society they lived in: feminism.

The UK: AIDS and birth control/abortion

One surprising factor that emerged from this research in the UK is the difference between women in Scotland, in

England and Wales and in Northern Ireland. With widely different policies towards abortion and reproduction, it was likely that women's attitudes to their bodies and the "sexual revolution" would vary greatly.

The issue of abortion rights surely affects women's perception of their sexuality, as a woman from Northern Ireland testifies: "When I was twenty-one I was raped, deflowered and impregnated at the same time. I was incapacitated by too much to drink and my date took advantage of me. Abortion was not easily available then, so I had to give my baby up for adoption. There was no family member I could turn to at the time, as I was living many miles away in another city, and I felt no one would understand. I would not wish this experience on my worst enemy."

In the UK, the sexual revolution was tempered by the feminist movement of the 1970s, which safeguarded abortion rights and worked for the rights of single mothers, women's right to work and earn equal pay (in theory), the right to sue for sexual harassment or discrimination at work, the right to speak up about rape, even in marriage, as well as about incest or having been molested. However, when the Conservatives came to power with the election of Margaret Thatcher, it became smart to be "post-feminist." Clothing styles followed suit and became power oriented: at first "power suits" with big shoulders were all the rage, then black leather outfits with silver studs or pierced jewellery emphasized a sexy toughness for women as the "new chic."

In the 1980s wider issues such as the menace of HIV infection influenced people's view of sex and the sexual revolution. Yet the impact of this disease was not quite as had been predicted, and did not produce more monogamous couples, according to this research. With the exception of the gay male community, no more "stable couples" than before surfaced, government statistics showed divorces continuing to increase, and the number of people living as "single" reached 50 per cent, as more and more couples visited counsellors.*

*These seemingly negative statistics are interpreted in *The Hite Report on the Family* as part of a largely positive process of democratization of families.

Only 41 per cent of women in this study said that they believed AIDs had changed their personal sexual behaviour—made them more monogamous or less sexually active—though they believed that the threat of AIDs has changed others' behaviour, as well as the general social climate ("back to basics", "family values").

Only 38 per cent of single women regularly ask or insist that a man use a condom during sex "because of AIDs or as birth control"; only 22 per cent of single women demand that a new partner take a test for HIV or show them recent test results before having sex. Thirteen per cent of single women have had sex with someone who was HIV positive, using protection.

New sexual activities: Clitoral stimulation with a partner to orgasm—and beyond

Given the amount of information available about the clitoris for the last twenty-five years (as opposed to earlier when virtually no information was available)—even though such information may have been partial and undermined by uninformed clichés—it would be logical to expect that more women now would practise stimulation of the clitoral area to orgasm with their partner, whether by hand or mouth until orgasm. (A partner need not worry that, after this orgasm, a woman will no longer be interested in coitus or sex, since the data show that female orgasm is not the "end" of sex for women, in the way that, for twenty minutes at least, male orgasm is an "end" for men.)

Is "clitoral stimulation to orgasm" ("The Activity for Which There Is No Name") a "normal part of sex" for women in the UK, Australia and New Zealand today?

UK women, as well as their Australian and New Zealand sisters, are more likely than other women studied to have orgasm with a partner via clitoral area stimulation—

sometimes several orgasms (a majority of women in the UK report having more than one orgasm often during sex with a regular partner; see Statistical appendices). However, UK women are also most likely to say that a new partner needs to be taught everything and that before that, he is completely unaware and misinformed!

Combining manual clitoral stimulation and vaginal penetration is an important sexual innovation now practised by 62 per cent of "thirty-something" British women. As one woman describes, "I often lie in his arms, when we are in bed naked together, and touch myself. While I am masturbating, he sometimes puts his fingers around my back and under my buttocks, into my vagina—or even my anus, sometimes both! Sometimes he uses a small vibrator, this drives me wild with passion, especially if he says rude things at the same time!" Other women describe how their lover performs stimulation of the mons clitoris by both hand and mouth, while at the same time inserting a finger or fingers into the vagina.

UK women seem to live in a world of extremes: of the 45 per cent who do not (yet?) enjoy clitoral stimulation to orgasm with a partner, most (36 per cent) report that there is no stimulation provided (even as foreplay) or understood at all, that they are severely pressured to conform to old stereotypes of female sexuality, i.e., be receptive to coitus.

Flashy photos of "young things having a wild time" in UK and Australian newspapers seem to imply that sex is everywhere. Do they represent reality for most UK, Australian and New Zealand women? Or do these photos represent only a small minority, hiding a private life for "the average woman" that is somewhat milder than that of many European neighbours—and perhaps less emotionally or psychologically intense at times than that of their American sisters? The impression given by this research is that a new kind of sexuality is developing that has very little to do with old-style media clichés of what is "sexy and wild."

English women seem to have a richer fantasy life, including fantasies they tell their partners, than women in Scotland and Northern Ireland (or perhaps those women simply do not, even with the anonymity of this study, feel free to express them). For example, a woman in Manchester said, "I used to imagine, sometimes when I was alone and no one would disturb me, and I could lie in my bed and dream, that I was intimately entwined in the body of a lover, while another individual at the same time was licking my cunt and inserting their finger into various of my holes. I would be lying face down on the body of my lover, pressing against it while this other person put—no, kept jabbing and removing fingers inside me, tantalizing me, then sucking me again. I would go crazy imagining this until I would shout out to be fucked. At this point I would rub my mons and soon have a great orgasm! Now I talk to my lover about this when we are rolling around in bed, I'm not the only one who likes to imagine there's someone else . . . ."

Under an apparent surface of tranquillity, women in many parts of the UK—for example, Scotland—are making radical changes in their daily sexual expression. For them, this does not mean conforming to a stereotyped or crude notion of "she's no lady, she's a sex devil!" Many Scottish women, for example, continue to believe in being "lady-like", and/or hold traditional non-sexual revolution values, while they also continue, despite the odds and the contra-dictions, to create their own process of sexual evolution and new forms of sexual self-expression and identity.

Images of women in magazines, no matter how shrilly the magazines shout "You are sexy! You can be sexy! You should be sexy!" leave many women feeling resentful, doubtful that they are sexy, at least, not in the way the mag-azine intends. Four out of five UK women reading a specific issue of a bestselling women's magazine replied to this researcher that yes, they found the magazine interesting, but they didn't think they were typical readers. "Why not?" "Because I'm not like the women in it." "How are you dif-ferent?" "Because . . . I would never, could never dress like that, I think it's fun to look at but it's not me, I am more intelligent than the women in it."

The sexual revolution image of women with short skirts

and little-girl body shapes and postures, lack of weight, lack of female shape, also give the message that women are lightweight, not serious; the best a woman can hope to do is "stay young" and "have fun," as in "girls just wanna have fun-un . . ." While girls do have fun, they also do other things—such as discover cures for cancer—and have fun doing them.

Do women in the UK still worry about whether they have orgasm during intercourse rather than during clitoral stimulation? UK, Australian, New Zealand and US women all agree: a social stigma lingers over clitoral stimulation and masturbation to orgasm even now, as if such orgasms were "more girlish" and "less mature"; a "grown-up women" should love coitus (following Freud's ideas).

The majority of UK women, when asked, "Do you ever fake orgasms during sex?" responded that they rarely act out spasms, but 61 per cent often do allow their partners to believe that they orgasm when they really have only been highly aroused and excited. Do women fake orgasms too when having sex with other women? Yes, according to this data, but much less frequently, usually in order to avoid embarrassment, and usually with a new partner, not a regular partner.

Women in Australia and New Zealand were less likely to "let things pass" than their British sisters, more likely to demonstrate their powers and go for their orgasm "after his orgasm." ("Why? To avoid being left out—no matter what he thinks of me.")

Case studies

Women in the UK, like women elsewhere, say that, sexually, their need for "special" attention to the clitoris in order to orgasm is still all too often overlooked and ignored by male partners, and that old patterns of sex keep being repeated.

Sixty-four per cent of women in the UK (and 59 per cent of women in Australia) say that the men in their lives, or men they know, are uninformed (under-informed) or insensitive to their needs:

"No, my partner is not sensitive to what I like and frankly doesn't seem to notice if I am enjoying what he does or not. If I say that I don't particularly like something he does, he stops doing it but will probably do it again a couple of minutes later. Physical affection is extremely important to me; I don't want to think that my husband can only be bothered to show any affection towards me when he wants sex. Nor do I want to feel that all physical affection and touching has to lead to sex either. I don't touch him as much as I would like, since unfortunately such touching is usually taken by him as an invitation to have sex, rather than just be close. So I often start to touch and then think twice and end up not touching at all. Flash: since it's the touching part of sex that I enjoy—the actual penetration is totally unfulfilling—I suppose I always have sex for the touching!"

"I am twenty years old and getting engaged in a few weeks' time. I'd just like to tell you that my boyfriend of two years is a wonderful, caring guy but sometimes there can seem like a lack of communication between us. One thing that annoys me is how men have always been told never to show their emotions and to never let a woman push him around . . . Our sex life is good but if I don't always orgasm he thinks he is doing something wrong. I know not many women orgasm from intercourse, but I have on a few occasions. I will admit that at times I have even faked it. That is only because I don't want my boyfriend to think that he is doing something wrong. He is a very sensual lover and has always pleased me every time we have intercourse. Because I like sex a lot, my boyfriend sometimes labels me as a nymphomaniac but I know it is only in fun."

"For me, touch is what makes me feel strong, whole, wanted, valid and worthwhile as a human being. Most of the time, I feel touch-starved and undernourished, small and loveless. When I am touched affectionately by friend, it can make me feel good all day, touch communicates so much! There is little touch in my marriage, which is a sign of, and a cause of, the increasing distance between us. We never row, we just act distant. During sex, we have a fairly fixed pattern, little touching outside the bedroom. I sometimes think that I'd love to have a room of my own and be able to sleep alone. That would ensure that in order to make love, my husband would have to seduce me, or I him! Being in each other's pockets (and beds) all the time does not excitement make on a Saturday night."

"Is my partner sensitive to the stimulation I want? I don't always tell him if I want something. Generally, I find that men can be a bit rough and not slow and gentle enough. Also, some men don't bother asking, they assume it will work on me because it's worked on other women. I usually allow the man to dictate the pace and style of sex, although sometimes I get carried away. My partner usually decides when it's over, when he's come, except one or two past partners have been more considerate and concerned about my satisfaction. I often subsume my own desires in order to satisfy a partner, pretend I'm getting pleasure even if I'm not, to please him. On rare occasions, if sex has started to become uncomfortable or painful, I have decided it's over.

"My greatest pleasure is having oral sex performed on me if the man knows how to do it and is gentle. But I feel guilty about receiving oral sex if I feel my partner is not particularly turned on by it. I dislike being hurt in any way and anything to do with anal sex; if I even think someone is going to try and do that, it gets me distressed. I feel really okay if I trust someone; and if he is aroused too. Then I don't feel guilty as long as he is involved helping me, i.e., sucking my nipples, masturbating himself or 'talking dirty' to me while I masturbate. If he makes it clear he doesn't like it, I'll wait until I'm on my own or he's asleep."

"The last five years I've been menopausal with hot flushes, panic attacks, etc., but strangely I've felt more need of sex and loving and things like that but my husband seems to have been running down, maybe he doesn't fancy me, but I still fancy him and find him very sexually attractive. It bothers me, I find myself fantasizing about sex . . . On the other hand, I try to tell him that we can just kiss and cuddle and it does not need to lead to sex, but he does not respond. I do not think that he is well informed about my body, though I have often tried to explain or asked him to read an article or a book I think would help. He is either too 'shy' or too uncaring to bother. He always wants to get down to it quickly, while the things I like, like being massaged or having my hair stroked, last four seconds. He almost never talks during sex. I would like to, but now I've become too embarrassed. How awful that sounds. I never thought we'd be like this when we were madly in love."

Yet 36 per cent of UK women (32 per cent in Scotland and 38 per cent in Northern Ireland) and 39 per cent of Australian women praise their husbands or lovers for their sexual skill, imagination, thoughtfulness and sexiness, as does the following woman who also comments on her own sexual development:

"I was born in Canada in 1970, educated in Scotland and live in Ireland, and am currently involved in a relationship of six months' standing. No children, one abortion when aged nineteen.

"I am fortunate, my boyfriend is very well informed about both what I like, and how much of it: he pays attention to what he is doing. Although naturally skilled, he has been known to ask for directions—which he scarcely needs, and, joy of joys, he doesn't stop too soon—even if he gets bored/hot/uncomfortable. He has even learned how to give me an orgasm with his hand, something that has failed with past lovers. As I have had too many experiences of the inept, he is very well appreciated, I can assure you! He is also good at stopping if I want him too. A past lover would give me a wonderful orgasm, and then insist on having intercourse with me. I eventually realised that I hated this, I never got to enjoy the post-orgasmic collapse. I told my present lover this, and he is perfectly willing to stop after I come, even if he has not done so. I needn't ask him to do this, he will often just ask me what I want. It's the stuff of dreams really!!

"In a non-sexual situation he is also 'sensitive to the stimulation that I want.' He hugs me for no other reason than I am in the room, will stroke my hair on demand, while we watch television for example, and is generally receptive to any touch that I offer him.

"We both set the pace of sex. Either of us has the ability to initiate sex or to veto it, even halfway through. Style more or less follows the form of suggestions made and either followed or turned down. I can't think of a situation in my current relationship which has been unlike this cooperative model. In the past, however, I have let a man set the style, simply because his repertoire was so narrow as to prevent him taking up one that would have suited me better. It was a very sad experience.

"Sex is over when one of us has had enough, or is too knackered to continue! I have often found that after an orgasm through intercourse, men are too exhausted to do anything else. If they come as a result of other means, then there is enough energy for other things. To try and combat this, I will often have an orgasm prior to intercourse if I want to have one, but there is always the possibility of delayed interest. I can become very aroused with intercourse and feel disappointed when it is over, sometimes I think that there should be a second man around to take over when the first one flags. (I have told my lover this, sometimes joking about it makes it less frustrating.) I wonder if intercourse is more-ish in this way in order to ensure that a woman will remain interested in it until the man has succeeded in ejaculating?

I find that the sensations of intercourse are always promising that they will improve, hence I continue. If it were the case that women got a very early one, prior to the male's ejaculation, this could be bad for reproduction.

"I have always hated when a lover has just taken his pleasure without regard to my wishes. In fact it has upset me enormously upon occasion, as it dawned upon me that they don't care about my pleasure and hence about me. I try to give pleasure to those whom I am with, and I expect them to do the same. When they don't even display the desire to, I get mad, and quite rightly too. Selfishness in bed is a complete give away about someone's character; having realized this I will never again become involved with a lover who turns out to be selfish. A person's character is very clearly displayed in how they act physically. When it comes to affection, actions do speak louder than words.

"The sensations of good sex are incredibly satisfying. I love to feel aroused whether it is a loving relationship or as a more impersonal lust. Pure lust is hard to manage as a satisfying experience, it is very short-lived and gets tangled up in the personalities as a matter of course. However, the sheer strength of it, and its ability to completely distract me from my everyday self means that I expect that I shall, more often than not, welcome it in my life. So far I have found it can make me feel incredibly proud of myself; very vibrant, strong, important—yet elemental and basic at the same time. It has also made me feel humiliated, as it seems to be a strong habit for me now. Thus, in the long run, it would be the shared closeness with another that I most enjoy about sex. I thrive in the trusting atmosphere which comes with good sex, and in the feeling of being desired and wanted, and in being able to desire and want. I like being able to give pleasure and sex gives me a forum for communication and closeness with another person that is difficult to equal in platonic relationships.

"What I hate most about sex is the influence of my

past in how I respond. I suspect that it is as a result of my having been beaten as a child that my sexual fantasies strongly feature 'punishment' or being in the control of others, i.e., spanking. I hate this internal reminder of the humiliation I suffered and wish that I did not respond in this manner. I have tried to shift these fantasies, but with little luck. Nowadays, however, I am less uncomfortable with this than I used to be, my efforts have paid off and I can enjoy sex without feeling intruded upon; it is not so strong that I cannot feel pleasure and orgasm without them. I have found little helpful literature to explain how fantasies work, etc., but what I have read has reassured me that my thoughts are very like those of others who have experienced physical abuse. I deeply resent that I have been 'given' such thoughts, and they caused me considerable distress when I was younger. I would accuse myself of actually having provoked the abuse because I secretly enjoyed it. I realize now that this self-blame was another effect of the beatings, but it took too long for me to learn this and it should not have been necessary that I do so in the case where a man treated me appallingly and yet my lust for him raged in spite of my self-respect. I put it down to my hormones, but it was intensely difficult to tolerate."

The majority of women in each of these studies think real sex with a man should entail the forging of a new definition of sexuality between them, rethinking the question of who orgasms when and how, which activities are included, experimenting together.

Lesbian women

Fifteen per cent of women in this UK study enjoy sex with other women, or are in a sexual relationship with a woman. An additional 8 per cent are "bisexual" and relate to both women and men. Seventy-four per cent of women who prefer women have never had sex with a man. A slight majority say they feel they were "born this way"; the rest say they discovered their feelings when they began dating in school. Also in Australia and New Zealand, as in the UK, women orgasm more frequently and in more varied ways with each other. (Charts giving more complete information, including data for Australia and New Zealand, can be found in the Appendices.)

The higher statistics on lesbianism in the UK, Australia and New Zealand* deserve comment. Though there is not sufficient space here to address all the issues, many important changes are taking place in how women relate to each other. As one young woman writes:

"Here on campus (University of London) you see girls together who have probably got crushes on each other, having fun together and so on. Is there more lesbianism than there ever was? The magazines make it trendy now but, I wonder . . . I must admit, I am curious and would like to try it with a pretty woman, one of those bleached blonde students I see with the short hair (tattooing and pierced nose and tongue might be too much), but so far I haven't had the courage. Anyway, how would I advertise myself, would I have to dress in tight black leather and wear steel chains to get the message across?"

A large number of women are open to investigating intimacy with another woman. Women choosing to relate to other women is one of the valid and authentic ways women are recreating their sexual identities.

Additionally, 33 per cent of women are relating in new non-"sexual" ways to other women, experimenting with new ways to live together:

"I now live with my best friend. We are both in our fifties. I was married, now divorced with grown children. I always had more fun with Ruth, but never dreamed of

*See Appendix 3.

living with her. Thought that would make me a lesbian. Now I laugh to think I ever thought that. Sure, we sit together on the sofa some evenings and she puts her head on my shoulder or I touch her hand, we watch television or talk or listen to music, but this doesn't make us gay women. It is a very satisfying way of life, but most people don't quite understand. Like my children . . ."

The women's movement has championed the right of women to live together and be lovers and/or create a family, as well as defending women's rights to have a traditional heterosexual family and reproduction. Lesbianism is a choice women increasingly feel they have the right to make, though social and official stigmas remain in the form of restrictions on maternity benefits, housing allowances and inheritance rights. Women today are beginning to take other women as seriously as they take men, seeing them as potential mates, not fearing the label "lesbian" but feeling proud of being with another woman. By doing this, they are making their presence felt publicly, changing laws and opinions.

Comparison of US, UK and Australian samples: Is your vulva beautiful?

Do UK women like their vulva—what it looks like and how it smells—more or less than US women? Australian women? The statistics look like this:

"Do you think your genitals are ugly or beautiful?"

UK women
12% ugly
49% beautiful
39% neither—interesting

US women
30% ugly
31% beautiful
39% neither—interesting

Scottish women
24% ugly
40% beautiful
36% neither—interesting

Australian women
18% ugly
44% beautiful
41% neither—interesting

Clearly, UK women now show a more positive regard for their sexual anatomy ("down there" as it is called in one of Madonna's songs) than US women. Is the discrepancy due to differences in culture and perspective between UK and US women, or to the time that has elapsed between the studies and subsquent advances in our thinking? Or perhaps the number of visual representations now available accounts for the change: i.e., recently people have seen more visuals of the female vulva in pornography, on television and in magazines. Even if the context of most of these images is negative, do they nevertheless give the subliminal message that a vulva is "pretty" because it is worthy of being photographed and thus an object of desire and beauty? Or (more likely) is the reason for UK women's positive self-image due to the energy of feminist ideas, i.e., that as women we are beautiful? Whatever the reasons, though of course not every woman in the UK thinks her vulva looks good, UK women feel better about their bodies than others and buy fewer vaginal deodorant sprays.

Women in Australia also have a good body image, according to this study, though the pressures to see one's own sexuality as a commodity to use in bargaining with others remains, according to Australian women.

A young woman in New Zealand speaks of how she sees her sexual organs: "When I was about six, I think, I first looked at my pussy. I remember I liked it, I thought it was clean and had smooth skin, cute sort of. Later, when I got hair there, I felt like something was wrong with me, my crotch was dirtier and hairier. It wasn't pretty like it had been before."

Her remark is interesting, as boys in our society often say that "the penis is a great thing," or "my penis is the best penis," and are proud of their bodies, showing them off to other boys in the bathroom (or at least bragging about them). Developing hair is a sign of manliness. Yet it is rare for a girl to speak, as this girl does, about looking at herself, or to describe her sexual vulva as "pretty." Perhaps this will become more common.

Male sexuality: Are men "beasts with raging hormones?"

For the record, though often confused, the sexual revolution is a separate phenomenon, with a different set of values from the women's liberation movement. The sexual revolution consists in large part of a belief that we are all "natural creatures" underneath society's veneer, and that our sexual nature is biologically structured depending on our gender: male sexuality is especially understood in terms of it being "animal nature". In this false view, a man is a "beast who can't help himself, certain things turn a man on and he just can't stop, it's nature's way of making him deposit his seed here, there and everywhere . . . a man can't really be monogamous, ethics are just a way of trying to make him into something he's not."

This attitude towards male "sexual nature" is widely accepted, as exemplified by 1990s' articles seen internationally about Viagra and the sexual scandal surrounding President Clinton. A pseudo-Darwinian idea of man-as-beast became especially prominent during World War II when propaganda promoted men as "real animals underneath the veneer of civilization, capable of storming through a jungle and killing other animals . . . with a great sexual appetite."

In the 1960s, an anti-establishment movement came about among US men in reaction to the Vietnam war, the injustices of racism and exploitation of black people, as well as the stressful conformist tendencies of post-war 1950s' America. First came the Beatnik movement, a rather limited "rebel" phenomenon, then the 1960s' "flower children" movement, when people around the world began to sing and speak of "peace and love" and "let it all hang out." This flowering of individualism, with its non-military version of masculinity, was the strongest statement of anti-conformity men had ever made (though the nineteenth-century romantic movement *à la* Byron, Schubert and others was not dissimilar). This rebellion against the traditional (or at least 1950s) man-as-head-of-the-family, breadwinner or hunter image of masculinity, with each man instead wanting to "search for himself," "find his space" and "be free," is ongoing today; not even the pro-family propaganda of the 1980s dissuaded men from their quest for "freedom" or assuaged their fear of "being tied down."*

What is "female sexual nature?"

No research has shown any evidence (nor could research show evidence, since all humans we know of have grown up with cultural influences) for what such a "nature" could be. Thus women's natures were simply assumed to be like men's, i.e., "women are sexual animals underneath it all, animals who crave satisfaction and that satisfaction is not orgasm but 'a good fuck from a man.' "

*Their fear is of being "tied down" to "the system", though many men say they fear being tied down to a relationship with a woman.

Women in the late 1960s and early 1970s discovered that in the "sexual revolution" movement, the slogans of peace and love—though in themselves positive and appealing—meant that men were expected to be the leaders in rallies, demonstrations and ideas, while women were expected to embrace naturally a secondary, "helpful" role. It was assumed that women in the peace and love movement would accept the belief in "free love"(sex with whomsoever you wanted whenever you wanted), take the birth control pill and "not demand men wear condoms," nor that men be faithful or monogamous. In short, in this male non-conformist movement, women were expected to "put out" sexually as often as asked, or be accused of being "unfree" and psychologically "messed up"—not in touch with their "true sexual natures."

Thus women's supportive role was expanded into the area of sexuality, where they were obliged to serve men's "sexual needs" (as men were programmed by society to have them), in addition to daily needs (meal preparation and cleaning). Of course the women's movement saw female sexuality in a different light.

The ideas about "raw nature underneath it all" (mixing in equal parts crude versions of Freudianism and Darwinism, sexist to the core) combined with a commercialist mentality, turning the new view of female "sexual freedom" into a profit-making opportunity. Previously ads appealed to "the civilized, well-groomed man" or "the modern woman"; now they would appeal to "the sensual male" or the "sensual woman," "the animal in us all." The new emphasis was on "the sexual animal underneath the veneer" in advertisements for cosmetics, cars, shaving creams, and cigarettes. The new "freedom" launched a whole industry of "lifestyle magazines," advice books, and an expanded pornography industry, exploiting and distorting the very legitimate experimentation going on in the idealistic peace, love and freedom (or "flower child") movement, and the new feminist movement.

The semi-pornographic images of women visible today, on so many advertising posters and in television commercials (and used by some Islamic fundamentalists to point to the "decadence of the secular West"), do not so much represent "who women are sexually" as the use and selling of women's bodies by a double standard tradition. It is no wonder, with female sexuality equated with what is shown in most advertising depictions of women, that many women wonder if "the old ways were best, when women were respected"— whether or not this were true.

Though the sexual revolution did not last long in its most overt manifestation, it combined with "flower power" and feminism to lead to various waves of experimentation and discovery that continue today.

Redesigning "sexual freedom": Why be ashamed of secularism?

On the positive side, the sexual revolution's challenge to the establishment, combined with feminist debates, produced and is continuing to produce new ideas and to open up thinking to a broad spectrum of choices about sexual identity, living arrangements, marriage, and the meaning of love, passion and relationships. Without the counterforce of the women's movement, it is questionable how beneficial the sexual revolution's effects would be. While not wishing to endorse a simplistic idea that "orgasm makes you free," or "getting in tune with your body makes everything right," in fact a false and rigid notion of what "sex" is (i.e., reproductive activity) has put blinkers on us about how we can best relate.

We need to redefine our idea of the physical. On one level, as women say in this study, it is not a question of simply "having more sex" or "dressing sexy when you want," but of deprogramming ourselves of the idea that the only way to touch another person intimately is to have sex with that person.

Also out of the combination of the sexual revolution

and women's liberation movement emerged a new and strong, forceful gay and lesbian movement that eventually—especially in the UK—branched out, searching for "alternative" forms of sexual expression, endeavouring to blur the lines between the genders, between "male behaviour and appearance" and "female behaviour and appearance", as well as to encourage new thinking and experimentation.

Some of the experimentation (whether "gay" or "heterosexual") seems to be expressed in ways previously thought of as perverse. During the 1980s and 1990s, a fashion for sado-masochistic themes in clothing and sex developed, in both heterosexual and homosexual-lesbian circles. Photographs by Helmut Newton in fashion magazine layouts, on Wolford stocking packages, or in ads for Karl Lagerfeld or Chanel clothing, popularized images (already seen in the streets of London, Sydney, New York and elsewhere) of women in black leather jackets and tight boots, riding motorcycles, often exposing flesh in a provocative sexual manner. Sado-masochistic themes, such as rape, spanking or domination-submission, being tied up or abused, were anathema to family-style procreative sexuality, yet began to be discussed and did reflect many people's desire to put sexual acts in a context other than the reproductive.

The appeal of the new experimental behaviour seemed to be widespread, yet also in part led to or fuelled the pro-family-values movement ("Back to Basics"), with its view that society is bankrupt, its moral values rotten, "Western cities are nothing but modern Babylons (as in the Bible) that will soon fall and be punished." The Taliban movement in Afghanistan, among other fundamentalist movements worldwide, at times voiced the idea that it would "inevitably" overcome the "decadent West" because of its purer spiritual values, i.e., adherence to the belief that one is pure when not "contaminated" by the body or physical desire, sexuality or women; sexuality is a behaviour of the "lower animal" not the higher human self, etc.

The sexual violence we see in many advertisements using the female body or on the Internet and in other pornography is reprehensible. Did the sexual revolution also lead to this, as well as to the increasing sexual violence to women we see in crime statistics? While many people have expanded their sexual experimentation and rethinking without any recourse to violence whatsoever, aggression during sex should not be confused with sexual violence to women. We should look for the root of the violence (to women) elsewhere, rather than somehow resigning ourselves to a false idea that sexuality is inherently violent ("you have to keep the lid on"). I would suggest that one of the most important places to start looking for the cause of deep-seated violence to women, sexual violence, is in unjust and non-equal family structures, as well as in the mind–body split (the idea that women are only valuable for their bodies and sexuality, the "religious" idea that the body is "impure"). (See *The Hite Report on the Family*, which contains a large-scale analysis of the basic mythology of the society, and the origins of violence in it.)

How does age influence sexual desire and the kind of stimulation and orgasms women enjoy? This will be the topic of a future analysis*; however, a few observations here about whether women feel they change, sexually, and in what way, are in order.

Though the cliché is that women "stop feeling sexy" around menopause, and certainly by the time they are "elderly" (now there may be a reverse cliché forming), the truth is that women's bodies change, but not in a stereotypical way. The fact that much of women's sexual anatomy is interior has already been noted, and this also means that as interior anatomy changes gradually over time, areas needing stimulation and feeling good may shift somewhat as well. Strength of orgasm during masturbation or other stimulation has been shown in clinical research to continue as strong or stronger as women age; one explanation given for increased strength in some older women's sexual feelings is that the

---

*If you would like a questionnaire, so that you can participate in this research, please send a self-addressed, stamped envelope to me c/o the publisher, or e-mail me at info@hite-research.com.

venuous network accepting flows of blood necessary during arousal and orgasm increases with use and age (see Sherfey).

What is mature sexuality? Much of the media seems to imply that "acting sexy" is a sign that a woman has become a sexual adult of "today", "a modern liberated woman." Yet mature sexuality is more subtle than that.

Another age-related cliché that should be put into the dustbin involves women in their thirties.

The enormous pressure on women to "get married by thirty-five" or "have a baby by thirty-five" is usually attributed to the "biological clock," yet I propose that it is caused not so much by biology as by social pressures, i.e., a woman may need (subconsciously) to fit into the society's mythological icon of a "good woman" by being reproductive and appearing to be part of a "traditional family," as a rite of passage; only this will "legitimize" a woman's existence—according to the substrata of archetypes that form our psychological landscape. This is not to say that many women do not have legitimate reasons to have children; however, many others are pressured into motherhood.

Redesigning sex to suit yourself*

Will women now continue to redefine sexuality? Women are making and have made many changes in how they see and practise intimate physical relations—how they express and share their bodies—but will make even more. Though the choices are theirs, really theirs, it can still take some time to wake up and see that one is free, in charge of one's life, that all decisions are possible. Like Sleeping Beauty waking up after 2,000 years of misinformation, women need a little time

*The idea that sex is a cultural rather than a biological institution—that our society's idea of sex is formulated to suit reproductive needs, not instinctive ones, was first proposed in this study (1976), and subsequently expanded by Foucault .

to begin thinking clearly and put into action all their ideas.

Sexual freedom for women is, first, economic independence (see chapter 6, Sexual slavery). Intimidation, because of economic dependence (as seen also in current discussions of sexual harassment at work), means that a woman cannot express herself; if she lives in fear, she will attend to the other person's needs, rather than expressing her own. She may even lose touch with them.

Sexual freedom is not a clichéd version of the attitudes the sexual revolution espoused, turning tradition on its head (for shock value) and imagining all that had been "repressed" is now "good" and "worthwhile", e.g., "I am married, twenty-eight with three children, and currently in the middle of a Greek-Anglo affair, which began while my husband and I holidayed in Greece recently. I consider myself a liberated lady of the nineties who is in tune with her own body and emotional condition."

As another woman explains, "Where today's 'female sexual freedom' goes off track is in thinking that 'being overtly sexy' is the same as being sexually alive and a 'new woman.' Neither is wearing black leather, whips and chains, or piercing your body somewhere weird automatically a sign of being able to take charge of your sexuality, though it can be a sign that someone is headed in that direction, trying."

Fortunately, the pressure on women that made them feel like "sexual commodities for men" has been tempered by the ideas of the international feminist movement, calling for a recognition by governments that women have the right to control their own reproductive and sexual choices (United Nations Declaration on the Rights of Women, 1995, Beijing, signed by 140 countries). The combination of "sexual freedom" (called "secularism" by some "religious" governments especially in the Middle East) and "feminism" has led to an interesting, ethically sophisticated mixture; incontestably, women have more rights and control over their own lives (more "freedom" and recognition within society as full human beings) than before the "sexual revolution." However, without the important, clear driving force and leadership of the feminist movement—with its in-depth analyses of the symbolic meaning of female sexuality in patriarchy—the "revolution" would have led to more exploitation than liberation.

It is nothing short of a miracle that, given the historical context, women are able to continue making a new path for themselves, carving out a new direction. A real "sexual revolution," women say, would work towards a new definition of sex—more ethical yet also more free—and towards a new female sexuality—the kind that many women are now engaged in creating for themselves, privately, in countries around the world.

Women 2000: A celebration

Women in the UK and elsewhere have made amazing advances in the last two decades, creating their own sexual independence, and removing from the society some of the ignorance, prejudice and misapprehension surrounding female sexual identity—above and beyond the confusing, false categories of the "sexual revolution." I am proud to have played a part in this. One of the big markers of this progress, as noted, is the United Nations Declaration of the Rights of Women, listing the most important ways in which women around the world have the right to autonomy and control over their own bodies.

Sexually, women in the UK, Australia and New Zealand seem more and more sure of their right to get what they want and need, both emotionally and physically, from relationships and work. They are more sure of their right to choose a way of life that makes sense to them, and is fulfilling on their terms—whether being single and on their own, married, living with another woman or being celibate—than previously. Women's psychology has changed enormously, or, in other words, women have changed their psychology and the world.

Appendices

Appendix 1: Questionnaire versions I, II and III

The purpose of the questionnaire is to try to understand ourselves better, both collectively and individually. On the one hand, asking yourself these questions is a good way to get further acquainted with your sexual feelings, and on the other hand, it is wonderful to hear what other women are thinking and feeling about the same things—especially since we never talk about them. The results will be published as a general discussion of what was said, with a few statistics, and a lot of quotes, like a giant "rap session" on paper.

The questionnaire is anonymous, so don't sign it. If any questions do not apply to you, just write "non-applicable." Please use a separate sheet of paper and number your answers accordingly. **Don't feel that you have to answer every single question** (although we would really like it if you did). You can just skip around and answer the ones that interest you—just let us hear from you!!!*

---

* This introduction or one similar appeared on each questionnaire.

Questionnaire I

September 1972

NATIONAL ORGANIZATION FOR WOMEN,
NYC CHAPTER
47 EAST 19 ST., NYC 10003

1. Is having orgasms important to you, or would you enjoy sex just as much without ever having an orgasm? Is having sex important to you? Why?
2. Could you describe what an orgasm feels like to you?
3. When do you usually have orgasms? During intercourse? Masturbation? Clitoral stimulation? Other sexual activities? How often?
4. Supposing all the psychological factors were right, what physical stimuli would cause you to have an orgasm?
5. In other words, if "a man has an orgasm when there is up-and-down friction on his penis, a woman has an orgasm when . . . " Fill in the blank.
6. Are your techniques for reaching orgasm the same in intercourse (vaginal penetration) as in masturbation?
7. Please give a graphic description or a drawing of how your body could be best stimulated to orgasm.
8. Do you usually have orgasm during intercourse? Never? Sometimes? Rarely?
9. What positions are best for having orgasm during intercourse? Do you like to be on top or on the bottom, or sideways, backwards, etc.?
10. Do penis size and shape make a difference to you? What shape and size do you find are most compatible with your body—long and fat, short and fat, thin and short, etc.?
11. Describe which techniques of vaginal penetration or intercourse would be most stimulating for you— softer or harder, with pressure to the back or front or neither, complete or partial penetration, etc.
12. Where (at what physical area) does the sensation of orgasm occur when you have it during vaginal penetration?
13. Is it easier for you to have an orgasm when intercourse is not in progress? In other words, do you have orgasms more frequently by more direct stimulation of the clitoral area?

14. Are these orgasms different from orgasms during intercourse? Which is stronger? Which is "better?" How?

15. What positions are best for having an orgasm during this direct (clitoral) stimulation? Does it matter if your legs are together, or can they be apart? Do you move very much, etc.?

16. What kind of stimulation of this general clitoral area do you prefer? Do you like a hard, medium, or soft massage? Do you like rhythmic movements? Do you like the position varied or remaining constant?

17. Please explain ways you and your partner practise this direct stimulation.

18. Do you have orgasms during cunnilingus? Do you have them during oral/clitoral contact or both? Explain how it should be done to suit you.

19. Do you use a vitrator to have orgasms? Where do you use it (what body area)? Is it used by you or your partner? During intercourse?

20. What physical preliminaries are important to you for reaching orgasm?

21. Do you like intercourse? Physically? Psychologically? Why? Do you ever have any physical discomfort?

22. Do you feel free to do all the things you would like, or do you think the other person(s) would be shocked?

23. Do you enjoy masturbation? Physically? Psychologically? Is it more intense with or without a partner?

24. How do you masturbate? Please explain with a drawing or detailed description. For example, what do you use for stimulation—your fingers or hand or a vibrator, etc.? What kinds of motions do you like—circular, patting, up and down, etc.? Do you use two hands, or if not what do you do with the other hand? Are your legs together or apart? Where do you touch yourself? etc.

25. What is the sequence of physical events that occurs when you masturbate? For example, one person might put her legs together, then massage the clitoral area with her hand, while pushing the lips together rhythmically between her legs, with the pelvis also moving slightly, etc.

26. Do you enjoy rectal contact? What kind? Do you enjoy penetration? How often are you requested to do this and how often do you do it?

27. What other sexual activities cause you to have orgasm?

28. Is the time of the month important? Do you have intercourse during your period?
29. What do you think about during sex? Do you have fantasies? What about?
30. Are sounds and words important to you? What sex words and phrases and sounds do you find stimulating? Dislike?
31. Does pornography stimulate you? What kinds, what actions?
32. What do you think of sado-masochism (domination-submission)?
33. What would you like to try that you never have? What would you like to do more often? What would you like to see incorporated into the usual bedroom scene? How would you like to see that scene changed?
34. What were your best sex experiences? Please explain.
35. How important are orgasms to you? Do you like them? Do they ever bore you? Is it more fun getting there or having the orgasm?
36. Do you think you look ugly or beautiful when you are having an orgasm?
37. How often do you desire sex? Do you actively seek it?
38. Is one orgasm sexually satisfying to you? If not, how many?
39. Do you go for long periods without sex? Does it bother you? Do you feel you are missing something when you are not sleeping with a partner?
40. If you almost never or never have orgasms, what factors do you think would contribute to your having them?
41. Do you prefer sex with men, women, either, or yourself?
42. Do you think men are uninformed about your sexual desires and your body? Do you think women are?
43. Do you like objects in bed with you? That is, do you like to use objects in love-making?
44. Do you ever fake orgasms? How often? Why? Under what conditions?
45. Do you feel you must have a climax to "perform" for your partner, because otherwise you are not normal, not a "real woman"? Do you feel that you should have an orgasm because it would be good for you, or a "fun experience"?
46. Is having an orgasm somewhat of a concentrated effort?
47. Are you shy about having an orgasm with a partner? Why? With only new partners or with everyone?
48. Do you feel embarassed asking for clitoral manipulation? Do you feel your partner is sacrificing to give it to you?

49. What is it about sex that gives you the greatest pleasure?
50. Do you feel most men get more pleasure from intercourse than from sexual play? Do you feel guilty about taking time for yourself in sexual play which is perhaps not that stimulating to your partner?
51. Does your partner realize you come when you come? Do you show any particular signs? What are they?
52. Describe how most men have had sex with you (if there are any standard practices, etc.).
53. Please describe how most women have had sex with you.
54. Do(es) your partner(s) masturbate you? Without being asked? For how long? Do they like cunnilingus? Without being asked?
55. Is there anything, any sexual practice, which you enjoy that you would like to share with or recommend to other women?
56. Do you ever find it necessary to masturbate to achieve orgasm after "making love"?
57. Which would cause you to become more excited, physical teasing or direct genital manipulation? Psychological teasing? Describe how you would like to be teased.
58. Would you free-associate sex with childbearing, going to the bathroom, pleasure, or love? Other?
59. Have your opinions about all of this changed over a period of time? Do you feel your body responses and interests have changed?
60. Do you feel that having sex is in any way political?
61. Have you read Masters and Johnson's recent scientific studies on human sexual response, or articles discussing their work? What did you think of them? Of Kinsey? Any other writers?
62. What things were not covered in this questionnaire that you wanted to say?
63. How did you like the questionnaire?

Questionnaire II

January 1973

NATIONAL ORGANIZATION FOR WOMEN,
NYC CHAPTER
47 EAST 19 ST., NYC 10003

1. Is having sex important to you? What part does it play in your life?
2. Do you have orgasms? When do you usually have them? During masturbation? Intercourse? Clitoral stimulation? Other sexual activity? How often?
3. Is having orgasms important to you? Do you like them? Do they ever bore you? Would you enjoy sex just as much without ever having them? Does having good sex have anything to do with having orgasms?
4. If you almost never or never have orgasms, are you interested in having them? Why or why not? If you are interested, what do you think would contribute to your having them? Did you ever have them?
5. Could you describe what an orgasm feels like to you? Where do you feel it, and how does your body feel during orgasm?
6. Is having orgasms somewhat of a concentrated effort? Do you feel one has to learn how to have orgasms?
7. Is one orgasm sexually satisfying to you? If not, how many? How many orgasms are you capable of? How many do you usually want during masturbation? During clitoral stimulation with a partner? During intercourse?
8. Please give a graphic description or drawing of how your body could best be stimulated to orgasm.
9. Do you enjoy arousal? For its own sake—that is, as an extended state of heightened sensitivity not necessarily leading to orgasm? What does it feel like?
10. Do you like to remain in a state of arousal for indefinite or long periods of time? Or do you prefer to have arousal and orgasm in a relatively short period of time?
11. Do you ever go for long periods without sex? (Does this include masturbation or do you have no sex at all?) Does it bother you or do you like it?

12. How often do you desire sex? Do you actively seek it? Is the time of the month important? Do you experience an increase in sexual desire at certain times of the month?

13. Do you enjoy masturbation? Physically? Psychologically? How often? Does it lead to orgasm usually, sometimes, rarely, or never? Is it more intense with someone or alone? How many orgasms do you usually have?

14. What do you think is the importance of masturbation? Did you ever see anyone else masturbating? Can you imagine women you admire masturbating?

15. How do you masturbate? What is the sequence of physical events which occur? Please give a detailed description. For example, what do you use for stimulation—your fingers or hand or a vibrator, etc.? What kinds of motions do you make—circular, patting, up and down, etc.? Do you use two hands, or if not, what do you do with the other hand(s)? Where do you touch yourself? Does it matter if your legs are together or apart? Do you move very much? etc.

16. What positions and movements are best for stimulating yourself clitorally with a partner? Do you have orgasms this way usually, sometimes, rarely, or never? Please explain ways you and your partner(s) practice clitoral stimulation.

17. What other sexual play do you enjoy? Is it important for reaching orgasm? How important is kissing (mouth stimulation), breast stimulation, caressing of hips and thighs, general body touching, etc.?

18. Do you like vaginal penetration/intercourse? Physically? Psychologically? Why? Does it lead to orgasm usually, sometimes, rarely, or never? How long does it take? Do you ever have any physical discomfort? Do you usually have adequate lubrication? Do you ever have a decrease in vaginal–genital feeling the longer intercourse continues?

19. What kinds of movements do you find most stimulating during penetration—soft, hard, pressure to the back or front or neither, complete or partial penetration, etc? Which positions do you find stimulating? Does the size and shape of the penis or penetrating "object" matter to you?

20. Do you have intercourse during your period? Oral sex?

21. Is it easier for you to have an orgasm when intercourse is not in progress? In other words, do you have orgasms more easily by clitoral stimulation than intercourse? Are the orgasms different? How?

22. Do you enjoy cunnilingus? Do you have orgasms during cunnilingus usually, sometimes, rarely, or never? Do you have them during oral/clitoral or oral/vaginal contact or both? Explain what you like or dislike about it.
23. Do you use a vibrator to have orgasms? What kind of vibrator is it? At which body area(s) do you use it? Do you use it during masturbation or sexual play or intercourse or at other times?
24. Do you enjoy rectal contact? What kind? Rectal penetration?
25. What do you think about during sex? Do you fantasize? What about?
26. Does pornography stimulate you? What kinds? Which actions?
27. What do you think of sado-masochism? Of domination-submission? What do you think is their significance?
28. Do you prefer to do things to others or have things done to you, or neither?
29. Which would cause you to become more excited—physical teasing, direct genital stimulation, or psychological "foreplay"?
30. Who sets the pace and style of sex—you or your partner? Who decides when it's over? What happens if your partner usually wants to have sex more often than you do? What happens if you want to have sex more often than your partner?
31. Do you usually have sex with the people you want to have sex with? Who usually initiates sex or a sexual advance—you or the other person?
32. Describe how most men and women have had sex with you (if there are any patterns, etc.).
33. Do most of your partners seem to be well informed about your sexual desires and your body? Are they sensitive to the stimulation you want? If not, do you ask for it or act yourself to get it? Is this embarrassing?
34. Do you feel guilty about taking time for yourself in sexual play which may not be specifically stimulating to your partner? Which activities are you including in your answer?
35. Are you shy about having orgasms with a partner? With only new partners or with everyone? Why?
36. Do you think your vagina and genital area are ugly or beautiful? Do you feel that they smell good?
37. Do you ever find it necessary to masturbate to achieve orgasm after "making love"?

38. How long does sex usually last?

39. Do you ever fake orgasms? During which sexual activities? How often? Under what conditions?

40. What would you like to try that you never have? What would you like to do more often? What changes would you like to make in the usual "bedroom" scene?

41. What were your best sex experiences?

42. How old were you when you had your first sexual experiences? With yourself? With another person? What were they? How old were you when you had your first orgasm? During what activity? At what age did you first look carefully at your vagina and genitals?

43. What is it about sex that gives you the greatest pleasure? Displeasure?

44. What can you imagine you would like to do to another person's body? How would you like to relate physically to other bodies?

45. Do you enjoy touching? Whom do you touch—men, women, friends, relatives, children, yourself, animals, pets, etc? Does this have anything to do with sex?

46. How important are physical affection and touching for their own sakes (not leading to sex)? Do you do as much of them as you would like? Do you ever have sex with someone mainly to touch and be touched and be close to them? How often?

47. Do you ever touch someone for purposes of sensual arousal but not "real" sex? Please explain. (If desired, refer to question #9).

48. Is there a difference between sex and touching? If so, what is that difference?

49. In the best of all possible worlds, what would sexuality be like?

50. Do you think your age and background make any difference as far as your sex life is concerned? What is your age and background—education, upbringing, occupation, race, economic status, etc.?

51. Do you usually prefer sex with men, women, either, yourself, or not at all? Which have you had experience with and how much?

52. What do you think of the "sexual revolution"?

53. How does or did contraception affect your sexual life? Which methods have you used? Did you ever take birth control pills?

54. Do you feel that having sex is in any way political?

55. Have you read Masters and Johnson's recent scientific studies on sexuality? Kinsey's? Others? What did you think of them?
56. Please add anything you would like to say that was not mentioned in this questionnaire.
57. How did you like the questionnaire?

Questionnaire III

June 1973

NATIONAL ORGANIZATION FOR WOMEN,
NYC CHAPTER
47 EAST 19 ST., NYC 10003

1. Is having sex important to you? What part does it play in your life, and what does it mean to you?
2. Do you have orgasms? If not, what do you think would contribute to your having them?
3. Is having orgasms important to you? Would you enjoy sex just as much without having them? Does having good sex have anything to do with having orgasms?
4. In most of your sexual encounters, does your orgasm(s) usually occur during cunnilingus, manual clitoral stimulation, intercourse, or other activity? Which of these activities usually lead to orgasm? How often?
5. Could you describe what an orgasm feels like to you during the build-up? Just before the orgasm? During the climax? After?
6. Is having orgasms somewhat of a concentrated effort? Did you have to learn how to have orgasms? Did they become better or easier for you with practice?
7. Is one orgasm sexually satisfying to you? If not how many? How many orgasms are you capable of, and how many do you usually want during masturbation? Intercourse? Clitoral stimulation with a partner? Cunnilingus?
8. Do your thoughts and emotions affect your desire for orgasms? How?
9. If you are just about to have an orgasm and then don't because of withdrawal of stimulation or some similar reason, do you feel frustrated? How do you feel? When does this tend to happen?

10. How often do you desire sex? Do you actively seek it?

11. How important are physical affection and touching for their own sakes (not leading to orgasm, or even necessarily to sex)? Do you do as much of them as you would like?

12. What do you think is the importance of masturbation? Did you ever see anyone else masturbating? How did they look? Can you imagine women you admire masturbating?

13. Do you enjoy masturbating? Physically? Psychologically? How often? Does it lead to orgasm usually, sometimes, rarely, or never? How long does it take? Do you prefer masturbating or the same activity with a partner?

14. How do you masturbate? Please give a detailed description. For example, what do you use for stimulation—your fingers or hand or a vibrator or sheets, etc.? What kinds of motions do you make—circular or up and down, etc? Where do you touch or rub yourself? Does it matter if your legs are together or apart? Do you move very much? Etc.

15. Do you practise clitoral stimulation with your partner(s)? How? Does it lead to orgasm usually, sometimes, rarely, or never?

16. Do you enjoy cunnilingus (oral sex)? Is it oral—clitoral or oral—vaginal or both? Does it lead to orgasm usually, sometimes, rarely, or never? What do you like or dislike about cunnilingus?

17. Do you like vaginal penetration/intercourse? Physically? Psychologically? Does it lead to orgasm usually, sometimes, rarely, or never? Did you have to learn to have orgasms during intercourse, or did you always have them?

18. If you have orgasms during vaginal penetration/intercourse, how long does it usually take? Do you prefer the penetrating "object," or penis, to be holding still or moving? Is any accompanying stimulus necessary to reach orgasm? What is it and how do you achieve it?

19. Which kinds of movements do you like to make during penetration to increase your stimulation—soft or hard, pressing to the back or front, using complete or partial penetration, or any other technique? Which positions do you find stimulating? Does the size or shape of the penis or penetrating "object" matter to you? Do you use vaginal or other muscles to help achieve orgasm?

20. Do you ever have any physical discomfort during intercourse? Do you usually have adequate lubrication? Do you sometimes feel less excited the longer intercourse continues?

21. Is the emotional and psychological relationship more important during penetration than other forms of sex? What is your emotional reaction to penetration?

22. Is it easier for you to have an orgasm by clitoral stimulation when intercourse is not in progress? If you had to choose between intercourse and clitoral stimulation by your partner, which would you pick? Why? Do orgasms with penetration feel different from orgasms without penetration? How?

23. How important is what you do to the other person for your own stimulation?

24. Do you fantasize during sex? If so, is it to help bring on an orgasm, or just in general? Exactly what fantasies do you have? What activities are involved?

25. Does erotic art or pornography stimulate you? Which kinds, with what activities? Would you prefer some other kind of erotica than you have seen?

26. Do you ever have a feeling of power during sex? When? How does it feel? Is it exciting or frightening, or what? What are your feelings towards your partner and yourself at such times? Do you ever want to attack or hurt or rape your partner?

27. Do you ever have a feeling of powerlessness or submission, or wanting to be "taken" during sex? When? How does it feel? Do you enjoy it, and what are your feelings at this time?

28. What part do your emotions and relationships play in sex in general? Do you like unemotional, "casual" sexual encounters? Do most of your sexual relationships start out being basically physical or basically emotional? Is it different with men and women?

29. Do you often feel your partner is not emotionally involved during sex? Or, what emotional responses do you most often feel from your partner? Are these usually different with men and with women?

30. What type of person usually attracts you? Are there certain physical or personality traits you often find attractive?

31. What have your deepest relationships been like, with both women and men? How were they satisfying or unsatisfying, both emotionally and physically?

32. Ideally, what kind of relationship would you like to have with a sexual partner?

33. If you have ever experienced something you called "love," which emotions were involved? Was it, or were they, a healthy or

unhealthy relationship? How did these relationships affect sex?

34. How often do you desire sex? Do you actively seek it?
35. What is it about sex that gives you the greatest pleasure? Displeasure?
36. Are most of your partners sensitive to the stimulation you want? If not, do you ask for it or act yourself to get it? Is this embarrassing?
37. Do you ever find it necessary to masturbate to achieve orgasm after "making love"?
38. Have you ever been afraid to say "no" to someone for fear of "turning them off"? If so, how did you feel during sex? Afterwards?
39. Do you ever fake orgasms? During which sexual activities? How often? Under what conditions?
40. Do you think your vagina and genital area are ugly or beautiful? What other parts of your body do you like or dislike? Are you comfortable naked with another person? Do you worry about how your body looks?
41. What would you like to try that you never have? What would you like to do more often?
42. Describe how most men and women have had sex with you.
43. How have these experiences influenced your current thinking or sexual behaviour? Did you have any one experience which drastically affected your sexual life?
44. How old were you when you had your first sexual experiences? What were they? With yourself? With another person? How old were you when you had your first orgasm? During what activity? At what age did you first look carefully at your vagina and genitals?
45. What is your age and background—occupation, education, upbringing, race? Do you usually live alone or with someone you have sex with? Where did you obtain the questionnaire?
46. Do you usually prefer sex with men, women, either, yourself, or not at all? Why? Which have you had experience with and how much? Was it mostly long- or short-term relationships?
47. What do you think of the "sexual revolution"?
48. Do you feel that sex is in any way political?
49. Do you think "sex," as we usually define it, is a conditioned response? That is, do we act in ways that, had we not been taught them since childhood, we would not consider "natural"?

50. What changes would you see as leading to a better sexuality or physical expression? In other words, in the best of all possible worlds, what would sexuality be like?
51. Have you read Masters and Johnson's recent studies on sexuality? Kinsey's? Others? What did you think of them?
52. Please add anything you would like to say that was not mentioned.
53. Why did you answer this questionnaire (thank you), and how did you like it?

Appendix 2:
Statistical analysis:
Who answered (US)

Questionnaire distribution

This questionnaire and the three different versions given in Appendix I were distributed to women all over the US between 1972 and 1976. Their purpose was to discover how women view their own sexuality. Great effort was put into mailing and distribution of the questionnaires in an attempt to reach as many different kinds of women, with as many different points of view, as possible.

Early distribution was done through national mailings to women's groups, including chapters of the National Organization for Women, abortion rights groups, university women's centres, and women's newsletters. Soon after, notices in *The Village Voice, Mademoiselle, Brides*, and *Ms.* magazines informed readers that they could write in for the questionnaires, and later there were also notices placed in dozens of church newsletters. In addition, *Oui* magazine ran the questionnaire in its entirety, and 253 replies were received from its Women Readers. Finally, the paperback *Sexual Honesty by Women for Women,* * which contains forty-five complete early replies, has asked readers to send in their own replies since its publication in 1974. All in all, 100,000 questionnaires were distributed, and slightly over 3,000 returned (more or less the standard rate of return for this kind of questionnaire distribution).

Replies to Questionnaire II include, besides answers from the women's movement distribution, answers from readers of *Mademoiselle, Brides*, and *Ms.* magazines.

*Published by Warner Paperback Library.

Questionnaires III and IV represent a mixture of women's movement distribution and church newsletter distribution.

Replies to Questionnaire I include those received from readers of the *Village Voice*, *Oui* magazine, and again from general distribution through the women's movement and various church and religious groups. Although these groups tended to be quite different in manner of expression, and in perspective on their situation (as will be readily apparent in the quotes), their answers did not differ in basic content—i.e., type of masturbation, stimulation necessary for orgasm, etc.

Statistics given in the book are generally broken down into the three populations—Questionnaires I, II, and III—as a way of demonstrating how closely results from all of the groups resemble each other. Since Questionnaire IV was distributed while tabulation of the results was already in progress, only replies to Questionnaires I, II, and III—are presented statistically (1,844 women total); however, quotes from replies to Questionnaire IV are included in the text. Also, replies from women who had read *Sexual Honesty* were not included in the statistics, since they might have been influenced by what the other women had said, but quotes from these replies are occasionally included in the text. The total number of women's answers received from all the sources is 3,019.

In this new edition, replies received from UK readers, after US publication of the original book, are included, forming approximately 57 per cent of the total amount of first-person testimonies. Statistical tabulation of these replies can be found in Appendix 3.

Geographic distribution of replies

Answers, according to postmarks, were received from the following American states:

Alabama 3
Alaska 6
Arizona 15
Arkansas 5
California 248
Colorado 25
Connecticut 29
Delaware 13
Florida 49
Georgia 18
Hawaii 1
Idaho 1
Illinois 64
Indiana 20
Iowa 7
Kansas 10
Kentucky 7
Louisiana 15
Maine 12
Maryland 30
Massachusetts 66
Michigan 38
Minnesota 27
Mississippi 1
Missouri 13
Montana 3
Nebraska 14
New Hampshire 13
New Jersey 88
New Mexico 12
New York 485
North Carolina 12
North Dakota 3
Ohio 59
Oklahoma 3
Oregon 25
Pennsylvania 107
Rhode Island 11

South Carolina 9
South Dakota 3
Tennessee 9
Texas 32
Utah 3
Vermont 13
Virginia 21
Washington 48
Wisconsin 35
Wyoming 3

Canada 36
APO 5
Washington, DC 28

Outside the US 13
    Australia 1
    France 2
    Germany 3
    Mexico 2
    Puerto Rico 3
    Singapore 1
    Sweden 1

TOTAL: 1817
27   unknown

"Marital status"

The following categories refer to the ways in which women described their own lives. As the division married/single is no longer sufficient for the classification of sexual relationships, this question was not asked specifically on any of the questionnaires.

	Q.I	Q.II	Q.III
Married (number of years not given)	182	250	46
Married 1–5 years	19	28	4
6–10 years	6	15	5
11–15 years	4	12	4
16–20 years	5	3	4
21–25 years	3	12	5
over 25 years	2	8	3
Divorced, now single	52	74	30
Widowed, now single	12	15	3
Single	186	246	55
Boyfriend	70	81	19
Living with lover*	75	104	43
Celibate	3	7	1
Total	619	855	222
Did not answer	71	64	13

*Includes lesbian relationships.

Breakdown by percentages

(percentages of those who answered the question)

	Q.I	Q.II	Q.III
Married	36.0	38.0	32.0
Divorced and widowed, now single	10.0	10.0	15.0
Single	30.0	29.0	25.0
Boyfriend	11.0	9.5	8.5
Living with lover	12.0	12.0	19.0
Celibate	0.5	1.0	0.5
Total	99.5	99.5	100.0

Age, religion, education, and occupation

Statistics on age, religious background, education, and occupation are not available for Questionnaire I, since this information was not requested in that version of the questionnaire. Since so many survey results have given the impression of categorizing and labelling people on a superficial basis, it was hoped that by not asking these types of questions, the questionnaires could break through to a deeper level of communication with the person answering. Quite a few women did appreciate this approach:

"I almost don't know how to handle not being required to put down age, sexual experience, marital status, occupation, etc. It was very objective and remarkably impartial. Great!"

"The questionnaire was good in that it completely avoided questions about age, how long you've been having intercourse, and whether it's with one partner or many. Statistics are easy to answer and to add up, but they encourage you to stereotype yourself on the other questions as well."

"You never asked if I ever had children or was married! Hooray for you!"

"I answered this questionnaire because it was the only one I've ever seen that didn't make assumptions or seem to be overconcerned with placing me in a sociological pigeonhole—like how many men I've slept with, how much experience I've had, that kind of thing."

However, information about age, religious background, education, and occupation was requested in Questionnaires II and III, and these results follow:

Ages of respondents

Age	Q.II	Q.III	Age	Q.II	Q.III
14	3		31	28	8
15	2		32	26	12
16	6	3	33	22	5
17	10	5	34	14	5
18	22	3	35	14	6
19	28	6	36	21	7
20	38	6	37	13	4
21	33	10	38	15	4
22	44	6	39	18	7
23	47	7	40	13	4
24	41	4	41	10	4
25	63	7	42	16	4
26	57	11	43	14	2
27	31	12	44	10	4
28	39	10	45	9	1
29	28	7	46	7	3
30	38	5	47	7	1

cont'd

Age	Q.II	Q.III	Age	Q.II	Q.III
48	4	1	66	1	
49	5	1	67		
50	8	6	68		
51	8	3	69		
52	5	2	70		
53	6	4	71	1	
54	2	1	72		1
55	9		73		
56	2	1	74	1	
57	2		75	1	
58	4	2	76		
59		1	77		1
60	4	3	78		1
61	1				
62	1	1			
63					
64	1				
65		1		853*	213†

*66 ages unknown
†22 ages unknown

Religious background

	Q.II	Q.III
Catholic	252	41
Jewish	198	40
Protestant	309	73
Did not answer	160	81
Total	919	235

In addition, over 95 per cent of all the women who answered indicated that they had been brought up with the idea that sex was "bad", or at the very least a subject that was never mentioned—implying that it was bad.

Race was not specifically asked about, and since only a small number of women identified themselves by race, these figures are not included here. However, it should be noted that, for purposes of this research about the female body, the position of the clitoris, vagina and other parts of the anatomy, is the same for all races; variations occur in individuals, not groups.

Education

	Q.II	Q.III
Less than high school	12	4
High school	145	24
Some college	264	60
Currently in college	139	31
Nursing degree	12	1
B.A./B.S.	179	35
Graduate school/ law school	39	8
M.A./M.S.W./M.B.A.	82	33
Ph.D.	23	12
Travel	11	—
"Well educated"	14	3
Total	741*	211†

*178 did not answer
†24 did not answer

Occupation

(The following terms are those used by the respondents.)

	Q.II	Q.III
Accountant	4	1
Actress	4	2
Administrative assistant	11	4
Advertising executive	2	—
Air Force	2	—
Artisan	1	—
Artist	17	10
Auditor and tax consultant	1	1
Barmaid	1	—
Bookkeeper	—	2
Broker	—	1
Cab driver	—	1
Call girl	1	1
Cashier	4	—
Chemist	1	—
Child care	—	1
Clerical	13	—
College administrator	1	—
Computer coder	1	1
Computer service	1	—
Conservation service	1	—
Costume design	1	—
Consultant	1	—
Counsellors		
abortion	2	—
disability determination	1	—
drug	—	1
guidance	1	2
problem pregnancy	—	1
sex therapy and counselling	1	2
vocational	7	1
Cryptanalyst	1	—
Dancer	3	—
Day care	1	—

cont'd

	Q.II	Q.III
Dental hygiene	1	2
Department manager	4	1
Diamond cutter	—	1
Dog trainer	1	—
Drug dealer	1	—
Editor	5	2
Factory work	1	—
Food economist	—	1
Greenhouse worker	—	1
Government job	1	1
Health food store stocker	1	—
Hospital worker	14	—
"Housewife"	262	34
Insurance	1	—
Interior designer	1	—
Key-punch operator	—	1
Librarian	3	4
Masseuse	1	—
Medical field	11	—
Medical technician	2	2
Microbiologist	—	1
Minister	1	—
Model	2	—
Music business	1	—
Nun (ex)	3	—
Odd jobs	6	1
Own business	1	—
Own secretary service	—	1
Personnel	1	—
Physical therapist	2	—
Physicist	1	—
Probation officer	1	2
Professional woman	15	—
Program director	3	—
Proofreader	2	2
Psychiatrist	1	—
Psychologist	2	3

		Q.II	Q.III
Psychometrist		1	1
Public relations		1	—
Radical collective		—	1
R.N.		17	4
Reporter		5	—
Research		6	3
Sales clerk		2	—
Sales representative		1	—
Scientist		1	—
Secretary		89	24
Slave		2	1
Social worker		9	6
Sociologist		2	—
Songwriter		—	1
Speech pathology		1	—
Stewardess		11	—
"Street rat"		1	—
Student	**Total:**	139	31
college	**Breakdown:**	(95)	—
graduate school		(11)	—
high school		(10)	—
law		(2)	—
nursing		(6)	—
Ph.D.		(4)	—
pre-medical		(1)	—
unclear		(10)	—
Switchboard operator		8	1
Teacher			
college		3	7
high school		75	11
Testing electronics systems		—	1
Unemployed		23	5
Waitress		5	—
Work for senator		1	—
Writer		25	12
X-ray technician		1	1
Total		**867**	**207**

Appendix 3:
Statistical Analysis:
Findings (US)

Masturbation (Chapter 1)

How many women in the study* masturbate

	Total population	Do masturbate	Didn't answer (may or may not masturbate)	Don't masturbate
Q.I	690	562 (81%)	23 (4%)	106 (15%)
Q.II	919	743 (81%)	31 (3%)	145 (16%)
Q.III	235	200 (85%)	11 (5%)	24 (10%)
Total	1844	1505 (82%)	64 (3%)	275 (15%)

*Only replies to Questionnaires I, II, and III were analysed statistically (1,844 women total), although quotes from the replies to Questionnaire IV are also included in the text, making a total of 3,000 women. Questionnaire IV was distributed while tabulation of the results was already in progress. In addition, replies from women who had read *Sexual Honesty* were not included in the statistics, since they might have been influenced by what the other women had said, but quotes from these replies were at times included in the text.

How many women orgasm during masturbation

	Do orgasm during masturbation	Didn't orgasm during masturbation	Didn't answer if orgasm during masturbation	Total population who does masturbate
Q.I	542	1	19	562
Q.I	714	5	24	743
Q.III	193	2	5	200
Total	1449	8	48	1505

Frequency of orgasm during masturbation

	Q.I	Q.II	Q.III
"Yes"	298	124	29
Always*	79	339	88
Usually	143	215	66
Sometimes	10	27	8
Rarely	2	9	2
Total	542	714	193

*In Questionnaire I the question was phrased, "Do you usually orgasm during masturbation?" In Questionnaire II the question was worded, "Does masturbation lead to orgasm usually, sometimes, rarely, or never?" In Questionnaire III "always" was added as a choice, since so many women gave this as their answer in Questionnaires I and II.

Percentage who answered "yes," "always," or "usually" to the question, "How often do you orgasm during masturbation?" (see above)

Q.I	530
Q.II	678
Q.III	183
Total	1391*

*96% of women who do orgasm at any time and who do masturbate orgasm regularly during masturbation.

How do you masturbate?

Total population	Did masturbate and did say how	Did masturbate but didn't say how	Didn't answer whether or not they masturbate	Didn't masturbate
1844	1391	114	64	275

Type of masturbation

Type I	1015
Type II	76
Type III	53
Type IV	46
Type V	31
Type VI	21
Women who masturbate in more than one way	149
Total	1391

Breakdown of types

IA	657	74%
IA1	67	8%
IA2	70	8%
IA3	12	1%
IA4	11	1%
IA5	20	2%
IA direct	56	6%
Total type IA	893	

IB	96
IB1	17
IB2	8
IB5	1
Total type IB	122

IIA	44 (+ 18 in combination with other types)
IIA1	4 (+ 2 in combination with other types)
IIA2	4 (+ 2 in combination with other types)
IIA5	0 (+ 1 in combination with other types)
IIA3	1 (+ 3 in combination with other types)
IIA4	3 (+ 2 in combination with other types)
IIB	15 (+ 8 in combination with other types)
IIB1	3 (+ 01)
IIB2	2 (+1 in combination with other types)
Total type II	76 (+ 37 in combination with other types)

III	40 (+ 28 in combination with other types)
III1	6
III2	1 (+ 1 in combination with other types)
Unusual III	6
Total type III	53 (+ 29 in combination with other types) (includes 11 who also held cloth between their legs simultaneously)

cont'd

IV	36 (+ 20 in combination with other types)
IV1	6 (+ 1 in combination with other types)
IV2	4 (+ 1 in combination with other types)
Total type IV	46 (+ 22 in combination with other types) (includes 25 who held a pillow or towel between their legs simultaneously)
V—tub faucet	17 (+ 33 in combination with other types)
V—shower	6 (+ 9 in combination with other types)
V—shower hose with head removed	1 (+ 2 in combination with other types)
V—tub faucet or shower hose	1 (+ 2 in combination with other types)
V—hose spray attached to tub faucet	3 (+ 6 in combination with other types)
V—exact method not given	3 (+ 1 in combination with other types)
Total type V	31 (+ 53 in combination with other types)
VI	21 (+ 10 in combination with other types)
Total type VI	21 (+ 10 in combination with other types) (includes 17 who use clitoral stimulation before entry)

Combinations of masturbation types (women who masturbate in more than one way)

IA and IB	5	IA3 and II	2	II and V	1
IA and III	10	IA3 and V	6	II and VI	1
IA and II	9	IA3 and III	2	II and IV	2
IA and IV	6	IA4 and II	1		
IA and V	26	IA4 and VI	1		4
IA and VI	2	IA5 and III	2		
		IA5 and IV	2	III and IV	7
		IA5 and VI	1	III and VI	2
IA1 and II	3	IA5 and II	1	III and V	5
IA1 and IA4	1			III and II	4
IA1 and IB	1		101		
IA1 and III	1				18
IA1 and V	4				
IA1 and VI	2	IB and IA5	1	IA and II and III	1
		IB and III	1	IA and II and V	1
		IB and IV	3	IA1 and II and V	1
IA2 and VI	1	IB and V	5	IA and III and IV	2
IA2 and III	2	IB and VI	1	IA and IV and VI	1
IA2 and IV	2	IB and II	2	IA2 and II and III	1
IA2 and IB	1	IB2 and III	1	IB and III and VI	1
IA2 and IA3	1	IB2 and VI	1	IA3 and I and V	1
IA2 and II	1	IB4 and II	1	II and III and V	1
IA2 and V	5				
			16		10

Total: 149

Type of insertion for masturbation type I

Total type I

OBJECT INSERTED

	Vibrator	One finger	Fingers	"One hand"	Wide object	Narrow object
A1 and B1	10	30	28	10	9	9
A2 and B2	11	31	35	16	17	12

MOTION

	In and out	Stationary
A1 and B1	10	36
A2 and B2	41	23

Most finger/fingers fell into the in-and-out category, especially moving in and out near the opening of the vagina, while objects tended to fall into the stationary category. All type III and IV inserts were stationary. Out of *all* the type Is, figures were:

In and out	Stationary	Occasional entry for lubrication
56	78	22

LEG POSITION

Apart:	90	Together:	31
Apart, then alternating:	13	Slightly apart:	6
Alternating:	14	Together, then apart:	2

Leg position used during type II masturbation

Legs apart:	17	Legs together:	30
Legs slightly apart:	5	Legs together at orgasm:	4
With a pillow between legs:	7	Scissor movement (butterfly):	3

What kind of motion was involved in manual stimulation during masturbation?

Descriptions such as these were given:

"My fingers play gently with myself,"

"I gently squeeze, rub, and pat the area,"

"I caress myself with a circular, up and down motion, sometimes pulling up towards the navel,"

"I rub lightly, almost shaking the whole area,"

"I keep my body fairly still, while I have a gentle and quick massage with a piece of clothing,"

"I press on the whole area, from clitoris to vagina, with my whole hand, heel on clitoris, fingers near vagina—press and release, press and release,"

"I rhythmically push some clitoral flesh into the lower fleshy folds of my vulva,"

"I move my finger on the area just below the clitoris, back and forth, sliding to below the vaginal opening, pausing slightly then back up, then down, etc., pressing in just a little at the lowest point,"

"I squeeze my clitoris between my labia, pushing the lips together rhythmically, using my fingers in a scissor-like motion,"

"I tickle the clitoris softly, then stroke back and forth."

All these motions, though remaining soft and light, became faster, sometimes with pressure slightly increased. Actually, some women believe that speed and circumference of rotation are not as important as the amount and *constancy* (reliability/predictability) of pressure and rhythm. It is true that, basically, any kind of gentle constant motion will enable you to begin feeling the exact spot that is sensitive to stimulation at any given time, and focus on it.

Then, for orgasm, a very rapid agitation of the area is usually necessary—not large strokes, just rapid, in effect simulating a vibrator as closely as possible:

"I jiggle skin over the whole area with a vibrating motion of my hand and arm."

"I make my whole body vibrate by tensing my arm and moving back and forth as fast as possible."

"At the end, I rub from left to right in one inch sweeps over my clitoral shaft as fast as possible."

"I just rub the sponge as fast as I can."

"Increasing the tempo, the stroking becomes almost a vibration or rapid agitation."

"Press—exert pressure then release very quickly. The effect is like a vibrator."

Other than fingers, sponges, pieces of clothing or bedding, washcloths and vibrators were used. Another way of making sure the clitoral stimulation is not too direct, sometimes referred to, is using your vulval lips as a covering of flesh for your clitoris—they form a perfect cushion to rub and massage through:

"I usually masturbate by rubbing the folds of skin that cover my clitoris; I don't usually touch my clitoris directly because that's usually uncomfortable."

"My fantasies go to work while I lightly and slowly fondle my clitoris. That is, I don't touch it directly. I cover it with some of the skin around it."

Using the surrounding skin, or labia, or some cloth to make a sort of covering, pressing the labia against the clitoris, and massaging that way, or putting a piece of soft cloth or a pillow or washcloth between fingers and clitoris can feel good, as can wearing clothes or underpants. One woman said, "Through pants is better because the material spreads the vibrations over a greater area, whereas rubbing the clitoris itself is just annoying."

Of course, types III and IV use no fingers, instead pressing the area against something soft, or between their own inner thighs, but the same kind of focusing of sensation is involved.

Orgasm (Chapter 2)

Arousal

What did women say when asked, "Do you enjoy arousal? For its own sake—that is, as an extended state of heightened sensitivity not necessarily leading to orgasm?"

Seven hundred and thirty-five women out of 919 in Questionnaire II said they enjoyed arousal; 11 said they did not enjoy it, and 2 said they enjoyed it with a partner but not during masturbation; 15 enjoyed it "sometimes"; 156 did not answer.

But as to whether or not they would enjoy it for its own sake, "not necessarily leading to orgasm," only 266 answered yes, while 260 answered no. Thirty-six said they would enjoy arousal for its own sake "sometimes," and 2 said it had been "okay as a teenager." Ten said orgasm always happened anyway, so that they really weren't able to say. Within the "yes" answers, some said it was okay for a short time, but not a long time, or that if involved in *direct* sexual activities, it was *not* enjoyable without orgasm. Three hundred and forty-five women did not address themselves to this part of the question.

When the same group of 919 women were asked, "Do you like to remain in a state of arousal for indefinite or long periods of time? Or do you prefer to have arousal and orgasm in a relatively short period of time?" the answers were:

349—long amount of time
  36—medium amount of time
198—short amount of time
  91—variable, depending on partner, mood, and time
  13—short amount during masturbation, but long with a partner
  35—both ways are good
  22—since orgasm did not end arousal or "sex," the question was inappropriate; these women preferred to keep having orgasms every so often, "never really coming down off them."
  18—"a few hours of the day in bed"

762 (out of 817 women who do orgasm in Q.II)*

*Throughout this appendix, the difference between totals given and the total number of women involved in the study represent the number who did not answer the question, unless otherwise stated.

Replies to this later question contained many complaints that long arousal was impossible with men because they would not leave things at that point for long without going on to intercourse and orgasm. Also, included in the above "long" answers were 20 who said the reason they liked long arousal was that the longer the arousal, the better the orgasm. Six other "longs" mentioned that it was especially enjoyable with a loved one. And two women who answered "short" declared that too long a state of arousal made orgasm impossible.

"When you are about to have an orgasm and then don't because of withdrawal of stimulation or some similar reason, do you feel frustrated? When does this tend to happen?"

    39—angry, furious and outraged
     4—terrible
  109—frustrated
     4—tense
     2—incomplete
     6—don't feel frustrated
     6—cheated
     5—let down, disappointed
     5—emotionally hurt and rejected
     3—depressed
     1—resigned
     4—sometimes frustrated
     4—I cry
     2—defeated and cheated, "ripped off"
     1—in pain
   10—never happened

205 (out of 205 women who do orgasm in Q.III)

It seemed from the reaction to the question that this had happened to most women many times, although many women did not answer the second half of the question, "When does this happen?"

- 35—when he comes before I do/during intercourse (a few of these mentioned "premature ejaculation")
- 19—phone rings, family interruptions, baby cries
- 5—partner is stoned, drunk, or tired
- 4—I lose concentration or interest
- 2—I'm tired
- 3—during intercourse when I am not getting any clitoral stimulation
- 6—when he changes position
- 7—when my partner stops stimulating my clitoris
- 1—it never happens any more since I've taken over responsibility for my own stimulation
- 3—when I don't tell my partner what feels good
- 8—with incompetent and inexperienced partners
- 8—with an insensitive partner

The seeming discrepancy between most women saying arousal without orgasm is "bad" here, and only approximately half saying "bad" in the preceding section, "Do you like long arousal?", is probably best interpreted to mean most women agree that not having an orgasm when you are on the verge is dreadful, but that just coasting along feeling aroused and sensual is great.

"Is one orgasm sexually satisfying to you? If not, how many?"

	Q. I	Q. II
Yes, one	258	370
1–2	31	52
1–3	12	24
2–3	41	27
2	15	17
24		1
2–5	8	2
14		4
34	24	15
3–5	3	6
1–6	1	6
3–6	3	2
3	9	10
4–5	5	6
6–8	S	1
7–10	4	2
5-6	4	2
6		1
8–10	1	1
2–20	1	1
18–19		1
15–25		3
One BIG one	12	10
One "vaginal" or several "clitoral"		18
What is important is satisfaction, not numbers		35
One is satisfying but prefer more		36
The limit is fatigue, nothing else	9	4
One "big" one, or several small ones	9	
One is okay sometimes	30	26
Multiple	4	6
No, one is not satisfying	24	19
One is okay, but usually have more		11
the more the better (as many as possible)		30
Total	**513***	**749†**

*out of 608 women who do orgasm
†out of 817 women who do orgasm

How many women in the study orgasm

Total population		Do orgasm	Don't orgasm
Q. I	690	608 (88%)	82 (12%)
Q. II	919	817 (89%)	102 (11%)
Q. III	235	205 (87%)	30 (13%)
Total	1844	1630 (88%)	214 (11.6%)

How many women who never orgasm do masturbate? Don't masturbate?

	Women who never orgasm	Do masturbate	Didn't masturbate	Didn't answer
Q. I	82	36	43	3
Q. II	102	33	57	12
Q. III	30	14	8	8
Total	214	83	108	23

Type of masturbation of women who never orgasm but who do masturbate

IA	37	IIA	1
IA1	3	IIB	1
IA2	4	III	1
IB	8	IV	1
IB1	2	V	3
IB2	1	VI	12
IA4	1	Didn't say how	4
IA4	3	Total	83
IA5	1		

Phrases most frequently used to describe orgasm

AROUSAL
- intense tingling
- tickling
- build-up of tension
- pressure
- whole body, a delicious aching rising from level to level, shifting gears
- filling up, swelling
- rhythmic moving or touching
- gradual build-up of tingling tension, body tenses
- will explode
- heat
- heightened sensuality/sensual ecstasy
- intense build-up (gradual)

PEAK
- reach peak
- explode
- sudden release of tension
- tense, rigid
- intense electric shock
- can't speak
- pressure, overflow
- body forgotten, only think of genitals
- mainly in genitals but also whole body

CONTRACTIONS
- rolling pulses
- throbbing
- waves
- spasms
- vaginal contractions
- vibrations
- pulsating
- shuddering
- uterine contractions
- starts in genitals and spreads from feet up
- waves of heat up through body

- relaxation
- alive
- peaceful
- free
- elation
- relief of tension
- euphoria

What is the difference in feeling between orgasm with penetration and without?

Questionnaire I: Are these orgasms (from clitoral stimulation) different from orgasms during intercourse? Which is stronger? Which is "better"? How?
Questionnaire II: Do you have orgasms more easily by clitoral stimulation than intercourse? Are the orgasms different? How?
Questionnaire III: Do orgasms with penetration feel different from orgasms without penetration? How?

	Q.I	Q.II	Q.III
Clitoral orgasm is stronger	86	4	19
Clitoral is better	36	9	
Stronger in masturbation	25		
Stronger in intercourse	42		
Intercourse more intense	8	23	3
Clitoral more intense	18	88	30
Clitoral more defined	2	1	2
Intercourse is better	55	12	
Intercourse because muscles hold tight to penis	3	3	11
Intercourse is more satisfying, more "complete"	6	19	
Clitoral more satisfying	2	5	

Clitoral more localized, intense; intercourse more diffused, whole body	21	46	24
Vice versa	1	3	
Yes, they are different	20	23	10
No difference	42	80	14
Intercourse is psychologically/ emotionally better	19	22	14
Clitoral is psychologically better		5	
Intercourse better because shared	12	8	5
Intercourse more internal, deeper, stronger	1	18	
Total	425	351	94

In Questionnaires II and III, only the answers of those women who did orgasm both during intercourse,* and during masturbation and/or clitoral stimulation by a partner were counted.

*With or without simultaneous manual clitoral stimulation.

Comparison of leg position and number of orgasms desired

	Q.I	Q.II	Q.III	Total
Legs together:				
one orgasm	58	57	10	125
more	51	68	21	140
Legs apart:				
one orgasm	102	110	17	239
more	91	80	44	215
Leg position not specified:				
one orgasm	80	99	15	194
more	62	89	36	187

Although these figures are not large (since so many women did not give their leg position), they do indicate a tendency for women who prefer their legs together to desire more orgasms.

Comparison between preferred leg position for orgasm, and whether orgasm is considered stronger with or without intercourse

(This chart does not include those who do not have orgasms during intercourse. Questionnaire II and III figures include those who orgasm via simultaneous manual clitoral stimulation during intercourse; Questionnaire I gives these figures separately.)

	Orgasm w/simultaneous manual clitoral stimulation	Orgasm during intercourse	Q.I	Q.II	Q.III	Total
Legs apart:						
stronger with intercourse			6	11	11	8	36
stronger without intercourse			4	30	27	15	76
Legs together:						
stronger with intercourse			4	12	3	0	19
stronger without intercourse			8	22	23	10	63
Leg position not given:						
stronger with intercourse			7	9	15	4	35
stronger without intercourse			12	25	32	14	83
			41	109	111	51	

Total stronger with intercourse: 90

Total stronger without intercourse: 222

Most of the remaining women answered only in psychological terms, the majority saying that intercourse was better emotionally.

Intercourse (Chapter 3)

Questionable orgasm definition group

In a few cases it was difficult to know with certainty from a woman's answers if she was actually having an orgasm. In most cases, by listening to other answers a decision could be arrived at. However, there were a few women whose answers were unclear, and these answers formed the "questionable orgasm definition" group listed separately in the statistics. Although the answers of this group were followed throughout the analyses of all the questions, it was found in the end that their numbers did not affect any of the overall results significantly, their answers usually being well distributed throughout the complete range of answers to any given question. They were not listed separately in any of the other chapters, to avoid over-complicating the figures. They were presented to provide the most complete and detailed breakdown possible. Examples of answers falling into this category are:

"I can have a constant orgasm for as long as he wants me to. He trained me that way."

"When I have an orgasm, I don't completely lose contact with what's happening around me but it's such a total feeling of pleasure. I become very content and receive this desire to be enveloped in something warm. I feel it in the lower part of my body and usually it goes up my back."

"I get *real* wet; my partner can tell, too. Then I start getting dry and if my partner isn't close to finishing, an artificial lubricant (whether spit or corn oil) *must* be used. Whereas *occasionally* I feel slightly unhappy or cheated after sex, if the above happens I always feel tired, relaxed, content. That's why I figure it's an orgasm. But there's no extra body or emotional feeling when it happens."

"I feel a sense of physical ecstasy, heat, and I tingle all over, especially my toes."

"I feel lost and floating and not in control of myself and slightly delirious."

"Turning inside out of my body, merging with another or my own mind, falling *up,* about to pass out, then release and relief."

"Very sensitive all over, totally shaken."

"Feelings vary from gentle floating to complete release from my genitals to my head. It starts in my genitals and streams all over my body. If it's great, it goes up through my head."

"It starts at my toes and sweeps over my body."

"High like floating."

"Orgasms are mind trips with feelings of floating, being separated from all corporal things."

"Other memorable occasions caused a great physical awareness to flood over my body, so that motions became the pleasure. I had a tingling sensation from my toes to my fingertips and a very aroused feeling of lightness and movement."

"I can't answer whether I have orgasms or not. A large part of the problem is semantic—the word is rarely defined and often seems to be an imitation of how men describe orgasms. Maybe I've never had an orgasm. With me it's a gradual sensory buildup that I feel all over. I've never experienced them as 'thems'— there's really no take-off point or cut-off point. Something like 'total sensory experience' is my best verbal attempt— sorry."

The last quote is reminiscent of a remark Sherfey made:

> *Many women seem innocently vague and uncertain when we ask them to describe the nature of their sexual sensations, or they sound like a marriage-manual recitation on the nature of the orgasm. One wonders if this well-known difficulty women have in reporting their sexual sensations does not stem from the fact that they deceive themselves and us about the nature of these feelings— because they are afraid that what they do feel is not what they should feel.*[1]

The general criterion adopted for orgasm description in this study was similar to that chosen most frequently by the women in Fisher's study: "Excitement mounts to a high tension followed by sudden release." Indeed, this was the most frequent common denominator of all the descriptions given in this study. It would be interesting to further investigate whether there are any correlations between a woman's description of her orgasm and the type of stimulation she prefers, or the activity during which she orgasms.

In addition, there were a handful of women who preferred to orgasm in terms of levitation, rising in the air, or the head being separated from the body:

"It feels like levitation. Waves of heat go up through my body to my head."

"I once thought convulsions and tightenings all over my body were the signs of orgasm. But I was thoroughly shocked once when my head and whole body seemed to be ecstatically removed."

"I feel the top of my head is coming off, and am unaware of what's happening."

"My head is separate from my body, lost to consciousness. It is always diffuse and I am not keenly aware of what my body feels like. Once my lover and I looked deeply into each other's eyes and felt a slow, sweet intense pleasure that was more mental love."

"High up in my vagina, there is a pleasurable sensation which becomes stronger until it is almost unbearable. Suddenly there is a break and the sensation decreases accompanied by contractions which seem to spread all over the body. With this goes a sensation of rising in the air.*

"At orgasm my head separates from my body at a higher elevation."

*This woman was not included in the questionable-definition population.

How was the 30 per cent figure for orgasm from intercourse arrived at?

Women who said they only orgasmed "sometimes" or "rarely" during intercourse were not counted in the final overall percentage of 30 per cent. The "questionable orgasm-definition" population *was* counted. In other words, this percentage is based on all women who answered "yes," "always," or "usually" to the question, including those whose definition of orgasm was questionable.

Since the questionable-definition group contains almost as many women as the "sometimes–rarely" group, the percentage could also be seen as reflecting half of both the "sometimes–rarely" group and the questionable-definition group.

This percentage may be slightly high, due to the inclusion of the questionable-definition group, and also because women are under such great pressure to have orgasm during intercourse, both from others and from themselves, that in cases of doubt they may very well have said yes, not wanting to think too carefully about the possibility of being "frigid." This brings to mind one woman who, worried about not having orgasms during intercourse, discussed the problem with her analyst. He assured her that she could say she had "climaxes" during intercourse, since she did reach a peak of feeling—even though she didn't really "orgasm."

Other women said they had orgasm during intercourse, but meant by "intercourse" *all* the physical activities with another person: "It seems that you take intercourse to mean penis in vagina, whereas I mean by intercourse all that happens from the time we start until the time we're done. So, if that's how you're using it, then I've never had an orgasm strictly through 'intercourse.' I always require some manual stimulation of my clitoris. Whew! Maybe I've been getting my terminology confused for a long time, but by your usage, I guess I've never had an orgasm during intercourse except by the incidental manual stimulation."

In conclusion, all of these factors may have slightly inflated the percentage arrived at in this chapter.

Frequency of orgasm from intercourse

	Q. I	Q. II	Q. III
"Yes"	30	47	5
	q.d. 18	q.d. 16	q.d. 7
Always	17	15	2
	q.d. 14	11	1
Usually	81	88	23
	q.d. 40	55	17
Sometimes	65	86	27
	q.d. 15	26	3
Rarely	29	54	16
	q.d. 0	6	1
	222+87 (q.d.)	290+114 (q.d.)	78+29 (q.d.)

q.d. = questionable definition

"Do you ever have any physical discomfort during intercourse?"

	Q.I	Q.II	Q.III
Yes	19	48	13
(no orgasm during intercourse)	8	45	28
Sometimes	73	69	12
(no orgasm during intercourse)	17	46	22
No	115	97	25
(no orgasm during intercourse)	26	48	44
Yes if:			
too long or too frequent	22	4	2
(no orgasm during intercourse)	8	2	1
not aroused/no lubrication	46	5	6
(no orgasm during intercourse)	13	2	13
thrusts too deep	29	6	3
(no orgasm during intercourse)	7	7	3

cont'd

	Q.I	Q.II	Q.III
always with the first few thrusts	6	9	0
(no orgasm during intercourse)	1	9	2
too large penis	24	10	5
(no orgasm during intercourse)	10	2	3
yes, due to yeast infection	12	8	4
(no orgasm during intercourse)	4	3	1
Total	**440**	**420**	**187**

"If the man is larger than average, there is some pain—sometimes too much to have orgasm, and I spend all my time trying to keep him from penetrating too deeply."

"I avoid positions that allow his penis to hit my uterus (like being on the bottom with my legs up). In other positions I can avoid his penis hitting my uterus by tightening the muscles in my vagina or by shifting my hips."

"I think my cervix is in an unnatural position because I often experience a sharp pain when the penis is thrust in me at certain angles. I can usually lie in a position that enables painless penetration."

"Occasionally I have a sharp pain with deep penetration. At one time I bled profusely after rough intercourse. Had a minor operation that ended the problem. My uterus is tipped backwards and my doctor attributes the discomfort to this. Sometimes discomfort is due to my diaphragm."

"Sometimes it hurts when he gets carried away with deep hard thrusts when he comes. I get a stomach ache, feel battered, and urination becomes painful."

"Sometimes it feels as though the man's penis is poking too hard against another more sensitive internal organ. It gives me a sharp pain."

"I'm easily hurt by too deep penetration or too vigorous thrusting, but adjusting my position to limit penetration usually takes care of it."

"The discomfort I experience during intercourse is because I have an extremely retroflexed uterus that gets 'banged' into sometimes, which hurts."

"Wow, I'm really glad to see this question. I thought I was weird like that—yeah, sometimes I sure do get sore, although my partner can't believe it. I don't know why. I used to think we didn't 'do it right' but after a few other guys that doesn't seem possible."

"I love intercourse, but I've had a lot of pain in the past, especially when I had severe vaginal infections where I thought I'd die from the pain. After the infection was supposedly cleared up, I probably carried psychological thoughts of the pain with me and that made it linger on. Nowadays I never have pain except if I'm dry (unusual) or the guy lasts longer than fifteen minutes—in which case I tend to swell up quite a bit and have trouble sitting down."

"When I have a fungus it causes burning especially after intercourse. I have also heard that the pill can make intercourse painful—more burning. But then the pill also makes you more prone to fungus. Maybe they're connected."

"Sometimes the first penetration hurts because some men don't realize the importance of going in slowly. Also, sometimes an IUD can get poked the wrong way."

"During penetration, I seem to wait, expecting pain. Then when I find it's in and okay, I relax."

"Sometimes it burns if my pubic hair is pulled by my being dry, or him being large, or penetration too sudden or deep. It hurts in another way not to come after a long time, with aching and tightness."

"The only time it is uncomfortable is when I am not ready for it and that is simply rape. If fucking is uncomfortable, then it is just that. That's when it's time to resort to some other kind of negotiation, and maybe that should involve, just possibly, parting the bastard's hair with a frying pan. Think about it."

Of women who don't masturbate, how many do and do not orgasm during intercourse?

(not including women who never orgasm in any way)

	Don't mastur-bate	Had not had inter-course	Don't orgasm during inter-course	Do orgasm during inter-course (regularly)	Some-times, rarely	Unclear how often	Only with simul-taneous manual clitoral stimula-tion
Q. I	67 =	1	7	23	15	12	9
Q. II	87 =	6	16	27	14	12	12
Q. III	13 =	1	4	1	4	0	3
Total	**167** =	8	27	51	33	24	24

Of those who orgasmed regularly during intercourse, by what method did they do it?

(*The second number given refers to women in the "question-able-orgasm definition" group.*) Since this question was not specifically asked in the questionnaires, some women did not give this information.

	"Yes"	"Always"	"Usually"
Questionnaire I:			
1. Did not describe how	9–12	7–9	36–27
2. Woman on top	8–5	6–3	16–2
3. Grinding of pubic areas together	1–0	1–0	6–0
4. Touching of pubic bones together during intercourse	8–0	0–1	11–2
5. Partial holding of the penis inside the vagina, allowing clitoral contact			
6. Frequent re-entry of the penis into the vagina, stimulating the lips	1–0	3–0	
7. After the first orgasm, one of the methods listed here is possible			
8. Extended "before play"	3–1	2–0	6–5
9. With one partner only; no explanation		1–1	2–0
Total	30–18	17–14	81–38

Questionnaire II:

1.	18–14	8–7	40–40
2.	13–1	3–2	20–7
3.	1–0		3–1
4.	6–0	0–1	11–0
5.	1–0		1–0
6.		3–0	1–0
7.	2–0	1–0	1–1
8.	2–0		9–5
9.	2–1	2–1	1–0
Total	45–16	17–11	87–54

Questionnaire III:

1.	2–6	1–1	10–13
2.			4–1
3.			1–0
4.	2–1		2–2
5.			3–0
6.			
7.			
8.		1–0	3–0
9.		1–1	0–1
Total	4–7	3–2	23–17

Frequency of orgasm during intercourse by simultaneous manual clitoral stimulation

	Q.I	Q.II	Q.III
"Yes"	25	67	20
"Always'	11	5	3
"Usually"	33	42	12
"Sometimes"	24	9	5
"Rarely"	10	10	3
Total	103	133	43

= 15% of total population

Clitoral stimulation (Chapter 4)

Other types of stimulation to orgasm

	Q.I	Q.II	Q.III
Tribadism	15	28	4
Penis stimulation of clitoris	54	46	
Leg or body stimulation of clitoris	11	42	
Other types:			
Dreams	21	14	
Breast stimulation	18	9	7
Nursing	1		
Mental stimulation (fantasies, etc., usually during other activities)	19	2	
Horseback riding	3		
Dancing	1		

"Do you enjoy rectal contact? What kind?"

	Q.I	Q.II	Q.III
Yes	211	230	
Sometimes	58	78	
No	268	363	
Don't know	80	106	

Types enjoyed, of those who answered yes or sometimes

	Q.I	Q.II	Q.III
Touching	63	142	
Penetration of penis	83	63	
Penetration of finger	77	70	

"Do you think your vagina and genital area are ugly or beautiful?"

	Q.I	Q.II	Q.III
Beautiful, I like them	245	71	
Fascinating	23	8	
Ugly	116	28	
Average/Okay	90	24	
Neither: neutral	192	30	
Part of the whole, natural, functional and utilitarian	53	18	
Varies, mixed feelings	17	4	
Strange	8	5	
Total	744	188	

"Do they smell good or bad?" (Q. II)

Good	206	Neither	8
Great	18	Bad	114
Good if clean	141	Sometimes good, sometimes bad	62
Okay	75	Funky	2
Earthy	5	Bad after intercourse	7
Interesting	8	Bad with discharge	2
Unusual	10	Odour with fungus	19
Sexy	25	Yummy	4
Natural	21		
Exciting and stimulating	16		
Desirable	1	**Total**	744

"Are men uninformed about your sexual desires and your body?" (Q. I)

Yes	334
No	87
Varies	49
Men are not uninformed, they just don't care	10
I inform them	35
In general most men are uninformed, but my partner is informed	71
Total	586

Sexual slavery (Chapter 6)

"Do you like vaginal penetration/intercourse?"

	Q.I	Q.II	Q.III
Yes	539	693	186
It's okay	12	23	6
Sometimes	21	38	8
Depends on the partner	18	13	6
No	27	41	6
Total	617	808	212

Since it has become general knowledge that the interior walls of the vagina are more or less insensitive physically, some sex researchers now talk about "proprioceptive feeling"—the sensations caused by the distension of the vagina by the penis rather than friction on the vaginal lining itself. Only a few women mentioned feelings that might come under this heading—that is, pleasurable *physical* feelings not connected to orgasm:

"Just the feeling of having a penis in my vagina can feel good, and has nothing to do with having an orgasm. It just satisfies a need to be touched internally."

"I like vaginal penetration, both physically and psychologically. Physically, it feels good to have the whole area moved around the way penetration does. It feels 'full.' That's probably psychological. Anyway, I like it a lot."

"I like being filled up. Love to eat. Before I stopped, I used to smoke and fill my lungs and found it very satisfying. Being penetrated is a nice feeling, not necessarily even sexual!"

"Physically it feels good to have the whole vaginal-clitoral area moved around the way penetration does—it feels full."

"Intercourse has never led to orgasm but I enjoy the bulk and the movements inside of me, and the enveloping feeling."

"Yes, it feels close and I feel filled, supported and moved about by the genital region. I think it derives from being lifted and carried as a baby. Horseback riding is also good this way."

There were several reasons given by those women who didn't like intercourse.

"I don't enjoy intercourse because it's a bore and I never come."

"Penetration is frustrating and boring because it doesn't excite me. Also I do not like being laid, come in, getting slightly excited and then being deserted."

"Having a sweaty jumpy body on top of me is physically uncomfortable."

"I like intercourse when it feels good physically—which is only during the first penetration. After that it gets boring and pointless, and feels like you're being pounded."

"Intercourse is the least pleasurable to me of all the sex acts, particularly if it lasts too long. I don't find it repulsive or painful, just fatiguing and boring."

"Physically it is slightly pleasant, but boring, as it

takes so long and never brings me to orgasm."

"Not really—because it's dreary and boring. There was a time when I did it a lot, hoping it would get better. It's okay, but I feel there must be something more."

"It's great with a musical and sensitive person—like dancing. But most often I find it boring and psychologically oppressive."

"Physically, I can take it or leave it. Psychologically, it's pleasant but not necessary—except for him. Penetration itself never leads to orgasm for me. I find that penetration has the effect of separating my partner from me. It becomes an act unto itself, and its necessarily increased motion (thrusting, etc.) is all well and good if it helps him, but it strikes me as unconnected with any concept of 'love' and therefore inappropriate and humorous. I don't get the suggestion of brutality or selfishness on his part—it's just that all that bouncy activity strikes me more as genital gymnastics or as 'making sex' than as 'making love.' It's close to masturbation in communication value—you wind up talking to yourself."

"It's grossly built up into something it's not. It's just a thing you have to do because guys expect it. You really have to talk to yourself into it."

"Physically it doesn't matter unless it's too rough or painful. Psychologically, I hate it. I didn't always. But now I feel assaulted, skewered, and I feel like the penis is a club or blunt instrument."

"Intercourse has always felt like rape to me, for a host of reasons: like, my partner is insensitive to my feelings, my partner is coercive, he does not treat me as an equal, he treats me like an object, and I could go on . . . "

"As of late, I just feel used and abused, and can't help having the feeling that he uses me because I'm convenient and won't say no. Of course even if I do say no, it doesn't matter and we do it anyway."

Other women had more mixed feelings.

"Not as much as I used to—I learned that it wasn't as much as I once thought it would be, and I don't need it to have an orgasm. Once in a while it feels sort of nice. I like to hold someone I care for closely."

"I don't miss it when I don't have it. Sometimes I enjoy it while it's happening. Usually during intercourse. I think about whether I am, in reality, aroused, or am I pretending and just caught up in the movements and making the man believe I am truly enjoying it?"

"I've only had intercourse ten times in the last year and a half. My favourite time is immediately after my orgasm because it feels good that way. It's not something I think of as the only way to have sex with a man . . . it's sort of something I do when I'm too lazy to satisfy a male partner. I guess I like it sometimes but not as something important in love-making."

"I like intercourse: it's a moving experience to be naked and together and warm and moving together unique and tender. But sometimes I'm not in the mood, and I get tired of having to go wash my vagina (otherwise it sticks together) and sometimes I'm swollen."

"I like the moment of penetration, but intercourse is often disappointing. As things stand, I prefer having my back tickled to having intercourse, but so far I haven't said this to a man."

"So far I haven't enjoyed it, *per se*, all that much— maybe because it hasn't been with the right person. I really prefer the warm affectionate touching, feeling, kissing, and being together, and hugging."

"I like the moment of penetration, sometimes best of all (and I've had male partners who agree with me). But the pain and discomfort of having my legs spread so far apart and a heavy body on top are distracting, and I find it hard to concentrate on the build-up of sexual feeling under those circumstances. I enjoy the feeling anyway, for a while, and I like to feel that the man is experiencing deep pleasure. If I really love him, I don't feel any resentment even if I'm uncomfortable; in fact his ecstasy is arousing to me. Sometimes the feeling comes and goes in 'spurts,' so that I vacillate between arousal and pain (and boredom) until either he comes or I come or (five times in my life) we both come at the same time."

"How I feel about it is inseparable from my mood and attitudes about my husband. I resent being used as a security blanket, i.e., when under tension, he increases his sexual demands for intercourse. I can only enjoy intercourse if I feel good about our relationship at the moment."

"Intercourse with a man without orgasms for this woman falls into one or another of the following categories . . . an accommodation of his needs experience, a nurturing parenting type thing, plain submission, a martyrdom or self-hate thing, or an extreme loneliness and just glad-for-the-company type thing."

"It's physically okay—rarely exciting, usually boring. Psychologically the most I get out of it is pleasing someone else. I love feeling close to someone but you don't need a penis to feel close!"

Some women didn't like intercourse for the reason mentioned: "that watching the man have an orgasm when you don't can be maddening."
"My husband is brash and too fast for me. I require direct stimulation, and feeling loved, which he usually doesn't give me, to have an orgasm. I'm usually not enjoying intercourse, although I pretend to. God! If he only knew!"

"I don't like intercourse so much because men get so aggressive and intense then, and I need slower gentler movements to have an orgasm."

"Usually I like intercourse, but sometimes I feel it isn't fair I don't experience orgasm too and so when I am penetrated I tense up and it isn't enjoyable. Men expect intercourse to satisfy me, and just refuse to understand that it doesn't."

"I could live without intercourse. If we are having sex, and by the time of intercourse I have not had an orgasm, I feel like it's all over, that my stimulation is now ended. I feel disappointment and anger maybe sometimes that I have to do it. Pissed off."

"I only like intercourse after I have orgasmed through another method, so I know that the anxiety about orgasm will not be there."

"I wish I had orgasms during intercourse. When I have had them during intercourse (rarely) it has made intercourse more satisfying. When I don't, it seems unbalanced—like the man got more pleasure out of it than I did. Also, I've been conditioned to think it's more 'normal' during intercourse."

"I feel psychological ambivalent about intercourse. Sometimes I feel good about myself, I feel I've willingly chosen it as a means of mutual pleasure. Other times I feel my pleasure is not important to my partner, that I'm merely a receptacle, and that virtually anyone or anything could be equally satisfying to him."

"It depends on the other person. The kind that just want their own release and don't give me enough time— I am usually thinking about that, and how I am aware that I am just beginning to relax or something and they are panting away and all done, ready to go to sleep— then I think about how it wasn't even worth getting into and starting myself up just to be frustrated cause I usually don't dig that faking . . . if they live with me I could cry, silently, later because I love them so much and they don't know how to appreciate me so I can give them more of my love and they're cheating themselves and I think about whether this can go on or how I can resolve it."

"I have made it my motto for the past year that no man will lie back relaxed after intercourse if I haven't come. Why should he come if I don't? Equal orgasms!!"

The sexual revolution (Chapter 7)

"How often do you desire sex?"

	Q.I	Q.II
More than once a day	72	64
Daily	124	139
1–2 times per week	80	122
2–3 times per week	84	128
3–5 times per week	106	105
"Often"	44	43
1–2 times per month	20	19
3–4 times per month	4	7
Varies	32	80
Infrequently	13	13
Never	3	9
Total	582	727

In fact, the figures for "How often do you desire sex?" are somewhat misleading, in that they were usually given by the women as averages, with the complete answers indicating a much more sporadic interest in sex.

For the majority of women, the desire for sex fluctuated according to desire for a certain person.

"How much sex I want really depends on the partner—the more attracted I am, the more I want. When I am interested in someone, several times a week is good. But since I don't have someone around permanently, sex usually consists of making love two or three times each night when I am with someone, and then doing without for days."

"I rarely desire sex without desiring some one person in particular. My husband has refused me so many times that I now get nothing out of sex with him and do not really desire it. But during the six months when I had a lover, I desired him at least one time every day."

"I only want sex if I am deeply attracted to another person, for the most part. For example, I used to want sex two or three times a week when my marriage was good, but then I lost interest as we grew apart. Now, with my current lover, I want it constantly again—just the sound of his beautiful voice turns me on."

"When I love someone very much, my desire is high every day, sometimes days and nights on end. It's like craving physical closeness, out of which sexual desire emerges."

"The sexual passion between my husband and myself has fluctuated greatly. The early feelings I had for him (rushes of emotional and sexual feelings) are much less frequent now, but I am much more sexually satisfied than I was three or four years ago. It seems like when you get to know a person, that special excitement dies down after a while—but it doesn't mean that I don't love him as much; I love him *more.*"

"In a long relationship, my interest in sex settles down to about two times a week. But in a new relationship, I want it daily at least. And some people make me more horny than others. On the other hand, when I'm alone, I almost forget about sex. Intense sexual activity, followed by periods of near celibacy, has been my pattern for so long I no longer know if it's imposed or chosen."

Some women mentioned that unhappy experiences or periods of depression cut down or ended entirely their interest in sex.

"I usually want it all the time, until I have it with someone who ends up fucking me over."

"If I am troubled, I have no, or very little, desire for sex. After the death of my son, two and a half years ago, I lost all desire for almost two years. I did not even wish to masturbate, and may have had three 'wet dreams' during these two years. Under normal conditions, I find

I am stimulated by my partner if I feel affectionate towards him, and if he is 'giving' to me in other ways."

"The better I feel about myself and my life, the better my sexual activity. When I am depressed I have less or no desire. Also, I have discovered myself feeling sexy after a big fight with my husband where I have strongly asserted myself."

Other women feel that sex is addictive: the more you have it, the more you want it, and the less you have it, the less you want it.

"My sexual desire seems to decrease without heavy sexual activity. Going without only bothers me after I've just had it and my body and emotions are used to sex and affection."

"If I go without sex for one month, then going six months is easy."

"After the initial month or two, I got used to not having sex and didn't miss it."

"Soon after my ex-lover and I split up, I ached for it, but as the separation became wider the aches became less."

"It is definitely habit-forming for me. Right now, since I haven't had it in so long, I don't desire it quite so much."

"Although I'm glad to have discovered my own sexuality and it is important to me, if I had to I think I could live very happily without sex, as I did for many years. I think if you have it, you want it regularly; if you don't have it regularly, the need decreases. Right now I am off cigarettes; I hope I shall never smoke another cigarette again in my life; I know that in some ways I shall always desire to smoke a cigarette, but it is not an all-consuming need for me now because I haven't had one for three years. I think people's need for sex is very similar, except of course there is no reason for people to have to go off the joy of sex."

Quite a few women didn't know for sure how often they would want it, since they were having it more often than they wanted.

"I want it one or two times a week, I think, but I have it five or six times a week. I think I'd enjoy it more if I had it less."

"We usually have sex about four or five times a month. Of course, being married and having access to sex any time, or giving it to him any time he wants it, I don't know how I would be if I could set my own desires."

"I really can't say. I can say that I have sex a lot when I don't desire it, due to my partner's desires."

"Before I was married I thought it was wrong for a girl to have any big desire for sex. I never did have any big desire for it. Occasionally I felt like masturbating. Now my husband wants sex so often that I haven't had any big length of time to build up a big desire for it."

"Is the time of the month important? Do you notice an increase in sexual desire at certain times of the month?"

(*Questionnaire I*)

Yes, before and during menstruation	320
During and after menstruation	24
After menstruation	30
During ovulation	62
"Yes" (did not say when)	99
Total	**571**

It is interesting to notice that women are generally more interested in sex during times of the month when they are not fertile. This agrees with findings of other sex researchers. Kinsey found that approximately 90 per cent of his sample preferred sex during the pre-menstrual phase, and Masters and Johnson have shown that women produce more lubrication at this time.

Towards a new female sexuality (Chapter 9)

"What is it about sex that gives you the greatest pleasure?"

	Q.I	Q.III
Orgasm	71	42
Touching, sensuality, body contact		
Emotional intimacy, tenderness, a closeness, sharing deep feelings with a loved one	86	47
Pleasing him/giving	37	7
A partner I like	13	2
Giving and receiving pleasure	13	8
His orgasm	16	2
Intercourse	17	5
Clitoral massages	5	2
Good cunnilingus	8	3
Foreplay	13	2
The sexiness of it	14	
Release and relaxation	15	
Intercourse with a loved one	6	
The "entry," penetration	12	1
Fellatio	4	
Being together after; the feeling after	13	1
General good feelings	5	3
The excitement just before orgasm—the passion and losing control	19	4
Fantastic physical sensations	5	4
Total	432*	176

*103 women in Questionnaire I were not asked this question, due to substitution of an alternative question.

"The greatest displeasure?"

	Q.III
Sexist men who demand to get laid, don't respect you, etc.; power trips, used as a sex object, conquered, exploitative sex	18
Insensitive partner	5
Selfish partner	7
Harsh and rough or abrupt treatment	3
Neurotic partner	3
Casual sex with no emotions, impersonal sex	8
No orgasm	12
Lack of passion, sex with no arousal	7
Not being into it but trapped anyway	7
(Marital) duty	3
Any form of forcing	1
Messiness after: changing sheets, diaphragm or condom, etc.	4
Only having intercourse	4
No displeasure	14
Vaginal infections	1
Jealousy	1
Penetration when not ready	1
Pain from sudden thrusting in intercourse	2
Exhaustion	2
Lack of feeling	1
Anal sex	1
Fellatio	1
No after-time together	1
Total	107

"Is having orgasms important to you?"

(Most women answered this question in terms of sex with a partner.)

Q.I

26—I would not enjoy sex without orgasm; I would feel frustrated.

157—I would not enjoy sex *as much* without orgasm.

115—Sex is okay *sometimes* without orgasm.

31—Orgasm is important but I can enjoy sex without it.

4—Orgasm is important, but over-all pleasure is more important (like kissing, talking, and tenderness).

7—Orgasm is important but not always with one you love.

16—It depends on mood, partner, degree of arousal, etc.

43—Orgasm is not important; I would enjoy sex as much without it as long as there is closeness and a feeling of oneness.

15—Orgasm is not necessary, but it is pleasant.

203—Yes, orgasms are important

617   **Total**

"How important are orgasms to you?"

Q.I

473—Very important

24—Not always necessary

8—Not important

4—Okay

33—Not really important

542   **Total**

"Is having orgasms important to you? Would you enjoy sex just as much without ever having them? Does having good sex have anything to do with having orgasms?"

(answered as one question):

Q.II	Q.III	
9		Having orgasms is not important
71	4	Having orgasms is important
152	45	Orgasm is important, but sex is sometimes okay without
13		Yes, but closeness is more important
14	6	Orgasm is not necessary but pleasant
325	54	I would not enjoy sex as much; good sex involves orgasm
60	29	I would not enjoy sex without orgasm
15	7	It depends on the mood, partner, etc.; sometimes closeness is enough
16		Sex can be okay without orgasm, but orgasm is necessary for good sex
50	23	Sex is only okay without orgasm if there is love and affection, emotion, and tenderness present
9	33	Good sex leads to orgasm
26	21	Orgasm is important, but not all there is to good sex, which involves affection, love, and sharing
51	13	Sex is fine with no orgasm; good sex has nothing to do with orgasm
811	235	**Total**

Appendix 4:
Statistical analysis:
Sexuality of women in the UK, Australia and New Zealand, 1994–2000

A statistical base was set up for this new data, comprising the answers of 511 women of all ages and occupations, living in the UK, Australia and New Zealand.

As in the earlier research for this book, their answers were given via an anonymous written questionnaire, containing the same or similar questions to those originally asked. Their answers were submitted by post.

Those answering included women between the ages of nineteen and ninety-five:

14% ages 13–18
25% ages 19–29
29% ages 30–45
23% ages 46–65
 9% ages 66–95

Approximately 55 per cent of those answering were currently married, or previously married for more than two years (37 per cent were currently married, 12 per cent were divorced, 6 per cent were widowed), and 41 per cent were single (13 per cent were in lesbian relationships). These figures are not dissimilar to government statistics on marital status (although no government has published statistics on lesbian relationships); approximately 50 per cent of the urban population is now reported to live as "single". Nevertheless, no claim is made here that the statistics of this study are absolutely representative of the UK, Australian or New Zealand populations in general.

Religious affiliation as well as religious fervour varies in this sample, though the great majority should be characterised as "moderately Christian".

Those wishing to know more about the general statistical methods of *The Hite Reports* (this book, as well as others) can find a fifty-page essay on the topic in the appendices of *Women and Love: A Cultural Revolution in Progress* (Alfred Knopf, 1987; Viking-Penguin, 1988) as well as in *Women as Revolutionary Agents of Change* (Bloomsbury, 1993; University of Wisconsin Press, 1994).

Statistics by chapter (UK, Australia and New Zealand)

(*Figures are percentages.*)

	UK	Australia	New Zealand
Chapter 1: Masturbation			
How often do you masturbate?			
Daily	39	41	38
Once a week	47	45	51
Never; do not masturbate	6	5	7
Only experimented a few times	5	8	4
Didn't answer	3	1	0
How do you feel about it?			
Guilty and anxious	16	8	10
Proud and happy	21	30	25
Mixed	63	63	65
How do you masturbate?			
Clitoral stimulation by hand	82	81	79
Water or shower stimulation	7	3	8
Insertion into vagina	0	2	1
Vibrator, exterior use	9	11	8
Tensing legs together	2	3	4
Chapter 2: Orgasm			
Do you have orgasm?			
Yes	91	89	85
No	4	6	7
Not sure	5	5	8

cont'd

	UK	Australia	New Zealand
How many orgasms do you have?			
During masturbation			
One	42	37	39
A few	58	63	61
During sex with a partner (many kinds of stimulation), if you orgasm then			
One	80	77	88
A few	20	23	12
Do you orgasm best with your legs together or apart?			
Together	26	21	14
Apart	63	70	72
Moving apart and together, 'butterfly'	11	9	14

Chapter 3: Intercourse

How often do you orgasm during the following activities with a partner?

	UK	Australia	New Zealand
Intercourse (with no additional stimulation)			
Always	16	14	13
Sometimes	20	23	19
Rarely	51	49	50
Never	13	14	18

cont'd

	UK	Australia	New Zealand
Clitoral stimulation by hand of partner (separate from coitus)			
Always	44	43	30
Sometimes	20	31	26
Rarely	21	24	35
Never	15	2	9
Masturbation, stimulation by own hand (during sex with a partner)			
Too shy to try	66	73	64
Sometimes	21	19	27
Rarely	13	8	9
Cunnilingus, oral sex by partner			
Often	29	33	32
Sometimes	28	25	30
Rarely	17	18	10
Never	26	24	28
Do you use any special technique to achieve orgasm during coitus?			
I am on top and push myself against him	33	40	32
We press our pubic bones together	19	11	14
We have extended foreplay before penetration	11	10	13
Stimulation by hand on my mons during penetration	37	39	41

	UK	Australia	New Zealand
Chapter 4: Clitoral stimulation			
Is there a regular pattern during sex with men?			
Yes, it is foreplay until coitus, then ends with his orgasm	62	53	44
Yes, but the foreplay and afterplay are extremely varied	17	28	31
No, my partner is a dream, imaginative	21	19	25
If there is a pattern, what does it include?			
Foreplay	97	94	95
Vaginal penetration and intercourse	96	97	98
Manual stimulation of me by hand until I orgasm	26	30	21
Manual stimulation of me to get excited (not to orgasm)	65	69	71
Oral stimulation of me until I orgasm	8	7	5
Oral stimulation of me to get excited	16	22	24
My oral stimulation of him to get excited	10	12	18
His orgasm	95	99	98
More than one orgasm for me	2	6	3
Is your partner able to stimulate you to orgasm by hand? By oral sex?			
Yes, oral sex	19	26	21
Yes, by hand	32	31	37
I enjoy these but they are "foreplay", not to orgasm	49	43	42

	UK	Australia	New Zealand
Are your partners well informed about your sexual desires and your body?			
Yes	17	21	25
No	61	65	70
Sometimes	22	14	5
Do you think your vulva and genital area is ugly or beautiful?			
Beautiful, attractive	49	44	50
Unattractive, "ugly"	12	15	14
Neither, just utilitarian	39	41	36
Do your genitals smell good or bad?			
Good	63	59	72
OK, or not very good	14	11	11
Cannot let anyone go there	3	4	1
Varies (time of month, washing, etc.)	20	26	16

Chapter 5: Lesbianism

	UK	Australia	New Zealand
Have you had a sexual relationship with a woman?			
Yes	15	19	18
No	85	81	82
Are you curious or would you like to try a sexual relationship with a woman?			
Yes	71	78	80
No	29	22	20

	UK	Australia	New Zealand
Does sex with a woman, in your experience, lead to regular orgasm?			
Yes, I always orgasm with her through her touch	52	60	61
Usually I have orgasm with her when she kisses my crotch	32	27	24
I am too shy so far to have orgasm with her	16	13	15
What is your reason for having sex with another woman, or for being lesbian?			
I have always had these feelings, I was born with them	51	46	40
I discovered the feelings I could have for a woman when I was a teenager	18	14	26
I discovered the feelings I could have for a woman when I fell in love	31	40	34

Chapter 6: Sexual slavery

Is having orgasm important for you (during sex with a partner)?

	UK	Australia	New Zealand
Yes	44	40	46
Depends	25	28	25
No, not during sex with a partner	31	32	29

	UK	Australia	New Zealand
Do you find it easier or more difficult to have sex with a man who deals with your finances (at home or at work)?			
Encourages me to have sex	10	13	15
Inhibits me	43	39	31
I try to avoid it; sex and money should not be mixed	47	48	54
Do you accept regular sex with a man if you don't often have orgasm with him?			
Yes	62	59	55
No	38	41	45

Chapter 7: The Sexual Revolution

	UK	Australia	New Zealand
Is the sexual revolution good?			
Yes, it increased openness	11	6	12
No, it cheapened sex	14	21	17
There was no real revolution	41	40	35
No, it increased social instability	12	18	16
Yes, it made sex 'OK' for women too	22	25	20
How often do you desire sex?			
Daily	29	22	24
Once a week	18	16	12
A few times a week	19	25	26
Depends	6	8	11
A few times a month	13	10	7
Infrequently or never	15	19	20

	UK	Australia	New Zealand
Chapter 8: Towards a new female sexuality			
Should the pattern or definition of sex be changed?			
Yes, expanded with more options	46	61	49
Yes, women's desires should be taken into account	14	11	18
No, it's impossible to change	40	28	33
What is the biggest problem today for women?			
The double standard: "sexy women are not as respectable"	43	49	51
Making a real "sexual revolution": finding a sexual expression that has integrity in the midst of a difficult social context	44	40	34
Integrating sexual identity with female spirtual identity (family values and family life), recreating our idea of what sex and sexuality are	13	11	15

References

1 Masturbation
1. Betty Dodson, "Liberating Masturbation," distributed by Betty Dodson, Box 1933, New York, NY 10001; Eve's Garden, 119 W. 57th St, New York, NY 10019; 1972, p.18.

2 Orgasm
1. Mary Jane Sherfey, *The Nature and Evolution of Female Sexuality* (New York: Vintage Books; 1973), pp. 93–4.
2. Ibid., pp.104–5.
3. Ibid., p.112.
4. Ibid., pp.134–5.
5. Helen Singer Kaplan, *The New Sex Therapy* (New York: Brunner/Mazel, 1974), p.31.
6. Sherfey, op. cit, p.116.
7. Ruth Herschberger, *Adam's Rib* (New York: Harper and Row Books, 1970), p.72.
8. Edward M. Brecher, *The Sex Researchers* (New York: Signet Books, 1969), pp.220–1.
9. Kaplan, op. cit, p.29.
10. Josephine Singer and Irving Singer, "Types of Female Orgasm," *The Journal of Sex Research*, Vol. 8, No. 4, pp.255–67, November 1972.
11. Brecher, op. cit, pp.214–15.

3 Intercourse
1. Edward M. Brecher, *The Sex Researchers* (New York: Signet Books, 1969), p.156.
2. Helen Singer Kaplan, *The New Sex Therapy* (New York: Brunner/Mazel 1974) pp.340–1.

3. William Masters and Virginia Johnson, *Human Sexual Inadequacy* (Boston: Little, Brown and Cornpany, 1970), p.218.
4. Mary Jane Sherfey, *The Nature* and *Evolution of Female Sexuality* (New York: Vintage Books, 1973), p. 80.
5. Ibid., p. 90.
6. Nancy Marval, "The Case for Feminist Celibacy," (New York: The Feminists, 1971 [pamphlet]).
7. Alfred C. Kinsey, et al., *Sexual Behavior in the Human Female* (New York: Pocket Books, 1965), p. 322.
8. Marval, op. cit.
9. Seymour Fisher, *Understanding the Female Orgasm* (New York: Bantam Books, 1973), pp.113-14.
10. Ibid., pp.213–14.
11. Ibid., pp.106–7.
12. Ibid., pp.219–20.
13. Sherfey, op. cit, pp.27–8.
14. Fisher, op. cit., p.238.
15. Ann Koedt, *The Myth of the Vaginal Orgasm* (Boston: New England Free Press, 1970).
16. William Masters and Virginia Johnson, *Human Sexual Response* (Boston: Little, Brown and Company, 1966), p.59.
17. Sherfey, op. cit., p.177.
18. Ibid., p.111.
19. Alix Shulman, "Organs and Orgasms," *Women in Sexist Society: Studies in Power and Powerlessness,* ed. by Vivian Gornick and Barbara K. Moran (New York: Signet Books, 1972), p.296.
20. Sherfey, op. cit, p.122.

4 Clitoral stimulation
1. Mary Jane Sherfey, *The Nature and Evolution of Female Sexuality* (New York: Vintage Books, 1973), p.168.

5 Lesbianism

1. Kinsey, et al., *Sexual Behavior in the Human Female* (New York: Pocket Books, 1965), pp.481–2.
2. Ibid., pp.448–50.
3. Ibid., p.450.
4. Pepper Schwartz and Philip Blumstein, "Bisexuality: Some Sociological Observations," a paper presented at the Chicago Conference on Bisexual Behavior, 6 Oct., 1973, available from the authors, Dept of Sociology, University of Washington, Seattle, Washington.
5. Ibid.
6. Janis Kelly, "Sister Love: An Exploration of the Need for Homosexual Experience," *The Family Coordinator*, October 1972, pp.473–5.

6 Sexual slavery

1. Helen Singer Kaplan, *The New Sex Therapy* (New York: Brunner/Mazel, 1974), p.404.
2. Seymour Fisher, *Understanding the Female Orgasm* (New York: Bantam Books, 1973), p.89.
3. Ibid., p.199.
4. Ibid., p.258.
5. Kinsey, et al., *Sexual Behavior In the Human Female* (New York: Pocket Books, 1965), pp.368–9.
6. Pepper Schwartz, "Female Sexuality and Monogamy," University of Washington, Department of Sociology; also appearing in *Renovating Marriage: Toward New Sexual Life Styles,* eds. Roger W. Libby and Robert Whitehurst (San Ramon, California; Consensus Publishers, 1973).
7. A Redstockings sister, "Brainwashing and Women," *The Radical Therapist,* by The Radical Therapist Collective, produced by Jerome Angel (New York: Ballantine Books, 1971), p.123.
8. Dorothy Tennov, "Prostitution and the Enslavement of Women," *Prime Time,* a magazine for the liberation of women in the prime of life, Vol. 3, #1, April 1975.

7 The sexual revolution

1. Theodor Reik, *Psychology of Sex Relations* (New York: Farrar and Rinehart, Inc., 1945), p.11.
2. Lester, Kirkendall, "Towards a Clarification of the Concept of Male Sex Drive," *Journal of Marriage and Family Living*, Vol. 20, 1958, pp.367–72.
3. Kinsey, et al., *Sexual Behavior in the Human Female* (New York: Pocket Books, 1965), p.612.

8 Mid-life and older women

1. Helen Singer Kaplan, *The New Sex Therapy* (New York: Brunner/Mazel, 1974), p.111.

9 Towards a new female sexuality

1. Rollo May, *Love and Will* (New York: Laurel/Dell Publishing, 1974). pp.71-2.
2. Marc Feigen Fasteau, *The Male Machine* (New York: McGraw Hill, 1974), p.1.
3. Kinsey, et al., *Sexual Behavior in the Human Female* (New York: Pocket Books, 1965), p.625.
4. Ibid., p.229.

Appendices

1. Mary Jane Sherfey, *The Nature and Evolution of Female Sexuality* (New York: Vintage Books, 1973), p.26.